MW00619585

MORTARS, PLASTERS, STUCCOS

Artificial Marbles, Concretes, Portland Cements and Compositions

BEING A

THOROUGH AND PRACTICAL TREATISE

ON THE

LATEST AND MOST IMPROVED METHODS OF PREPARING AND USING LIMES, MORTARS, CEMENTS, MASTICS AND COMPOSITIONS IN CONSTRUCTIVE AND DECORATIVE WORK, INCLUDING A PRACTICAL TREATISE ON REINFORCED CONCRETES

PREPARED, COMPILED AND EDITED BY

FRED T. HODGSON, O. A. A.

AUTHOR OF

"Treatise on Uses of The Steel Square," "Modern Carpentry," "Architectural Drawing Self-Taught," "Up-to-Date Hardwood Finisher," "20th Century Bricklayer," "Modern Estimator," "Art of Wood-Carving," Etc.

PROFUSELY ILLUSTRATED

With Working Drawings and Sketches of Tools, Appliances, Ceiling Designs and Examples of Ornamental Stucco Work

Fredonia Books
Amsterdam, The Netherlands

Concretes, Cements, Mortars, Artificial Marbles, Plasters & Stucco:
How to Use and How to Prepare Them

Prepared, Compiled and Edited by
Fred T. Hodgson

ISBN: 1-4101-0221-1

Copyright © 2003 by Fredonia Books

Reprinted from the 1916 edition

Fredonia Books
Amsterdam, The Netherlands
http://www.fredoniabooks.com

All rights reserved, including the right to reproduce this book, or portions thereof, in any form.

In order to make original editions of historical works available to scholars at an economical price, this facsimile of the original edition of 1916 is reproduced from the best available copy and has been digitally enhanced to improve legibility, but the text remains unaltered to retain historical authenticity.

PART I

CONCRETES, CEMENTS, PLASTERS AND STUCCOS—THEIR USES AND METHODS OF WORKING SAME.

INTRODUCTORY

This book, or rather compilation, is largely made up of the very best material available on the subjects it proposes to discuss. All the latest improvements and methods in the mixing, proportioning and application of plaster, mortar, stucco and cement will be described and laid before the reader in as simple and plain a manner as possible.

The art of using mortars in some shape or other, is as old as civilization, as we find evidences of its use in ruins that date long before historical times, not only in the older countries of Asia and Europe, but also in the ruins of Mexico, Central America and Peru; and the workmen who did their part, or most of this work, were evidently experts at the trade, for some of the remains of their work which have come down to us certainly show that the work was done by men who not only had a knowledge of their trade, but that they also possessed a fair knowledge of the peculiar qualities of the materials they used. "Plastering," says Miller in his great work on Mortars, "is one of the earliest instances of man's power of inductive reasoning, for when men built they plastered: at first, like the birds and the beavers, with mud; but they soon found out a more lasting and more comfortable method, and the earliest efforts of civilization were directed to plastering. The inquiry into it takes us back to the dawn of social life until its origin becomes mythic and prehistoric. In that dim, obscure period we cannot penetrate far enough to see clearly, but the most distant glimpses we can obtain into it show us that man had very early attained almost to perfection in compounding material for plastering. In fact, so far as we yet know, some of the earliest plastering which has remained to us excels, in its scientific composition, that which we use at the present day, telling of ages of experimental attempts. The pyramids of Egypt contain plaster work executed at least four thousand years ago (some antiquaries, indeed, say a much longer period), and this, where wilful violence has not disturbed it, still exists in perfection, outvying in durability the very rock it covers, where this is not protected by its shield of plaster. Dr. Flinders Petrie, in his 'Pyramids and Temples of Gizeh,' shows us how serviceable and intelligent a co-operator with the painter, the sculptor, and the architect, was the plasterer of those early days, and that to his care and skill we owe almost all we know of the history of these distant times and their art. Indeed the plasterer's very tools do yet remain to us, showing that the technical processes then were the same we now use, for there are in Dr. Petrie's collection hand floats which in design, shape and purpose are precisely those which we use today. Even our newest invention of canvas plaster was well known then, and by it were made the masks which yet preserve on the mummy cases the lineaments of their occupants."

The plaster used by the Egyptians for their finest work was derived from burnt gypsum, and was therefore exactly the same as our "plaster of paris." Its base was of lime stucco, which, when used on partitions, was laid in reeds, laced together with cords, for lathing, and Mr. Miller, who has examined a fragment in Dr. Petrie's collection, finds it practically "three coat work," about 3/4 of an inch thick, haired and finished just as we do now.

Plaster moulds and cast slabs exist, but there does not appear any evidence of piece moulding, nor does any evidence of the use of modelled work in plaster exist. That some process of indurating plaster was thus early known is evidenced by the plaster pavement at Tel-el Amarna, which is elaborately painted. The floor of this work is laid on brick; the first coat is of rough lime stucco about 1 inch thick, and the finishing coat of well-haired plaster about 1/8 inch thick, very smooth and fine, and showing evidence of trowelling, the setting out lines for the painting being formed by a struck cord before the surface was set, and the painting done on fresco. It is about 60 by 20, and formed the floor of the principal room of the harem of King Amenhotop IV., about fourteen hundred years before Christ, that is, between three thousand and four thousand years ago. Long before this, plastering of fine quality existed in Egypt, and so long as its civilization continued it aided the comfort of the dwellings of its people and the beauty of its temples.

Nor was it merely for its beauty and comfort that plaster work was used. Even then its sanitary value was recognized, and the directions given in Leviticus xiv, 42-48, which was probably written about one hundred years before this date, show that the knowledge of its antiseptic qualities was widely spread, and the practice of it regarded as religious duty.

Unfortunately there is no direct evidence that the adjacent Assyrian powers of Nineveh and Babylon used plaster work. Possibly the fine clay brought down by the rivers of the Euphrates and the Tigris sufficed for all their purposes. Their records are in it: their illustrations on the sculptured walls of their palaces are in stone, their painting is glazed on their bricks, and for them there seems to have been but little need for plaster work, nor do we find until the rise of Grecian art anything relating to our subject.

Very early in Greek architecture we find the use of plaster, and in this case a true lime stucco of most exquisite composition, thin, fine and white. Some has been found at Mycenae, a city of Homeric date. We know that it existed in perfection in Greece about five hundred years before the Christian era. With this the temples were covered externally, and internally where they were not built of marble, and in some cases where they were. This fine stucco was often used as a ground on which to paint their decorative ornament, but not infrequently left quite plain in its larger masses, and some of it remains in very fair preservation even to this day. The Temple of Apollo at Bassae, built of yellow sandstone about 470 B. C., has on its columns the remains of a fine white stucco.

Pavements of thick, hard plaster, stained, of various colors, were common in the Greek temples. One of these, that of the Temple of Jupiter Panhellenius at Ægina, built about 570 B. C., is described by Cockerell as existing in the early part of the century, in good condition, though the temple itself was destroyed; and I have seen at Agrigentum plaster existing in perfect state, though scarcely thicker than an egg-shell, on the sheltered parts of a temple built at least three hundred years before our era, whilst the unprotected stone was weather worn and decayed.

What care the ancient Greeks bestowed on their stucco may be inferred from Pliny's statement that in the temple at Elis about 450 B. C., Panaenus, the nephew of Phidias, used for the groundwork of his picture "stucco mixed with milk and saffron, and polished with spittle rubbed on by the ball of the thumb, and," says he, "it still retains the odor of saffron." Lysippus, the first of the Greek "realists" in sculpture, was the first we hear of who took casts of the faces of living sitters about 300 B. C., so the art of plaster casting must have advanced a good deal by that time, as he made presents of copies to his friends. Afterwards we read of many sculptors who sent smaller plaster models of their works to friends. These were, however, probably carved in the plaster rather than cast.

Whether the Greeks used stucco for modelling is a somewhat doubtful point amongst antiquarians. From certain passages in classic writers I am induced to think they did. Pausanius, who describes the temple at Stymphalus, an almost deserted and ruined city when he visited it about 130 A. D., describes the ceiling of the Temple of the Stymphalides, built about 400 B. C., as being "either of stucco or carved wood," he could not decide which, but his very doubt would imply that stucco or wood were equally common. Now, this ceiling was ornamented with panels and figures of the harpies—omens of evil, half woman and half bird, with outspread wings. He also mentions a statue of Bacchus in "colored stucco." Of course these are not definite proofs of early Greek stucco modelling, but as the city of Stymphalus had decayed and become depopulated before 200 B. C., there is certainly presumptive evidence of the ancient practice of the art. Again, figures of unburnt earth are mentioned in contradistinction to those of terra cotta, and sundry other allusions to plastic work occur, which lead me to the opinion that quite early in Greek art this mode of using plaster began. At any rate, we know that it was early introduced into Grecia Magna—the earliest Southern Italian colony of the Greeks; and as colonists invariably preserve the customs and traditions of their fatherland even long after they have fallen into disuse in their native home, we can have no reasonable doubt but this art was imported rather than invented by them. Thence it spread to the Etruscans of Middle Italy, a cognate people to the Southern Greeks, by whom both plain and modelled stucco was largely used. The Etruscans, as we have seen, were more closely allied to the Greek than the Latin race, but in the course of time these two races amalgamated, the former bringing skill in handicraft, the latter lust of power, and patriotic love of country and of glory, whilst the Grecian element, which blended harmoniously with the first of these, added a love of art.

This union, however, took long to ripen to artistic fruitfulness. The practical Etruscan element firstly constructed the roads and the sewers, and gave health to Rome. The Latins added to their territory until it embraced half of Europe, giving wealth to Rome, and not till the luxury and comfort thus created did the artistic element of the Greek come in, giving beauty to Rome, and the day of decorative plaster work approached its noontide glory, making Rome the attraction of the world. The absorbance of Greece as a Roman province took place B. C. 145, and the loot of it began, giving an enormous impetus to Roman art. Thousands of statues were brought to Rome, and to be deemed a connoisseur in things artistic or a patron of the arts became the fashionable ambition. But it was not until the century just preceding the Christian era that it became especially noteworthy. Of coursé there is hardly anything left to us of the very early plaster work of Rome. The constant search for some new thing was inimical to the old. Old structures were pulled down to make way for new, which in their turn gave way to newer, and until the age of Augustus we have but little of the early work left. Strabo, who visited Rome about this time, complains of the destruction caused by the numerous fires, and continued pulling down of houses rendered necessary, for even pulling down and rebuilding in order to gratify the taste is but voluntary ruin; and Augustus, who boasted that "he found Rome of brick and left it of marble," in replacing the brick with marble destroyed the plaster work. How that plaster work was wrought we shall learn more from Vitruvius, who wrote his book on architecture about 16 B. C., and dedicated it to the emperor, "in order to explain the rules and limits of art as a standard by which to test the merits of the buildings he had erected or might erect."

Now, Vitruvius was a man who had travelled and seen much. He was with Julius Caesar as a military engineer in his African campaign in 46 B. C., or ten years after Caesar's invasion of Britain. Afterwards he became a designer of military engines, what we should call head of the Ordnance Department, and also a civil engineer, persuading himself that he had a pretty taste in architecture, just as though he were an R. E. of today. Thus he had a practical and also an artistic training, and here is what he says on matters connected with plaster work in Book VII, Chapter 11.

On tempering lime for stucco: "This requires that the lime should be of the best quality, and tempered a long time before it is wanted for use; so that if any of it be not burnt enough, the length of time employed in slaking it may bring the whole mass to the same consistency." He then advises it to be chopped with iron hatchets, adding that "if the iron exhibits a glutinous substance adhering to it, it indicates the richness of the lime, and the thorough slaking of it." For cradling out, and for ceiling joists, he recommends "the wood to be of cypress, olive, heart of oak, box and juniper," as neither is liable to "rot or shrink." For lathing he specifies "Greek reeds bruised and tied with cords made from Spanish broom," or if these are not procurable "marsh reeds tied with cords." On these a coat of lime and sand is laid, and an additional coat of sand is laid on to it. As it sets it is then polished with chalk or marble. This for ceilings. For plaster on wall he says: "The first coat on the walls is to be laid on as roughly as possible, and while drying, the sand and coat spread thereon. When this work has dried, a second and a third coat is laid on. The sounder the sand and coat is, the more durable the work will be. The coat of marble dust then follows, and this is to be so prepared that when used it does not stick to the trowel. Whilst the stucco is drying, another thin coat is to be laid on: this is to be well worked and rubbed, then still another, finer than the last. Thus with three coats and the same number of marble dust coats the walls will be solid, and not liable to crack. The wall that is well covered with plaster and stucco, when well polished, not only shines, but reflects to the spectators the images falling on it. The plasterers of the Greeks not only make their stucco work hard by adhering to these directions, but when the plaster is mixed, cause it to be beaten with wooden staves by a great number of men, and use it after this preparation. Hence some persons cutting slabs of plaster from ancient walls use them for tables and mirrors." (Chapter III.)

You will see by these remarks the great care taken through every process, and how guarded the watchfulness over the selection of materials, and you will also note the retrospectiveness of Vitruvius' observation, how he felt that the work done before the frantic haste of his own time was the better: very much as we find now. Time is an ingredient in all good work, and its substitute difficult to find.

There are other "tips" contained in this work which are worth extraction, as, for instance, his instructions as how to plaster damp walls. In such case he primarily suggests a cavity wall, with ventilation to insure a thorough draught, and then plastering it with "potsherd mortar," or carefully covering the rough plaster with pitch, which is then to be "lime whited over," to insure "the second coat of pounded potsherds adhering to it," when it may be finished as already described. Further, he refers to modelled plaster work which, he says, "ought to be used with a regard to propriety," and gives certain hints for its appropriate use. Speaking of pavements "used in the Grecian winter rooms, which are not only economical but useful," he advises "the earth to be excavated about two feet, and a foundation of potsherd well rammed in," and then a "composition of pounded coal lime, sand and ashes is mixed up and spread thereover, half foot in thickness, perfectly smooth and level. The surface then being rubbed with stone, it has the appearance of a black surface," "and the people, though barefoot, do not suffer from cold on this sort of pavement.'' Now all this bespeaks not only theoretical knowledge, but practical observation and experience, and was written nearly two thousand years ago, from which you can surmise how far advanced practical plastering had then become. This written evidence is almost all we have of the work of Vitruvius' own time, for even of the time of Augustus hardly anything remains to us, as the great fire of Nero utterly destroyed the greater part of the city in the year A. D. 64, and almost the only authenticated piece of plaster work done before or during his reign is the Tabula Iliaca, a bas-relief of the Siege of Troy, still preserved in the Capitol Museum at Rome. That this was modelled by Greek artists is proved by the fact that its inscriptions are all in the Greek language, and by some it is considered to be of very much greater antiquity. So much for the ancient history of the art of plastering, and I trust I will be pardoned if I continue this sketch, bringing it down to a more recent period and show in what high respect the plasterers' art was held in the Sixteenth Century, and later. Quoting from an old work, giving an account of the institution of ''The Worshipful Company of Plaisterers,'' and making use of the quaint language then in use we are told that: ''The Plaisterers' Company, which ranks as forty-sixth among the eighty-nine companies, was incorporated by King Henry VII., on March 10, 1501, to search, and try, and make, and exercise due search as well in, upon, and of all manner of stuff touching and concerning the Art and Mystery of Pargettors, commonly called Plaisterers, and upon all work and workmen in the said art or mystery, so that the said work might be just, true, and lawful, without any deceit or fraud whatsoever against the City of London or suburbs thereof. The Charter gave power to establish the Company as the Guild or Fraternity in honour of the Blessed Virgin Mary, of men of the Mystery or Art of Pargettors in the City of London, commonly called Plaisterers, to be increased and augmented when necessary, and to be governed by a Master and two Wardens, to be elected annually. The Master and Wardens and brotherhood were to be a body corporate, with perpetual succession and a common seal, and they were empowered to purchase and enjoy in fee and perpetuity lands and other possessions in the City, suburbs and elsewhere. And the charter empowered the said Master and Wardens to sue and be sued as "The Master and Wardens of the Guild or Fraternity of the Blessed Mary of Pargettors, commonly called Plaisterers, London."

THE OLD COAT OF ARMS.

The Company under the powers to make examinations, appears to have inflicted fines on offending parties for using bad materials, and for bad workmanship. Search days appear to have been annually appointed up to 1832, but not since, and the Company has not exercised any control over Plaisterers' work for many years.

Another charter was granted by Queen Elizabeth in 1559, but it has been lost, and there is no record of the contents. The Queen granted a new charter in 1597, which confirmed the privileges of the Company, and extended the authority of the Master and Wardens to and over all persons exercising the art of plaisterers, as well English as aliens and denizens inhabiting and exercising the said art within the City and suburbs and liberties, or within two miles of the City.

THE PRESENT COAT OF ARMS.

Charles II., by a charter dated June 19, 1679, confirmed the privileges granted by the previous charters. Having in view the rebuilding of the City, he forbade any person to carry on simultaneously the trades of a mason, bricklayer or plaisterer, or to exercise or carry on the art of a plaisterer without having been apprenticed seven years to the mystery. The jurisdiction of the Company was extended to three miles' distance from the City.

There were two orders made by the Court of Aldermen (exemplified under the mayoralty seal, April 1)

1585) for settling matters in dispute between the tilers and bricklayers and the plaisterers as to interfering in each other's trades. The observance of these orders was enforced by an order of the Privy Council dated June 1, 1613, and a general writ or precept issue to the same effect on August 13, 1613.

INDIAN CENTRE-PIECE.

There was also an order of the Court of Aldermen (29 Elizabeth, February 14, 1586-7) relating to the number of apprentices to be kept by members.

An act of Common Council was passed, under date of 18 James I., October 5, 1620.

An act of Common Council (6 William and Mary, October 19, 1694) was also passed to compel all persons using the trade of plaisterer in the City of London or the liberties thereof, to become free of the Company under penalty to be recovered as therein mentioned. In the East the Art of ornamental plastering was well known and almost universally practiced before Mahomet established a new order of things, and the enriched plaster work of India, Persia and other Eastern Empires are evidences of the high character of the workmanship of the Oriental workers in plaster. The Arabian and Moor brought back the Art of the Western World in the early part of the thirteenth century, and it is to them we owe the splendid plaster work of the Alhambra and other work still in existence in Spain. In the Mosque at Medina, built in 622, are still to be seen some fine specimens of old plaster work that was wrought on the building at the time of its completion. The Mosque of Ibu-tubun, Cairo, Egypt, which was finished in A. D. 878, abounds with beautiful plaster work. It contains a number of arches and arcades, the capitals of which, like the rest of the building, are enriched with plaster buds and flowers made in elaborate designs. Even in Damascus, that old and far-off City indulged in ornamental plaster-work when the people of Western Europe were cutting one another's throats for political ascendency. We illustrate a few examples of old work taken from existing specimens. These will to some extent, give an idea of what the old plasterers could do. See illustrations attached.

During the middle ages in Europe plastering and stucco existed only as a craft, and its highest function was to prepare a surface to be painted on. Sometimes it was used as an external protection from the weather but rarely was it employed for direct ornament. Sometimes small ornaments were carved in plaster of Paris, but it played no important part in decorative Art, excepting perhaps, as gesso, though this belonged rather to the painter than the plasterer. Nor was it until the commencement of the Renaissance in Italy that it showed any symptoms of revival.

ARABESQUE FROM THE GREAT MOSQUE, DAMASCUS.

With the commencement of the fifteenth century old learning and old arts began to be studied, the discovery of the art of printing and the consequent multiplication of the copies of the lore heretofore looked up in old manuscripts gave invention and progress new life, which has lasted until the present day. Italy has always been the nursing mother of plasterers, and in Mr. G T. Robinson's "Glimpse of the History of the Art and Craft," he has shown something of her great and glorious past, and how she sent her sons over almost all Europe to raise the art and status of this craft.

PERSIAN CENTRE-PIECE.

Even during the depressing times of her history she religiously preserved its ancient traditions and processes, and in almost all her towns there was some one or two plasterers to whom was confided the restoration, the repair and the conservation of its frescoes or its stuccos. The art dwindled, but it survived. So late as 1851 an English architect, when sketching in the

Campo Santo at Pisa, found a plasterer busy in lovingly repairing portions of its old plaster work, which time and neglect had treated badly, and to whom he applied himself to learn the nature of the lime he used. So soft and free from caustic qualities was it that the painter could work on it in true fresco painting a few days or hours after it was repaired, and the modeller used it like clay. But until the very day the architect was leaving no definite information could he extract. At last, at a farewell dinner, when a bottle of wine had softened the way to the old man's heart, the plasterer exclaimed, "And now, signor, I will show you my secret!" And immediately rising from the table, the two went off into the back streets of the town, when, taking a key from his pocket, the old man unlocked a door, and the two descended into a large vaulted basement, the remnant of an old palace. There amongst the planks and barrows, the architect dimly saw a row of large vats or barrels. Going to one of them, the old man tapped it with his key; it gave a hollow sound until the key nearly reached the bottom. "There, signor! there is my grandfather! he is nearly done for." Proceeding to the next, he repeated the action, saying: "There, signor! there is my father! there is half of him left." The next barrel was nearly full. "That's me! exclaimed he; and at the last barrel he chuckled at finding it more than half full: "That's for the little ones, signor!" Astonished at this barely understood explanation, the architect learned that it was the custom of the old plasterers, whose trade descended from father to son for many successive generations, to carefully preserve any fine white lime produced by burning fragments of pure statuary, and to each fill a barrel for his successors. This they turned over from time to time, and let it air—slake in the moist air of the vault, and so provide pure old lime for the future by which to preserve and repair the old works they venerated. After-inquiries showed that this was a common prac-

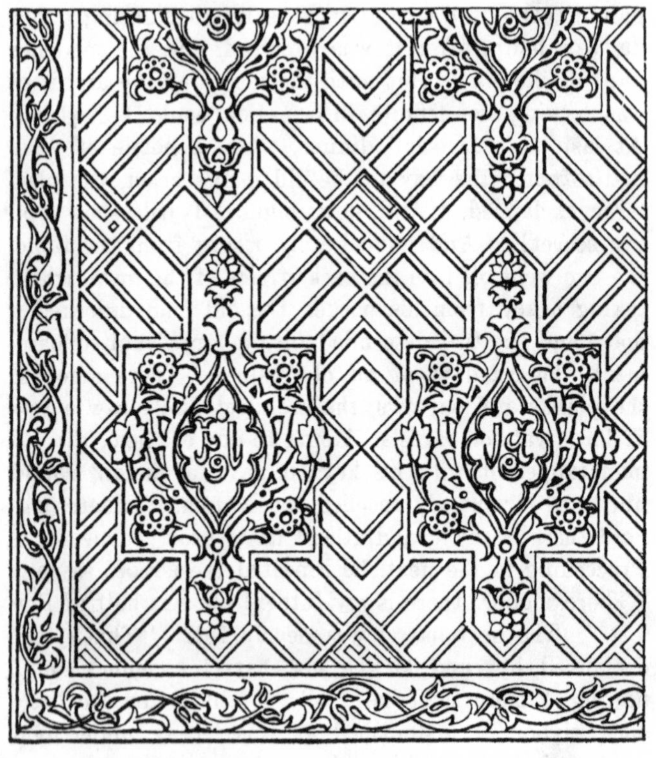

PORTION OF A CEILING FROM TEHERAN, PERSIA.

tice in many an old town, and thus the value of old air-slaked lime, such as had been written about eighteen hundred years before, was preserved as a secret of the trade in Italy, whilst the rest of Europe was advocating the exclusive use of newly burnt and hot slaked lime. Was there in the early part, indeed even in the middle

DIAPERED PLASTER PANELLING IN THE ALHAMBRA, SPAIN, THIRTEENTH CENTURY.

of the present century, any plaster image seller who was not an Italian? Indeed, at this present time, almost all the "formatore" or piece moulders for the majority of the sculptors of Europe are of Italian nationality or descent, and chiefly by these has the national craft been maintained.

When after the long European wars of the eighteenth and the commencement of the nineteenth century Italy had rest and power to "make itself" (faro de se), the first revival of its industry was felt by her plasterers, and as there was then, as now, more workmen than

PLASTER FRIEZE IN MOSQUE OF SULTAN HASAN. FOURTEENTH CENTURY.

work, they emigrated to the neighboring countries; and the major part of the plasterers along the Revieda, in the southern provinces of Germany and Austria, are Italians who go off with and return with the swallows, to earn that wage the poverty of their own country cannot afford them. With this brief historical summary I conclude the Introductory notice, and will now pass on to the more practical domain of the Plasterers' Art.

MATERIALS.

LIMES, CEMENTS, MORTARS, SAND, PLASTERS AND LATHS.

LIMES.

The Lime Principally Used for internal plastering is that calcined from carbonate of lime, in which the impurities do not exceed 6 per cent., and is known as fat lime, pure lime or rich lime. It is unfit for any purpose where strength is required, or in situations where it is exposed to the weather, as it has no setting power, and is easily dissolved by wet.

Hydraulic Limes are those which, in order to set, do not require any outside influences, their own chemical composition of lime and silica, when burnt, being sufficient for the purpose. The name is given for their capability of setting and hardening under water. Hydraulic limes are obtained mostly from the lias.

Good Hydraulic Limes are obtained from many places in the United States and Canada, the best known is "The Rosendale Hydraulic Cement."

Artificial Hydraulic Limes may be made by mixing a sufficient quantity of clay with pure lime to obtain a composition like that of a good natural hydraulic limestone. The lime, if soft, may be mixed with the clay and burnt raw, or, as is more usual, may be burnt, slaked, ground, and then mixed with the clay and reburnt.

The Purer the Lime the quicker will it slake. Great care should be taken that the lime is properly burnt or otherwise it will not slake properly, and will probably "blow" in the work.

The Perfect Slaking of the burnt lime before being used is very important, as it will slake eventually, and cause blisters in the work. In order to effect thorough slaking, the lime should be "run" as soon as the building is commenced. It should not be used unless it has been slaked at least three weeks.

A Bushel of Lime requires in slaking about a gallon and a half of water.

Lime which Slakes Quickly and with great heat is generally considered to be the best for plasterers' work.

When Lime "Falls" in dry weather without any sufficient apparent moisture, it is considered to foretell rain.

The Lime Should Be Run in couch on the site, where it can be seen by the architect. Care should be taken that as much lime is run as is required for the whole of the building.

The Plasterer, partly, perhaps, to avoid the money outlay, and partly to avoid the necessity of having to cart away any lime, has a tendency to run an insufficient quantity of lime. The result of this is that he, commencing at the top, the usually less important part of the building, has used up his lime by the time he has reached the principal rooms on the ground floor, and has to have recourse to possibly insufficiently seasoned lime, with an unfortunate effect on the work, as stated above.

SAND.

The Functions of Sand as used in plaster are (1) the production of regular shrinkage and the prevention of excessive shrinkage, otherwise cracking is the result; (2) to form channels for the crystallization.

Sand should be clean, sharp, and hard. The size of the grains does not influence the strength of the mortar, but, of course, the finer the plaster is required to be the finer must the sand be. Fine sand is best for hydraulic lime and coarse for fat limes, coarse stuff and Portland cement for floating. Uniformity of size is not desirable.

The Proportion of Sand to Lime will vary considerably, according to circumstances, and is difficult to determine. One part of lime to two parts of sand is a usual mixture.

Sand is Cheaper than Lime, and it must be remembered that this is an inducement to use too large a proportion of sand in order to cheapen the plaster.

Sand is Obtained from rivers, pits, or the sea. Sea sand, or that from tidal rivers, should be avoided, as the salt never dries, and will come out on the surface sooner or later, discoloring the wall papers, paint, etc., and keeping the walls damp.

River Sand is often used, but it is not to be recommended, because the sharpness of the grains is worn off by the action of the running water. It is easily obtained, however, and the light color of much river sand causes it to be used in internal work with the white cements.

Pit Sand is the best. It sometimes contains loam or clay, which should be carefully washed out.

All Sand for High-Class Plastering is best washed.

HAIR.

Hair is used in plaster in order to bind it together.

Good Hair should be long, curled, strong, and clean. Ox or cow hair is most generally used, and there are three qualities.

It Should Be Well Separated before being mixed with the plaster, and care should be taken in the mixing that the hairs are not broken.

CEMENTS.

Portland Cement, with a large proportion of sand, as much as 90 per cent., is useful for internal work; it may be used as a backing for a thin floating of the white cements.

The Heavier and Slower in Setting cements are generally the stronger; but in such plasterer's work as rendering walls the quicker setting cements may be used without disadvantage.

Roman Cement is a "natural" cement. It is liable to effloresce on the surface, but is useful where quick setting with expansion is required, as in underpinning or repairs, without any great ultimate strength.

Other "Natural Cements" very similar to Roman are Medina, Rosendale, Windsor, etc., and are also useful where quick setting is required.

The Use of the Natural Cements is much restricted at the present time as compared with artificial cements, such as Portland.

Parian Cement is valuable for internal work, by reason of its hardness, nonporosity, and quick setting properties. It is hence useful in cases where the walls mouldings, etc., have to stand rough usage. It is also washable. This cement will not admit of being reworked.

Keene's Cement is one of the most useful of the artificial cements. It is harder than the other kinds made from plaster of Paris, and is much used for pilasters, columns, etc., as it sets quickly and can be polished, and takes paint excellently.

Martin's Cement is much the same as Keene's, and used principally for dadoes, etc. In proportion to its bulk it covers a large proportion of surface. It can be painted, etc., as Keene's.

Robinson's Cement has many advantages, among which are its fire-resisting qualities and suitability for use on concrete. It is also cheaper than other like cements.

Adamant is another white cement, which is useful for work where hardness, facility of application, quick drying, and a fine surface are required.

The Above Cements have plaster of Paris (calcined gypsum) for their base, and are only adapted for internal uses, to which they are eminently suited. They can all be brought to a good surface, and can be painted almost at once.

Selenitic Cement is based on the property which sulphate of lime as plaster of Paris, when added to lime possessing hydraulic properties, has of causing its more rapid setting. It also increases the proportion of sand which it will bear. It is useful in plastering as a backing for the white cements, such as Parian.

PLASTER OF PARIS.

Plaster of Paris is made by the gentle calcination of gypsum, previously ground. It is known in the plastering trade as plaster.

The Principal Use of Plaster of Paris is in mixing with ordinary putty in order to produce greater rapidity in setting, but the fast setting plasters of Paris are not, of course, the best for working with, nor do they become as hard as the slower setting.

The Proportion of Plaster of Paris to ordinary lime putty varies greatly from about 1 in 4 to 1 in 20, depending on circumstances, such as the state of the weather, the speed with which the work has to be finished, etc. It is also used largely for cast ornaments, in cornices, etc., and, by reason of its quick setting and expansion when setting, for stopping holes, etc.

LATHS.

Pine, Cedar and Metal are used for laths for modern work; only the best quality should be used.

Oak Laths and Cypress formerly used, are very liable to warp.

The Defects to Be Avoided in Laths are sap, knots, crookedness, and undue smoothness. The sap decays; the knots weaken the laths; the crookedness interferes with the even laying on of the stuff; and the undue smoothness does not give sufficient hold for the plaster on the lath.

Riven Laths, split from the log along its fibres, are stronger than sawn laths, as in the latter process the fibres of the wood are often cut through.

Laths May Be Obtained in Three Sizes, namely: "Single" (average 1-8 in. to 3-16 in. thick), "lath and half" (average ¼ in. thick) and "double" (⅜ in. to ½ in. thick).

The Thicker Laths should be used in the ceilings, because of the strain upon them, and the thinner in vertical partitions, etc., where there is but little strain. Where walls and partitions have to stand rough usage the thicker laths are necessary.

Laths Are Usually Spaced with about ⅜ in. between them for key.

A Bunch of Laths usually contains a hundred pieces, and such a bunch nailed, with butt joints, cover about

$4\frac{1}{2}$ yds. super., and requires about 500 nails if nailed to joists 1 ft. from center to center.

The Lengths of Laths vary from 3 ft. to 4 ft., the latter the usual length.

Laths Are Best Nailed so as to Break Joint entirely, as for various reasons there is a tendency to crack along the line of the joints if nailed with the butt ends in a row. This may be obviated by using 3 ft. and 4 ft. laths together. Ceilings are much stronger if so nailed. Laths, however, are usually nailed in bays, about 4 ft. or 5 ft. deep.

Every Lath should be nailed at each end, and wherever it crosses a joist or stud.

Lap Joints at the end of laths, which are often made in order to save nails, should not be allowed as this leaves only $\frac{1}{4}$ in. for the thickness of plaster. Butt joints should always be made.

Joists, etc., which are thicker than 2 in. should have small fillets nailed on their under side or be counter-lathed, so that the timber surface of attachment be reduced to a minimum and the key be not interfered with.

Walls which are liable to damp are sometimes battened or strapped.

Metal Lathing is now extensively used for its fireproof qualities and freedom from rot or harboring of vermin.

Lathing Nails are usually of iron—galvanized, cut, wire, or cast; where oak laths are used, the nails should be galvanized or wrought. Galvanized nails should also be used with white cement work. Zinc nails, which are expensive, are used in very good work, because of the possibility of the discoloration of the plaster by the rusting of iron nails.

The Length of Lathing nails depends on the thickness of the laths, ¾ in. long nails being used for shingle laths, 1 in. nails for lath and half laths, and 1¼ in. nails for double laths.

MEMORANDA.

One Yard Rendering requires 1-3 cu. ft. lime, ½ cu. ft. sand, 2½ oz. hair, and 1¾ gal. water. One yard render and set requires ½ cu. ft. lime, ½ cu. ft. sand, 3 oz. hair, and 2 gal. water.

One yard render, 2 coats and set, requires 3-5 cu. ft. lime, 2-3 cu. ft. sand, 3 oz. hair, and 2½ gal. water.

One yard render and float requires ½ cu. ft. lime, ¾ cu. ft. sand, 2½ oz. hair, and 2½ gal. water.

One yard render, float and set, requires 3-5 cu. ft. lime, ¾ ft. sand, 3½ oz. hair, and 2¾ gal. water.

Two bushels of gray lime, or 3 of blue lias lime, or 3 of Roman cement, or 2 of Portland cement, or 14 lbs. plaster of Paris, equal one bag.

1 lb. hair is allowed to 2 cu. ft. of coarse stuff for good work, and 3 cu. ft. for common work.

100 yd. super. of lime whiting, if once done requires 1½ cu. ft. of lime; and if twice done, 2 cu. ft. of lime.

WORKMANSHIP.

EXTERNAL WORK.

Portland Cement is unquestionably the best material for external plastering. For weather resisting properties, strength, and capacity for moulding and painting, it is unequalled.

The Cement for Rendering requires to be mixed with sand in the proportion of about 1 of cement to 4 of sand, but for projecting cornices, etc., the proportion of sand should be only about half this, as, of course, the addition of sand decreases the adhesive power of the cement. The fining coat is mixed in the proportions of about 2 to 1.

External Facades in Portland Cement are usually laid in two coats; the first coat, known as the rendering or floating coat, is worked to screeds, and is from ½ in. to ¾ in. thick. This coat must be carefully cleared and well wetted for the second coat, which is known as the finishing or fining coat, which is about 3-16 in. thick, and is worked with a hand float.

The Key for External Plastering on brick work may be obtained either by building the walls roughly with the mortar projecting or by raking the joints at least ¾ in. Stone work should be hacked.

The Surface Must Be Well Wetted, or the wall will absorb the water from the rendering coat.

There is a Tendency to Mix Fat Lime with Portland cement in order to make it work more freely, but this should not be allowed.

Stucco is the term which is loosely applied to all kinds of external plastering, whether of lime or cement. An enormous amount of "stucco" was done at the end of the eighteenth century and the beginning of the nineteenth, but is now out of fashion, except for country and suburban residences. The term is also applied to some forms of internal plastering. The principal varieties of stucco are common, rough, bastard, and trowelled, but cement has largely superseded them.

Common Stucco was principally employed for exterior work, and was composed of 1 part hydraulic lime and 3 parts sand. The surface of the wall should be rough and wet as for Portland cement rendering.

Rough Stucco was used on a floated ground in positions where it was desired to imitate stone. It was worked with a hand float covered with a material such as rough cloth, in order to raise the sand and produce a stone-like appearance. Cement is now used for the same purpose.

Bastard Stucco and Trowelled Stucco were chiefly adapted for painted internal work, and each is laid on the second coat as a finish; the first and second coats being as for ordinary three-coat work.

Trowelled Stucco consists of 1 part sand to 2 parts fine stuff. It is worked with the hand float till a very fine smooth surface is produced.

Bastard Stucco contains a little hair and has not so much labor expended upon it.

Sgraffito is the name given to ornament which is scratched on plaster work. Patterns may be obtained by laying differently colored coats (usually two or three) on ordinary roughened Portland cement rendering, and removing portions of each coat in the form of a pattern.

The Design for the Sgraffito is applied in a cartoon and pricked and pounced on the work in the usual way. If more colors are required than the coats provide, the background may be washed and a combination of sgraffito and fresco used. The cutting should be deep enough to give a sharp appearance, but not too deep to hold dirt and wet.

Rough Cast, also known as pebble dashing, is the coarsest kind of external plastering. It is very durable if properly mixed. Its use in this country dates back to very early times. The wall is first plastered, and gravel, shingle, or other materials such as spar, broken bricks and glass bottles, broken pottery, etc., are thrown or dashed at it while it is soft. If the gravel is mixed and laid with the plaster there is a tendency in laying for it to tear the plaster away from the wall, and as the gravel is covered with plaster its appearance is not so good. The lime for rough cast should be weather resisting, and is generally used hot.

Depeter is a form of rough cast on which the gravel is pressed in by the hand. Ornamental patterns in color may be worked in it. Effective but simple decorations for external plaster may be made in various ways. Patterns, such as sunflowers, etc., may be incised in it, and a very effective decoration has been obtained by merely tapping the plaster with a scratch six or seven times alternately in a diaper pattern. In half-timber work the plaster is much more pleasing if carefully laid with a carelessly unlevel surface, and, of course, set back from the timber face about ¾ in.

INTERNAL WORK.

Lime Plastering is compounded of lime, sand, hair and water. The proportions of these materials vary according to their nature and the position of the plaster. For successful work good materials and skillful mixing are essential. It is applied in one, two, or three coats, and by the number of these the plaster is named.

The Thinner the Coats of plaster are the better, as the plaster has a better chance of drying and hardening.

One-Coat Work, necessarily the commonest and cheapest, is limited to very inferior buildings, such as outhouses and places where it will not be seen, as behind skirtings. One-coat work on laths is specified as "lath and lay," or "lath and plaster," and on walls simply as "render."

Two-Coat Work is that usually employed in inferior work, such as factories, warehouses, etc., but it is also used for the least important rooms in better class buildings. Common setting for walls and ceilings is generally used for this class of work. Two-coat work on laths is specified as "lath, lay, and set," or "lath, plaster, and set," and on walls as "render, and set."

Three-Coat Work is that used in all good buildings, and forms a most satisfactory wall finish, when well done. Three-coat work on laths is specified as "lath, lay, float, and set," or "lath, plaster, float, and set," and on walls as "render, float, and set."

The Processes in Plastering ordinary three-coat work are as follows:

For the First Coat a layer of well-haired coarse stuff known as pricking-up is laid to a thickness of about ½ in. This should be laid diagonally and with each trowelful overlapping. If on laths it should be soft enough to be well worked through them to form a key. The surface is then scratched with a lath to form a key for the next coat in lines about 4 in. apart. It is ready for the second coat when too hard to receive an impression from ordinary pressure.

The Coarse Stuff used in the first coat is mortar composed of sand and lime, usually in the proportions of 2 to 1, with plenty of hair, so that when a trowelful is taken up it holds well together and does not drop.

The Second Coat known as floating, is next laid. Four processes are involved in laying the second coat, namely: Running the screeds, filling in the spaces, scouring and keying the surface. The scouring is done with a hand float, the surface being sprinkled by a brush during the process. The keying consists in lining the scoured surface with a broom or nail float to form an adhesive surface for the finishing coat.

The Floating is of finer quality than the coarse stuff, it does not contain as much hair, and is used in a softer state.

The Third Coat is the finishing coat, and is known as the setting coat. Great care must be taken in laying this coat in order to obtain uniformity of surface, color, smoothness, and hardness. The second coat should be uniformly keyed, clean and damp before the third is laid. The processes involved are laying, scouring, trowelling, and brushing.

Fine Stuff, which should be used for the finishing coat if the walls are to be papered, consists of pure lime, slaked and then saturated till semi-fluid, and allowed to stand till the water has evaporated and it forms a paste. It may then be thoroughly mixed with fine sand in the proportion of 3 parts of sand to 1 part of fine stuff.

Plasterers' Putty is much like fine stuff, but is carefully sieved.

Gauged Stuff is plasterers' putty and plaster of Paris in the proportion of three or four to one. If too much plaster is used it cracks in setting. It is largely used in cornices, and also where the second coat is not allowed time to dry, and the work has to be done in a hurry. As it sets rapidly, it must be mixed in small quantities.

The White Cements (such as Parian, etc.), of which plaster of Paris is the base, are usually laid in two coats; the first, of cement and sand, is about ½ in. to ¾ in. thick, and the second of the cement neat.

Cracks in Plaster Work are caused, apart from the natural settlement of the building and the use of inferior materials and workmanship, by the too fast drying of the work, the laying of the plaster on walls of too great suction, by laying one coat on another before the lower one has properly set, and by the use of too little sand.

Joist Lines on Ceilings are very unsightly, and are caused by the filtration of dust through the intervening spaces. They may be prevented by using a good thickness of plaster, and working it well, that it may be hard and nonabsorbent and as the dust comes from the top and filters through, by protecting the upper side of the plaster.

Pugging consists in laying a quantity of plaster between the joists of a floor or between the studding of a partition for the purpose of preventing the passage of sounds or odors. In the first case, which is the more common, the plaster is laid on thin, rough boards fixed to battons on the sides of the joists; in the second case. which is called "counterlathing" in some parts of the country, by plastering on laths nailed between the partition studs.

Pugging Should Not Be Used Too Wet. There are three objections to this—the first that it takes a very long and inconvenient time in drying; and secondly, that the water is liable to be absorbed by the wood, and to cause it to rot; and thirdly, it is liable to crack in the drying. For this last reason it should always be laid in two coats.

The Battons should all be nailed at an equal depth from the tops of the joists, and the plaster should be of an equal thickness throughout, which is obtained by drawing a trammel along the joists.

Mineral Wool is far more sanitary than ordinary pugging, has considerable sound and fire resisting qualities, it does not absorb moisture and so rot the laths and timbers, is a preventive of vermin, and is light in weight.

Lime Whiting or Whitewash which is lime dissolved in water, is a useful and sanitary covering for the walls of cellars and outhouses.

If Lime-Whited Walls Have to Be Plastered, the wall should be first carefully picked, as if the lime is left on, the plaster is liable to scale.

Fibrous Plaster is composed of plaster, canvas, wood, etc. It is light and dry and can be quickly fixed.

Ornamental Plaster ceilings may be either modelled throughout in situ, or cast in pieces, or formed by working the ornament on a previously formed flat ceiling. The first method is the more costly, but more feeling is thereby obtained.

SPECIFICATION CLAUSES.

MATERIALS.

1. The sand for plastering is to be fresh-water river, or pit sand, and free from earthy, loamy, or saline material, to be well screened, and to be washed if required.

2. The laths to be straight-riven or saron pine of the strength known as lath and half, well nailed with lin. oxidized lath nails, properly spaced for key, and with butt-headed joints, double nailed, and breaking joint in 3 ft. widths.

The lathing to be "Expanded metal," No. — gauge.

3. The lime for coarse stuff to be approved well-burnt grey-stone lime, to be run at least one month before being required for use, to be kept clean, and well mixed as required with two parts sand and one part lime.

4. The coarse stuff for ceilings, lath partitions, and elsewhere where directed to have 1 lb. of good, long curled cowhair, free from grease, leading, or other impurities, well beaten in, and incorporated with every 3 cu. ft. of coarse stuff.

5. Approved lime, free from lumps, flares, or core, is to be used for setting, putty, etc., and is to be run at least one month before being required for use.

6. The Portland cement is to be of the best quality and description for plastering purposes, from an approved manufacturer, and must on no account be used fresh, but be spread out to cool for at least .... weeks in a dry shed or room.

All suitable cement and all other materials required in plastering are to be of the best of their respective kinds and descriptions.

7. Provide all plasterers' plant, necessary scaffoldings, tools, moulds, running rules, straight edges, templates, etc., of every kind and description necessary for the proper execution of the work.

WORKMANSHIP.

8. Lath, plaster, float, and set all wood joist ceilings, soffits, and stud partitions, and finish partitions to line in trowelled stucco.

The concrete ceilings and soffits are to be well hacked for key and floated and set in gauged stuff, and the concrete partitions are to be floated and set.

Do all dubbing out where required to concrete ceilings, soffits, and partitions in gauged stuff.

The concrete soffits of strong rooms to be finished with one coat of putty gauged with plaster only.

9. Cover all chases containing pipes, etc., with heavy wire lathing suitable for plastering on, securing the same in a thorough manner. The wire lathing to be wetted in lime water before being put on.

10. Render, float, and set all walls where not otherwise described. The walls to ...... to be finished in trowelled stucco.

11. All cornices and moulded work throughout to be run clean and accurately to the sections given.

All mitres and returns to be truly worked, and all enrichments and modelling to be to architect's approval, and strictly in accordance with the models and instructions given.

Run moulded plaster cornices .... girt to .... rooms,

with all mitres, returned, stopped, and mitred ends, etc., as required.

The cornices to .... are to be run in fibrous plaster, fitted and fixed with proper oxidized nails, and made good to.

12. All narrow reveals, splays, and returns to be finished in suitable cement on a Portland cement backing.

Run strong cement angles and arrises on Portland cement backing to all projecting angles except the following, which are to be moulded, viz.: ....

Run rounded angles to ...... of 3 in. girt in strong cement as before.

Run avolo moulded angles 3 in. girt with 2 in. wings to .... opening, finished with moulded stops and short lengths of angle and arris to detail, all in best cement.

All exposed surfaces of concrete lintels and girder casings are to be finished in white cement internally and Portland cement externally, kept flush with faces of brickwork; all with arrises and angles excepting those otherwise described.

13. Run Portland cement flush skirting 9 in. high to basement, where plastered, with flush head to top and trowelled face.

The skirting to ...... to be 12 in. high and 1 in. projection, sunk and twice moulded in white on Portland cement backing.

Float off the concrete floors of .... in Portland cement to the required level to receive mosaic and the pavings.

14. Run all necessary quirks, splays, arrises, etc., and make good to all mantelpieces; cut away for and make good after all other trades, and cut out and make

good all cracks, blisters, and other defects, and leave plaster work perfect at completion.

15. Ding walls where shown on plans with a coat of Portland cement 1 part, sand 2 parts, pea-grit 1 part, and ground chalk 1 part. Finish walls where shown with a rough coat of Portland cement 1 part and sand 3 parts, and rough cast with fine pea-grit.

16. Stop and twice lime white soffits and walls of . .

17. Twice distemper white all ceilings, soffits, and cornices, and twice distemper to approved tints the walls of all rooms.

PREPARATION OF BILL OF QUANTITIES.

MATERIALS.

Materials and Plant, etc.—1 to 7. These items appear in the heading under Specification clauses.

WORKMANSHIP.

Ceilings, Partitions, and Walls.—8 and 10. These are all billed at per yd. super. including lathing where required, also hacking concrete and any dubbing in the latter, stating the thickness. Keep all plaster work less than 12 in. wide separate in "narrow widths."

Wirelathing.—9. These being narrow, it is advisable to measure them at per ft. run, stating the width.

Cornices.—11. Cornices and mouldings under 12 in. girt are measured at per ft. run and those over this girt at per ft. super. number all mitres, stoppings, etc.; those to the running items following same, and those to the superficial items averaged for girt. See whether bracketing is required; if so, take the girt required at per ft. super., numbering angle brackets to mitres and returned ends, and averaging the girt.

Measure the walls and ceilings less by the height and projection of the cornice, and add to the girt of the cornice 2 in. (i. e., 1 in. for each edge) for the portion up to the ceiling and walls.

Enrichments are measured at per ft. run, giving the girt and description, and including the modelling. If of exceptional character, a provision for modelling is sometimes inserted.

Angles.—12. These appear in bill in feet run with the girt of moulding or bead (if any) and also the widths of returns. Number the stops, mitres, etc., allowing each to follow the item to which they apply.

The finishings to concrete beams, lintels, etc., is kept separate as in "narrow widths to beams, etc.," and all arrises, etc., being measured at per ft. run.

Skirtings or Dadoes.—13. Describe skirtings or dadoes giving height and projection, and also finish at top, and measure at per ft. run, numbering all mitres, ends, etc. Include the dubbing with the item. The general wall plastering is deducted for these.

Floating for mosaic and tile pavings appears in the bill in yard super.

Quirks.—14. Labor to splays, quirks, arrises, etc., are measured at per ft. run.

The attendance on trades is frequently measured in detail, as "making good around mantels" or gratings, etc.

The cutting-out and making good appears at the end of the bill in the form here given.

Rough Cast.—15. As clauses 8 and 10.

Lime Whiting and Distempering.—16 and 17. These appear in the bill in yd. super. In the case of distempering, if the colors are in any way special mention this, and also if in dadoes and filling, taking the dividing line in feet run.

Distempering on cornices is usually measured in ft. super., stating the number of tints, and if lines picked out in ft. run; as is also distempering on enrichments, taking the latter as "extra to," the distempering to cornices being measured over enrichments.

LATHS GENERALLY.

General opinion is undoubtedly in favor of split laths, and split laths are sometimes specified by architects for ceilings and partitions. Sawn laths, unless cut from specially selected straight-grained stuff, would most assuredly have weak places from uneven grain, and in order to avoid this weakness the sawn laths would have to be made thicker than split laths, and only the best quality should be used. Oak laths, formerly used, are very liable to warp. The defects that are to be avoided in laths are sap, knots, crookedness, and undue smoothness. The sap decays; the knots weaken the laths; the crookedness interferes with the even laying on of the stuff, and the undue smoothness does not give sufficient hold for the plaster on the lath. Riven laths, split from the log along its fibres, are stronger than sawn laths, as in the latter process the fibres of the wood are often cut through. Sawn laths are, however, cheaper than riven laths, and have superseded them, which is not desirable in good work. Thick laths, because of the strain upon them, should be used in the ceilings, and the thinner laths should be used in vertical partitions, etc., where the strain is but small. Some walls and partitions have to stand rough usage; in such cases the thicker laths are necessary. Laths are usually spaced with about 3/8 in. between them for key. A bunch of laths usually contains 360 lin. ft. and such a bunch nailed with butt joints, covers about 4½ super. yd., and requires about 400 nails if the laths are nailed to joists 16 in. from center to center. The length of laths varies from 3 ft. to 4 ft. Laths are best nailed so as to break joint entirely, because, for various reasons, there is a tendency to crack along the line of the joints if the laths are nailed with the butt ends in a row. This may be obviated by breaking joints; ceilings are much stronger if the laths are nailed in this way. Laths, however, are usually nailed in bays, about 4 ft. or 5 ft. deep. Every lath should be nailed at each end, and also at the place where the lath crosses a joist or stud. Lap joints at the end of laths, which are often made in order to save nails, should not be allowed, as this leaves only 1/4 in. for the thickness of plaster. Butt joints should always be made. Joists, etc., that are thicker than two in., should have small fillets nailed to the under side, or be counter lathed, so that the timber surface of attachment may be reduced to a minimum and the key not interfered with.

Lathing nails are usually of iron, and are galvanized, cut, wrought, or cast; where oak laths are used, the nails should be oxidized or wrought. Oxidized nails should also be used with white cement work. Zinc nails, which are expensive, are used in very good work, because of the possibility of the discoloration of the plaster by the rusting of iron nails. The length of lathing nails depends on the thickness of the laths, 3/4 in. nails being used for single laths, and 1 1/4 in. nails for double laths.

TOOLS AND APPLIANCES USED BY THE PLASTERER.

The illustrations shown at Figs. 1 and 2 show a number of tools and appliances made use of by the plasterer, and others—special—will be shown further on, when it is necessary to describe and illustrate some special process or method of working. The tools the plasterer requires are many and varied, and may be enumerated about as follows: They consist of moulds for running cornices, and center moulds, which may never be used only in the one piece of work, as the designs and styles of cornices and centers are continually changing. As these tools do not cost much, however, the changes do not fall heavily on the workman; but it is as well, whenever it can be done, to charge each mould against its own particular job of work. A good spade and shovel will be absolutely necessary to the plasterer's outfit, and will be among the first tools he will require. These should be light and strong, and well handled, or helved; after using they should have all the lime and mortar cleaned off them, and should be placed away where they will not be exposed to the weather.

The following list and descriptions of tools will give a new beginner an idea of the kind and character of tools he will be likely to require before he can successfully carry on the plastering business. Most of these tools will be illustrated further on:

The Hoes and Drags.—These are tools so well known that they require no description here. They are used

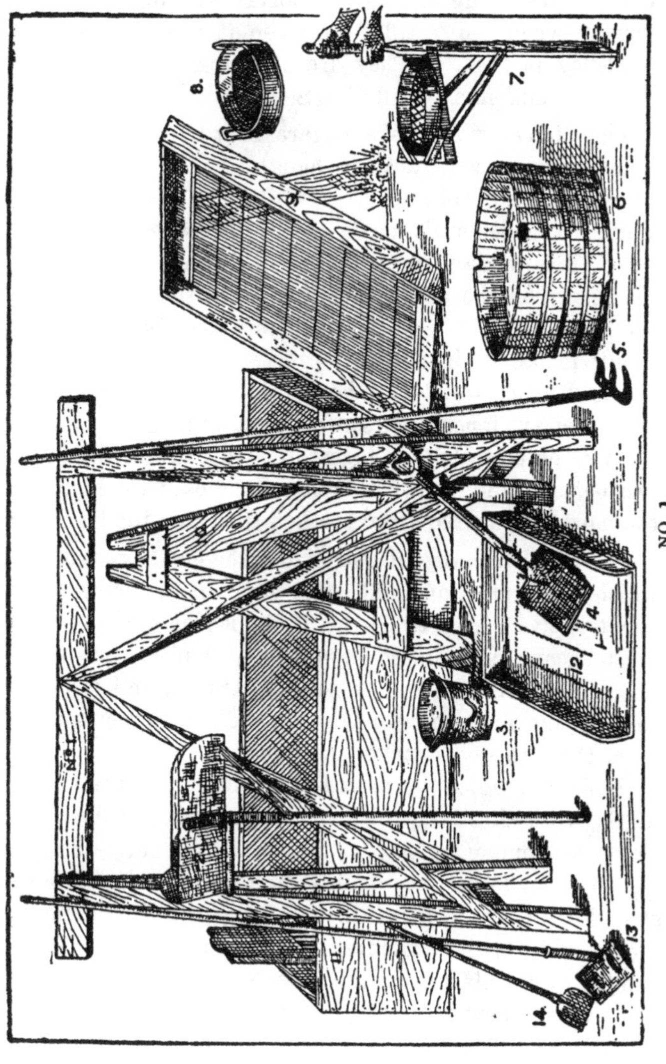

NO. 1

chiefly for mixing hair in the mortar, and for loosening mortar when too "stiff," or when it has developed a tendency to "set." They are also used for preparing "putty" and fine "stuff." (See Fig. 2.)

The Hawk, which is a square board about thirteen inches square, with a short handle on the under side. It is used for holding stuff while the operator is at work. It is generally made of pine or some other light wood; it is made thin on the edges, being beveled from the center on the under side to each of the four edges; the handle should be about six inches long, and one and a half inches in diameter.

The Mortar-Board is a board similar to a table top, and is about forty inches square; it is made by jointing two or more boards together, which are secured by two battens, and screws or nails. It is used for holding the mortar delivered from the hod direct by the laborer.

Trowels, which are of two kinds: the ordinary trowel, which is formed of light steel four inches wide and about twelve inches long; this is the laying and smoothing tool, and is the most important in a plasterer's outfit. The other is termed a gauging trowel, and is used for gauging fine stuff for courses, etc.; it varies in size from three to seven inches in length.

Of Floats, which are used for floating, there are three kinds, viz.: the darby, which is not a proper float, is single or double, as may be required; the single being for one man to use, the double for two. The single one should be four feet five inches long, and about four inches wide, with a handle near one end, like a hawk handle, and a cleat near the other end running lengthwise of the blade; the long darbys have a hawk handle on each end. The hard float, which is used in finishing, and the quick float, which is used in floating angles.

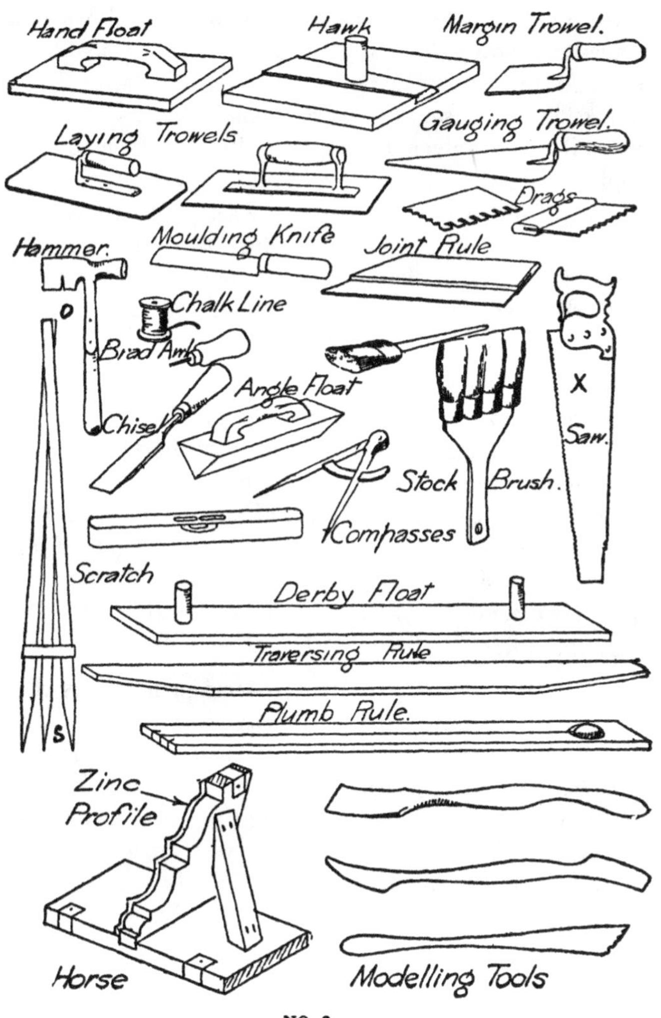
Hand Float
Hawk
Margin Trowel.
Laying Trowels
Gauging Trowel.
Drags
Hammer.
Moulding Knife
Joint Rule
Chalk Line
Brad Awl
Angle Float
Chisel
Stock
Brush.
X
Saw.
Compasses
Scratch
Derby Float
Traversing Rule
Plumb Rule.
S
Zinc Profile
Horse
Modelling Tools

NO. 2

The hard float is made of good pine, and has a semicircular handle on the back; a strip of hard wood is sometimes dovetailed into the blade, and the handle is screwed fast to the strip previous to the latter being driven in the dovetail; this is a good way, as there are no nails then driven through the blade, which, by the rapid wearing of the latter, would soon project above the blade and scratch the plaster where it was intended to have it smooth. The quick float is seldom used in this country; it is shaped like the angle it is intended to work down, and is a trifle handier for this purpose than the ordinary hard float.

Moulds.—These are used for running stucco cornices, and are infinite in shape and variety. The reverse of the contour of the cornice is cut out of sheet copper or iron, and is firmly attached to a piece of wood which is also cut out the reverse shape of the intended moulding. Their uses will be explained under the head of Operations. Moulds or matrices for leaves, flowers, or other ornaments are made of plaster and glue, or beeswax; these will be discussed hereafter.

Center-Moulds are made on the same principle as the reverse moulds for linear cornices, with an arm attached which is perforated at different radii to suit the diameter of center-piece. Sometimes the moulds for cornicing are so formed, by placing the plates at an angle of forty-five degrees, that they will finish the cornice right into the angle and form the mitre; more frequently, however, the mitres are finished by hand.

The Pointer is nearly the same shape as a bricklayer's trowel, but it is not so large, being only about four inches long. It is chiefly used for small jobbing, or mending broken or defective work.

The Paddle is simply a piece of pine wood less than three inches wide and six long, by one thick; it is made wedge shaped on one end, the other end being rounded off for a handle. Its use is to carry stuff into angles when finishing.

Stopping and Picking-Out Tools, or, as they are frequently called, Mitering Tools, are made of fine steel plate, seven or eight inches long, and of various widths and shapes. They are used for modeling, and for finishing mitres and returns to cornices by hand where the moulds cannot work.

Mitering-Rod.—This is a tool one foot or more long, and about one-eighth of an inch thick, and three inches wide; the longest edge is sharp, and one end is bevelled off to about thirty degrees. It is used for cleaning out quirks in mouldings, angles, and cornices.

The Operator also requires a good whitewashing brush with a short handle. The best should be obtained, as it will prove the cheapest in the end.

A Scratcher is generally made of short pieces of pine two inches wide and one inch thick; three or four of them are nailed to two cleats, and are placed about an inch apart. The center slat should be about eighteen inches longer than the others, so as to form a handle. See illustrations. The slats on the opposite end to the handle should be cut off square with one side and pointed. Its use is to make grooves, or bond in what is called the scratch coat. When completed it has somewhat the appearance of a gridiron.

Hod.—This is formed by two boards, eleven and twelve inches wide, respectively, and eighteen inches long, the wide board being nailed on the edge of the narrow one, making a right-angled trough; one end is closed, and the end piece is rounded over the top; the boards forming the sides are rounded at the opening. A handle about four feet long and two inches in diameter is then fastened about two inches forward of the middle nearer to the open end, and a piece of wood called a pad is fitted with a groove on the angle just back of the handle. The object of this block is to prevent the arris of the hod from chafing the shoulder of the laborer. Much controversy has taken place among workmen at various times regarding the exact size of hod, but this, I think, should be governed more by the strength of the person who has to use the particular hod than by any fixed rules. Hods for carrying mortar need not be so large as hods intended for carrying bricks. (See No. 2, Fig. 1.)

Sieve.—This is used for straining through putty for finishing; it requires to be very fine for the purpose. Sometimes a hair sieve is used, but they are not lasting, and should never be used when a wire sieve is obtainable. Sometimes a hair sieve may prove convenient where dry plaster or cements have to be run through a sieve of some kind before it can be used; so, on the whole, the plasterer who desires a full and complete outfit, should provide himself with one good hair sieve, and at least two sieves of wire. (See Fig. 7, No. 1.)

Sand Screens are usually twenty-one inches wide inside by about six feet long. On small work they are stood up at an angle of forty-five or more degrees, and the sand is shovelled against them; in some large works the screen is suspended, and one man shovels in the sand and a second one swings or shakes the screen. These screens, to be lasting, should have their sides and ends made of sheet iron, and the bottom should be formed with parallel rods of small round iron having wires running across them at regular intervals. These cross wires should be attached to the iron rods so as to hold them in place. The parallel rods may be placed at such distances from each other as will be most convenient for the work in hand.

Mortar Beds are made of rough lumber of any kind, and should be built partly in the ground, where circumstances will permit. They require to be strongly put together, as they have considerable weight to sustain. The writer has seen mortar beds built up with bricks and cement where large works have been under construction. Sometimes, master workmen, who do a large business, and who employ a great number of men, keep a large mortar bed or two in the rear yard of their shop and tool house, in which they keep always on hand a supply of ready-made stuff, which enables them to do small jobs or repairs at a moment's notice.

The Slack Box.—This is generally made of boards, and is eight or nine feet long, and from two to four feet wide, and twelve or sixteen inches in depth. An opening about eight inches square is left in one end, with a slide door attached, so that it can be opened or closed at pleasure. The opening should be covered on the inside with a grating, so that when the lime is run off no lumps or stones will get through. The grating may be made with iron rods, or may be formed with wooden laths or slats. The bottom of the box should be made as close and tight as rough boards will permit. (See No. 1, Fig. 11.)

Lathing.—It frequently happens in towns and country places that the plasterer has to do his own lathing, or at least have it done under his own supervision, therefore it will be necessary to have something to say on this subject, and on the tools employed by the workman whose duty it is to prepare the walls for the plasterer. These tools need not be extravagant ones or many in number. They consist of the following:

Lather's Hatchet.—This is a small hatchet with a blade not more than one and a half inches wide, and rather larger in proportion than ordinary hatchets. The opposite end to the cutting edge is a hammer, with which the lather drives the nails. Sometimes the face of the hammer end is grooved, which makes it cling to the nails if the latter are not struck fairly on the head. An expert lather, however, will prefer a flat hammer face for driving lath nails. The cutting edge is used for "nipping" off laths when they are too long, or when short spaces of lathing are required to be made. In cutting lath with the hatchet, the workman gives the wood a short sharp blow with the tool at the point where the severance is required, and the lath is invariably cut at the first blow, if the operator is an expert. (See 0, Fig. 2.)

Nail Pocket.—Perhaps the best nail pocket a lather can have is made from a portion of an old boot leg cut off to about four inches deep, and having a bottom of semi-circular shape made of wood, and to which the portion of the boot is fastened by means of broad-headed tacks. The pocket is fastened to the workman's waist by means of a strap, or other suitable device, and hangs in front of him in a convenient position. Sometimes nail pockets are made of canvas, but these are not so handy, as the top is apt to close and then nails are difficult to get at. This never occurs with the boot leg pocket.

Cut-off Saw.—A cross-cut saw is an indispensable tool to the lather for cutting lath in larger quantities for short spaces, and for rigging up platforms to work on, and for cutting supplementary studding or strips where such are necessary. The saw should have rather coarse teeth and have plenty of set. Usually, the lather thinks that almost any old used-up saw is good enough for this purpose, and we find him struggling away with all his strength cutting through a bundle of lath, when, if he had a saw that was worth anything—as a saw—he would perform his labors with about one-half the effort, and one-third of the time. It is all wrong to think of being able to work satisfactorily with inferior or imperfect tools. There is no economy in using tools of this kind, and any lather who fancies he is going to make or save anything by making use of an old buckled, mortar-stained saw, makes a terrible mistake. Get a good saw and keep it in good order, and it will pay you in two weeks. (See X, Fig. 2.) Besides these enumerated, there are many other tools and appliances that the plasterer will require, such as jointing rules, moulding knives, modelling tools, drags, chisels, compasses, plumb rules, etc.

PLASTER, LIME, CEMENTS, SAND, ETC.

Plaster of Paris.—Gypsum, from which plaster of Paris is made, is a sulphate of lime, and is so named from two Greek words—ge, the earth; and epsun, to concoct, i. e., concocted in the earth. In Italy it is known by the name of gesso; in Scotland it is called stucco; in this country it is known as calcined plaster; and in the English trade as plaster. The term "plaster" will henceforth be used in this book. The writings of Theophrastus and other Greek authors prove that the use of plaster was known to them. A stone, called by Theophrastus gypsos, chiefly obtained from Syria, was used by the ancients for converting into plaster. Gypsum is mentioned by Pliny as having been used by the ancient artists, and Strabo states that the walls of Tyre were set in gypsum. The Greeks distinguished two kinds—the pulverulent and the compact. The latter was obtained in lumps, which were burnt in the furnaces, and then reduced to plaster, which was used for buildings and making casts.

Gypsum is found in most countries—Italy, Switzerland, France, Sicily, The United States, and some of the South American States; also in Newfoundland and Canada. The latter is said to be the finest deposits in the world. It is found in England in many places. The finest gypsum is called "alabaster," and is soft, pure in color, and fragile. This white translucent material is a compact mass of crystalline grains, and is used for making small statuary, vases, and other ornaments. Gypsum is found in immense quantities in the tertiary strata of Montmartre, near Paris. This gypsum usually contains 10 per cent. of carbonate of calcium, not always in intimate union with the sulphate, but interspersed in grains. This sulphate gives the Paris plaster some of its most useful properties. Pantin, near Paris, has large beds of gypsum, one bed being horizontal and over 37 ft. thick.

The term "plaster of Paris" was mainly applied to it because gypsum is found in large quantities in the tertiary deposits of the Paris basin. Another reason is that lime and hair mortar is seldom used in Paris for plaster work, plaster of Paris being used for most kinds of internal and external work. Plaster is known in the color trade as terra alba. Plaster of Paris was known in England by the same name as early as the beginning of the thirteenth century. The gypsum, in blocks, was taken from France, and burnt and ground there. It continued to be burnt and ground by the users until the middle of the nineteenth century. The burning was done in small ovens, and the grinding in a mill, sometimes worked by horse-power, or more often by hand.

Plaster is the most vigorous as it is the oldest vehicle for carrying down generation after generation the masterpieces of art with which the golden age of sculpture enriched the human race. For reproductive uses, plaster enables youth to contemplate antiquity in its noblest achievements. Today plaster is revolutionizing industrial art for us, and in all probability for those who are to come after us. Plaster, lowly and cheap, but docile and durable, is the connecting agent with this greatest of men's endorsement in the past. Plaster thus employed in duplicating works of marble, pottery, and metal work, is today extending the finest industries, modern and ancient. Plaster is one of the best known fire-resisting materials for building purposes. After the conflagration at Paris, it was found the beams and columns of wood which had been plastered were entirely protected from fire. In cases where limestone walls had been ruined on the outside by the flames passing through the window openings, the same walls internally escaped almost unscathed owing to their being protected with plaster. Plaster in some climates has great lasting properties. The Egyptians covered their granite sometimes, and sand stone always, with a thin coating of stucco. The Greeks coated even their marble temples with plaster, and the plaster portions are now in better preservation than unprotected masonry, particularly at Agrigentum in Sicily.

Quick and Slow Setting Plaster.—M. Landrin, in giving the results of his long continued studies relative to the different qualities of gypsum, states that the more or less rapid setting of plaster is due to the mode in which it is burned. Its properties are very different when prepared in lumps or in powder. The former when mixed in its own weight of water sets in five minutes, while the latter under similar conditions takes fifteen minutes. The reason probably is that plaster in powder is more uniformly burned than when it is in lumps, which tends to prove this fact, that when the latter is exposed longer than usual to the action of heat it sets more slowly. Gypsum prepared at a high temperature loses more and more of its affinity for water, retaining, however, its property of absorbing its water of crystallization. Plaster heated to redness and mixed in the ordinary manner will no longer set; but if, instead of applying a large quantity of water, the smallest possible portion is used (say one-third of its weight), it will set in ten or twelve hours, and becomes extremely hard. To prepare good plaster, it should not be burned too quick to drive off all its moisture, and for its molecules to lose a part of their affinity for the water. If the plaster is exposed to heat until it has only lost 7 or 8 per cent. of its moisture it is useless, as it sets almost immediately. If, however, the burning is again resumed, the substance soon loses its moisture, and if then exposed to the air it very rapidly retakes its water of crystallization, and absorption continues more slowly. It then sets slowly, but attains great hardness.

Testing.—The quality of plaster may be tested by simply squeezing it with the hand. If it cohere slightly, and keeps in position after the hand has been gently opened, it is good; but if it falls to pieces immediately it has been injured by damp. Although plaster does not chemically combine with more than one-fourth of its weight of water, yet it is capable of forming a much larger quantity into a solid mass, the particles of plaster being converted into a network of crystals, mechanically enclosing the remainder of the water. Sulphate of lime (plaster) is soluble in water to the extent of 1 part in about 450, the solubility being but little influenced by temperature. It is on account of this solubility in water that cements which have to a large extent plaster for their bases are incapable in this raw state of bearing exposure to the weather. The setting of plaster is due to hydration, or its having but little water to take up to resume a state of consolidation. Plaster is used with hydraulic limes to stop the slaking, and convert the lime into cement. These are then called "selenitic."

In 100 parts of gypsum there are 46 acid, lime 32,

and water 22 parts. Good plaster should not begin to set too soon, and it should remain for a considerable time in a creamy state. When once set it should be very hard. Plaster should set slowly, as it gives more time for manipulation, but principally because one which sets quickly and swells never becomes so hard as slow-setting material. The quality of plaster cannot be determined by its color, the color being regulated by that of the gypsum; but all things being equal, the whitest and hardest generally yields the best plaster. But as the exception proves the rule, it may be mentioned that some plasters (such as Howe's) are of a delicate pink tint, and of a very fine grain, and exceedingly strong when gauged. This pink plaster is much appreciated by many plasterers for making originals, as owing to its fineness and density it is very suitable for cleaning or chasing up models taken from the clay, and also for durable moulding pieces. One of the whitest plasters known, which is also very close in texture, is that manufactured by Cafferata. For cast work the color of plaster is of small moment, because the cast work is sooner or later colored with paint, and moreover, unfortunately daubed over with distemper, or worse still, with whitewash. Coarse plasters are darker in color than fine. Coarse plasters of a sandy nature, and which rapidly sink to the bottom when put in water, contain too much silica, or improperly burnt gypsum, or are derived from a bastard gypsum, and are generally of a weak nature.

Compressive and Adhesive Strength.—The compressive resistance of properly baked plaster is about 120 lbs. to the square inch when gauged with neat water and 160 lbs. when gauged with lime water; thus showing that lime water hardens and improves the affinity of plaster. The adherence of plaster to itself is greater than to stone or brick. The adhesion to iron is from 24 to 37 lbs. the square inch.

French Plaster.—A considerable quantity of French plaster was formerly used in this country but our own is more uniform in quality and cheaper in price, so the use of the French material is somewhat limited. In Paris various kinds of gypsum mortars are in general use, raw gypsum and other materials being often intermixed. They also contain free carbonate of lime, according to the degree of heat to which the raw stone has been subjected. The Hotel de Platres, in Paris, affords a good illustration of the constructive uses to which plaster can be put, some of the blocks being about a hundred years old.

Limes.—Lime is one of the most important materials in the building trades. Limestone is the general term by which all rocks are roughly classified which have carbonate of lime for their basis. They are obtained from many geological formations, varying in quality and chemical properties. The carboniferous consists of nearly pure carbonate of lime. In the limestone of the lias carbonate of lime is associated with silica and alumina (common clay), in proportions varying from 10 to 20 per cent. Carbonate of lime is found in a state of chemical purity in rhombohedral crystals as Iceland spar. It is also found in six-sided prisms, known to mineralogists as arragonite. Its purest form as a rock is that of white marble. Colored marbles contain iron, manganese, etc.

The lias strata consists of a thin layer of hard limestone separated by another of a more argillaceous character, or shale, containing various proportions of carbonate of lime.

Hydraulic Limes.—Hydraulic limes are those which have the property of setting under water or in damp places, where they increase in hardness and insolubility. The blue lias lime formation is that from which hydraulic lime is principally made. This lime, while it has excellent hydraulic properties, can hardly be classed as a cement. The stones which produce these limes contain carbonate of lime, clay, and carbonate of magnesia. The clay plays an important part in giving hydraulicity to the lime, consequently this power is greater in proportion to the amount of clay contained in the lime. The proportion of clay varies from 10 to 30 per cent. When lime contains clay it is not so easily slaked as pure lime, and does not expand so much in doing so, and therefore does not shrink so much in setting.

Lias lime (called blue lias from the color of the stone from which it is produced) is very variable in quality and is generally of a feeble nature, but is sometimes of an hydraulic nature. M. Vicat divides them into three classes: feebly hydraulic, ordinary hydraulic, and eminently hydraulic. "Those belonging to the first class contain from 5 to 12 per cent. of clay. The slaking action is accompanied by cracking and heat. They also expand considerably, and greatly resemble the fat limes during this process. They are generally of a buff color. Those of the second class contain from 15 to 20 per cent. of clay. They slake very sluggishly in an hour or so without much cracking or heat, and expand very little. They set firmly in a week. The eminently hydraulic limes contain from 20 to 30 per cent. of clay, are very difficult to slake, and only do so after a long time. Very frequently they do not slake at all, being reduced to a powder by grinding. They set firmly in a few hours, and are very hard in a month."

A natural hydraulic lime is obtained from what appears to be a sedimentary limestone that has been formed by being deposited from water which held it in solution. It is very fine-grained, and contains almost no fossils, and scarcely the trace of a shell is to be seen, except at the top and bottoms of the divisions, which are four in number, and in all from 9 to 12 ft. thick. When first worked, the stone was slaked in hot kilns, but now this is effected by grinding. According to the "M'Ara" process, the "lime shells" from the kiln are ground in the same way as the clinker of Portland cement. Beginning with a stone-breaker, the lime passes from this to a pair of chilled crushing rollers, and finally to the millstones, after which the powder is carried by screw-conveyor and elevator to a rotary screen, 12 ft. by 4 feet, covered with wire cloth, which retains and returns to the millstones any residue in excess of the required fineness. Sifting is a very important factor in the process, as it is scarcely possible to have the millstones so perfect that they will not pass a few large particles.

The residue of imperfectly ground lime will doubtless slake when mixed with water, but at long or uncertain periods, so that it is obvious that fine grinding is a necessity, and the setting properties are not fully and safely developed unless the whole is finely pulverized. With regard to "Fat lime": the general practice is for lime producers to show their lime as rich as possible by analysis, and for users to prefer a rich lime, for the reason that it makes a more plastic and better working mortar with the usual quantity of sand. Now, it has been proved by experiments, many and varied, and extending over a long period, by the most eminent authorities, French, German, English and American, that this preference should exactly be reversed, and that the poorer common limes will make the best mortar, and will, in a comparatively short time, show some light setting power, whereas the very rich limes never take band, except in so far as they return to their original condition of carbonate by the reabsorption of carbonic acid from the atmosphere, and by the slow evaporation of the water of mixture. If it does not evaporate, the mortar remains always soft. If it evaporates too quickly, the mortar falls to powder, a result which must be in every one's experience who has witnessed the taking down of old buildings, and the clouds of dust created by the removal of every stone.

Some of the stones from which fat lime is produced contain a portion of sand as an impurity. They therefore yield an inferior substance. This, though cheaper, is not so economical as pure lime, as it does not increase its volume so much when slaked. The pure or fat lime should only be used for plastering, as it is easily slaked, and therefore not so liable to blister as most hydraulic limes. It expands to double its bulk when slaked, and can be left and reworked again and again without injuring it.

The Romans are said to have prepared their limes. This "lime putty," prepared by immersion for a longer or shorter period—seldom less than three weeks—before being used, is laid on in a very thin coat, and gives a hard skin to the surface. This hardness is largely, if not wholly, due to the fact that the lime is laid on in a thin layer on the floating coat that has already absorbed carbonic acid from the air. This thin layer becomes harder than the main body of the plaster.

The whole process of preparing lime and laying it on the walls in thin coats, with a considerable space of time between the coating, is conducive to the ultimate hardness of the whole. The lime is first slaked, and then made into coarse stuff, and setting stuff, all this time being exposed to the carbonic acid of the atmosphere. Again, each coat is long exposed to the same influence before being covered with the next, although in marked contrast to the system of using the mortar in building.

Calcination.—The process of "lime burning" is carried out in several different ways. But whether the operation be carried out in the simplest manner, or in kilns constructed on the most scientific principles, it will still depend (both as regards the quality and quantity of lime produced) upon the kilnsman, as it is only by constant observation from day to day that the man becomes capable of judging whether the proper temperature has been reached or that a correct opinion can be formed as to the effects produced by the various disturbing causes which exert an important influence upon the working of a kiln, such as its size, shape, the quality of the fuel, and the state of the atmosphere. The kilns vary in size and shape in different districts, though they are generally inverted cones or ellipsoids, into which layers of limestone and fuel are alternately thrown. When worked continuously as running kilns, the lime is periodically withdrawn from below, fresh quantities of fuel and stone being filled in at the top. When lime has not been properly calcined, or "dead burnt," it will not slake with water. This may arise from two causes—from insufficient burning, when the limestone, instead of being entirely caustified, has only been changed into a basic carbonate, consisting of two equivalents of lime and one of carbonic acid, one-half only of its carbonic acid having been expelled. This basic carbonate, on the addition of water, instead of forming a hydrate of lime, and being converted into a fine and impalpable powder, attended with the production of a large amount of heat, is changed, with little elevation of temperature, into a mixture of hydrate and carbonate. In the case of hydraulic limes which contain a considerable amount of silica, this "dead burning" may arise from the limestone having been subjected to a too high temperature, whereby a partial fusion of the silicate of lime formed has been produced, giving an impervious coating to the inner portions of the stone, retarding the further evolution of the carbonic acid. On this account the eminently hydraulic limes require to be carefully calcined at as low a temperature as practicable; and hence it is not infrequently found that lias lime has been imperfectly calcined. Pure limes, if subjected to an excessive temperature, exhibit somewhat less tendency to combine with water than is the case with lime properly calcined. Caustic limes unite with water with great energy, so much so as to evolve a very considerable amount of heat. When water is poured upon a piece of well-burnt lime heat is rapidly generated, and the lime breaks up with a hissing, crackling noise, the whole mass being converted in a short time into a soft, impalpable powder, known as "slaked lime."

Slaking.—Chemically speaking slaked lime is hydrate of lime—that is, lime chemically combined with a definite amount of water. In the process termed "slaking" one equivalent or combining proportion of lime unites with one equivalent of water, or in actual weight 28 lbs. of lime combines with 91 lbs. of water (being nearly in the proportion of three to one) to form 37 lbs. of solid hydrate of lime. The water loses its liquid condition, and it is to this solidification of water that the heat developed during the process of slaking is partly due.

Slaking is a most important part in the process of making coarse stuff and putty lime. Unless the slaking is carefully and thoroughly done, the resultant materials are liable to "blister" or "blow," owing to small particles still remaining in a caustic state. Blisters may not show until a considerable time has elapsed. There are three methods of slaking "lump-lime"—the first by immersion; the second by sprinkling with water; and the third by allowing the lime to slake by absorbing the moisture of the atmosphere. Rich limes are capable of being slaked by immersion, and kept in a plastic state. They gain in strength by being kept under cover or water. Pliny states that the Romans had such great faith in this method that the ancient laws forbade the use of lime unless it had been kept for three years. All rich limes may be slaked by mixing with a sufficient quantity of water, so as to reduce the whole to a thick paste. Lump lime should first be broken into small pieces, placed in layers of about six inches thick, and uniformly sprinkled with water through a pipe having a rose on one end, or by means of a large watering-can having also a rose, and covered quickly with sand. It should be left in this state for at least twenty-four hours before being turned over and passed through a riddle. The layer of sand retains the heat developed, and enables the process of slaking to be carried out slowly throughout the mass. Any unslaked lumps may be put into the middle of the next heap to be slaked. The quantity of water should be perfectly regulated, as if over-watered a useless paste is formed. If a sufficient quantity is not supplied, a dangerous powdering lime is produced. Slaking by sprinkling and covering the lime lumps is frequently done in a very imperfect and partial manner, and portions of the lime continue to slake long after the mortar has been used. Special care must be exercised, and sufficient time must be allowed for the lime to slake when this method is employed.

Different qualities of lime require variable amounts of water; but the medium quantity is about a gallon and a half to every bushel of lime. No water should be added or the mass disturbed after slaking has begun. In most places the lime for making coarse stuff is generally slaked by immersion, and is run into a pit, the sides of which are usually made up with boards, brick work, or sand, the lime being put into a large tub containing water. When the lime is slaked, it is lifted out by means of a pail, and poured through a coarse sieve. It is sometimes made in a large oblong box, having a movable or sliding grating at one end to allow the lime to run out and also to prevent the sediment from passing through.

In preparing lime for plaster work, the general practice is to slake it for three weeks before using. Not only so, but a particular cool lime is selected, for the reason that it is not liable to blister and deface the internal walls when finished. Now, while all this precaution is taken in regard to plastering, in making mortar for building the lime is slaked and made up at once, and it is frequently used within a day or two. But this is not all. Limes which are unsuitable for plaster work, known as hot limes, and which, when plasterers are obliged to use, must be slaked for a period of—not three weeks, but more—nearly three months before using, and are then not quite safe from blistering, are the limes mostly used for building purposes. It will at once be seen that when mortars of these limes are used immediately, the unslaked particles go on slaking for a long time, drying up the moisture, and leaving only a friable dust in the joints. This should help in understanding the old Roman law which enacted that lime should be slaked for three years before using. If three years should seem to us an absurd time, yet it may be justly said that at least three months are required to slake completely, and to develop fully the qualities of many of the common limes in everyday use. Major-General Gillmore, the eminent American specialist on the subject of Limes and Cement, mentions that in the south of Europe it is the custom to slake the lime the season before it is to be used.

Mortar.—This is a term used for various admixtures of lime or cement, with or without sand. For plaster work it is usually composed of slaked lime, mixed with sand and hair, and is termed "coarse stuff," and sometimes "lime and hair," also "lime." In Scotland the coarse stuff is generally obtained by slaking the lump lime (locally termed shells) with a combination of water sprinkling and absorption. The lime is placed in a ring of sand, in the proportion of one of lime to three of sand, and water is then thrown on in sufficient quantities to slake the greater portion. The whole is then covered up with the sand, and allowed to stand for a day; then turned over, and allowed to stand for another day; afterwards it is put through a riddle to free it from lumps, and allowed to stand for six weeks (sometimes more) to further slake by absorption. It is next "soured"—that is, mixed with hair ready for use. Sometimes when soured the stuff is made up in a large heap, and worked up again as required for use. This method makes a sound, reliable mortar. In some parts lime slaked as above is mixed with an equal part of run lime. This latter method makes the coarse stuff "fatter" and works freer. All slaked limes have a greater affinity for water than the mechanically ground limes.

Grinding is another process for making mortar or "lime," and if made with any kind of limestone is beneficial. It thoroughly mixes the material, increases the adhesion, adds to the density, and prevents blistering. When there is a mortar-mill, either ground or lump lime can be used, and the coarse stuff may be made in the proportion of 1 part lime and 3 parts sand. The lime should be left in the mill until thoroughly reduced and incorporated, but excessive grinding is detrimental The process should not be continued more than thirty minutes. Both material and strength is economized if lump lime is slaked before being put in the mill.

When a mortar-mill is used for grinding the lime, the sand may be partly or wholly dispensed with, and excellent results are obtained by using old broken bricks (clean and well burnt), stone chippings, furnace cinders (free from coal), or slag. It is most essential in all cases that the materials used should be perfectly clean. It should be borne in mind that a complete incorporation of the ingredients is essential in the slaking and mixing for coarse stuff, whether done by hand or machine. The sand or other material used can be tested by washing a portion in a basin of clean water, then sifting through a fine sieve. If there is an undue residue of clay, fine dust or mud in the water or sieve, the whole of the aggregate should be washed or rejected. Lias lime should be mixed dry with sand and damped down for seven or ten days to ensure slaking. It should not be used fresh for floating or rendering. Pure or rich limes are not so well adapted for outside work, or places exposed to the action of damp, as hydraulic limes. Mortar should be well tempered before using. Pliny states that it was an ancient practice to beat the mortar for a long time with a heavy pestle just before being used, the effect of which would be not only more thoroughly to mix the materials, but to take from the outside of the sand the compound of lime and silica (if such had been formed during the period of seasoning) and by incorporating it with the mass, dispose it more rapidly to consolidate. Smeaton found that well-beaten mortar set sooner and became harder than mortar made in the usual way. Mortar made from hydraulic limes should be mixed as rapidly as is compatible with the thorough incorporation of the materials, and used as soon as practicable after mixing, because if put aside for any length of time its setting properties will deteriorate.

Pure limes may be rendered hydraulic by mixing them with calcareous clays or shales, which have been so altered by the agency of heat that the silica they contain has to some extent assumed the nature of soluble silica. In good coarse stuff each granule of sand is coated over with the lime-paste so as to fill the interstices; the lime-paster is to hold the granular substances in a concrete form. If too much lime-plaster is present, it is called "too fat"; if the lime-paster is deficient it is "too lean" or "poor." This can be tested by taking up a portion on a trowel; the "fat" will cling to the trowel while the "lean" will run off like wet sand. The coarse stuff can be tested by making briquettes and slowly drying; the good will stand a great pressure, whereas the bad will not—in some cases falling to pieces. Some coarse stuff will appear "fat" on the trowel, but it may be the fatness of mud, not the fatness of lime, because sometimes sand is adulterated with fine-screened earth. When this stuff is made in the form of briquettes and dried, it will be extremely friable and easy to crush; or if put into water until soft, the earthy matter can be seen. Fine-screened earth, when dry and in bulk, does not seem an objectionable material; but in a wet state it is dirt or mud, and should at once be sent off to the works. All limes increase in strength by the addition of sand, being the reverse of Portland cement, which is weakened by this addition. Mr. Read made four samples of mortar with the proportions of ground lime and sand as follows: "Ground lime mixed with 4, 6, 8 and 10 parts of clean washed sand to 1 part of ground lime respectively. All set and went hard. One of each was placed in water; that made with 4 parts of sand expanded and went to pieces; those with 6, 8 and 10 parts of sand remained whole, and continued to get harder." The addition of a small proportion of brick dust to mortar will harden and prevent the disintegration of mortar. The proportions are 1 part of brick dust, 2 parts of sand and 1 part of lime, mixed dry and tempered in the usual way.

Adhesive Strength.—The adhesive strength of mortar varies according to the amount of sand used. The more sand used in the mortar, the less its adhesion. The following table shows the force required to tear apart bricks bedded in mortar made with the usual proportions of sand at the end of twenty-eight days:

ADHESIVE STRENGTHS OF LIMES AND CEMENTS.

Fat lime and sand	(1 to 3)	4¾ lbs. per Sq. In.
Common lias lime and sand	"	9 " " " "
" " " " "	(1 to 4)	6¾ " " " "
Portland cement " "	(1 to 4)	23 " " " "
" " " "	(1 to 6)	15½ " " " "

The old mortar which was held in such high esteem by the Romans is said to have consisted of lime mixed with puzzolana or trass. Trass is a material similar in its nature to puzzolana, obtained from extinct volcanoes in the valley of the Rhine, also in Holland, and is largely employed in engineering works. The name trass is derived from a Dutch word meaning a binding substance. Much has been written and said about the ancient and the old Roman mortars, but it may be safely said that, from the year one up to the present time, no cement or mortar has the strength, or could excel, or stand our variable climate as well as Portland cement. The primary cause of the premature decay which takes place in stuccos and cements, when used externally as a coating to walls, is the presence of muddy earth and decayed animal and vegetable matter in the sand used in the lime and cement. To this may be added the frequent impurities in the limes and cement themselves. The impurities in the sand may be eradicated by a thorough washing, and the lime should be carefully selected, prepared and manipulated. Having now briefly reviewed the principal parts and process of mortar, the practical conclusions to be drawn are, that the quality of the lime is of as great importance as the quantity, and thorough slaking is imperative; that the proportions of sand may vary considerably, and that it should be coarse and irregular in size, and of a clean and hard nature.

The Hardening of Mortar.—According to the results obtained from tests and experience, the hardening of mortar is due to several causes acting collectively. These causes appear to be absorption of carbonic acid from the atmosphere, and the combination of part of the water with the lime which act upon the sand, dissolve and unite with some of the silica of the sand is composed, thus forming a calcium silicate (silicate of lime). Some authorities state that the silicate of lime is formed by the reaction of lime and silicate of mortar, and to this is due the hardness of old mortar. In mortar from the pure lime, the initial setting is due to the evaporation of water, and to the production of minute crystals of hydrate of lime, which slowly absorbs carbonic gas from the air, the rapidity of this absorption necessarily decreasing in proportion to the difficulties presented to the free access of air. The setting and hardening of hydraulic limes are due mainly to crystallization brought by the action of water on the silicate of lime and not mere absorption of carbonic gas from the atmosphere, as is the case of fat limes.

The Romans were convinced that it was owing to prolonged and thorough slaking that their works became so hard, and were not defaced by cracks. Alberti mentions that he once discovered in an old trough some lime which had been left there five hundred years, as he was led to believe by many indications around it, and that the lime was as soft and as fit to be used as if it had been recently made. Common mortar made of rich lime hardens very slowly, and only by the evaporation of the water of the mixture, and by the absorption of carbonic acid from the atmosphere, with which it forms a crystalline carbonate of lime. This process, however, is so slow, that it gave rise to the French proverb that "Lime at a hundred years old is still a baby"; and there is a similar proverb among Scotch masons, "When a hundred years are past and gane, then gude mortar turns into stane." Mortar from the interior of the pyramids, where it has been exposed to the action of the air, still contains free lime, although it is five thousand years old. It has been ascertained that in rich lime mortars the carbonic acid penetrates about one-tenth of an inch into the joint in the first year, forming a skin or film which opposes the further absorption of carbonic acid, except at a decreasing ratio, so that the lime remains soft for an indefinite period. In illustration of this several cases have been cited, amongst others one by General Treussart, who, in the year 1822, had occasion to remove one of the bastions erected by Vauban in 1666. After these 156 years the lime in the interior was found to be quite soft. Dr. John, of Berlin, mentions that in removing a pillar of 9 ft. diameter in the Church of Saint Peter, Berlin, eighty years after erection, the mortar was found to be quite soft in the interior.

General Pasley mentions several instances at Dover Harbor, and at Chatham dock yard, the latter in particular, when part of the old wall was pulled down in the winter of 1834. The workmen were obliged to blast the brickwork fronting the river, which had been built with Roman cement, but the backing, done with common lime mortar, was in a state of pulp; the lime used had been prepared from pure limestone or chalk. But it is unnecessary to go back so far for knowledge of the absence of the setting quality in the rich limes, as there have been frequent experiences of it in the present age. While these remarks are true of the richer limes, many of our limes are comparatively poor in carbonate, and associated with silica, alumina, magnesia and oxide of iron, which may either be partially combined in the natural state, or enter into combination with the lime during the process of calcination, and these limes might be termed slightly hydraulic.

M. Landrin, who submitted to the French Academy the results of some experiments on the hydraulicity and hardening of cements and lime, came to the conclusion that (1) silicates of lime raised to high temperature set with difficulty, and in any case do not harden in water; (2) for the recalcination of cements to exert a maximum influence on the setting, in connection with water of the compound obtained, the process must be carried sufficiently far for the limes to act on the silica so as to transform it into hydraulic, and not fused silica; and (3) carbonic acid is an indispensable factor in the setting of siliceous cements, in as much as it is this substance which ultimately brings about their hardening. The comparative strengths of various mortars are shown in the following table:

TABLE.

Comparative Strength of Grey Lime and Portland Cement Mortar, also Portland Cement Mortar with the addition of Lime and Mortar.—Redgrave.

No.	No. of Tests	Proportions.				Breaking Strain on 2 25 square inch in lbs.	Breaking Weight per square inch in lbs.	Ratio as compared with Lime Mortar.	Ratio as compared with Cement Mortar.	Remarks.
		Sand.	Cement	Lime.	Water.					
1	17	2.00	...	1.00	1.33	61.06	27.18	....	....	Three samples.
2	27	2.00	...	1.00	1.33	106.07	47.09	....	....	Grey lime.
3	27	2.00	...	1.00	1.33	82.00	36.44	....	....	Water includes that required for slaking lime.
1	15	6.00	1.00	...	1.25	233.53	103.79	2.81 to 1	....	Cement taken from bulk in store.
2	20	8.00	1.00	...	1.66	154.80	68.80	1.86 to 1	....	
3	35	10.00	1.00	...	2.00	112.88	50.16	1.36 to 1	....	
1	70	6.00	1.00	0.50	1.50	165.31	73.47	2.00 to 1	0.70 to 1	Water includes that required for slaking lime.
2	74	8 00	1.00	0.66	2.00	132.62	58.94	1.60 to 1	0.85 to 1	
3	85	10.00	1.00	0.83	2.50	95.27	42.34	1.14 to 1	0.84 to 1	
				Loam.						
1	21	6.00	1.00	0.50	1.00	136.80	60.80	1.64 to 1	0.58 to 1	Yellow loam, fresh dug, and rather damp.
2	25	8.00	1.00	0.66	1.33	86.48	38.43	1.04 to 1	0.55 to 1	
3	19	10.00	1.00	0.83	2.00	64.50	28.66	0.77 to 1	0.57 to 1	

Magnesia in Mortars.—Magnesia plays an important part in the "setting" of hydraulic limes as well as in Portland cement. Vicat, after many experiments, was led to recommend magnesia as a suitable ingredient of mortars to be immersed in the sea, stating that if it could be obtained at a cost that would admit its application to such purposes, the problem of making concrete unalterable by sea water would be solved. General Gillmore, speaking of the American lime and cement deposits, says: "Magnesia plays an important part in the 'setting' of mortars, derived from the argillo-magnesian limestone such as those which furnish the Rosendale cements. The magnesia, like the lime, appears in the form of a carbonate. During calcination the carbonic acid is driven off, leaving protoxide of magnesia which comports itself like lime in the presence of silica and alumina, by forming silicate of magnesia and aluminate of magnesia. These compounds become hydrated in the presence of water, and are pronounced by Vicat and Chatoney to furnish gangues, which resist the dissolving action of sea water better than the silicate and aluminate of lime. This statement is doubtless correct, for we know that all of these compounds, whether in air or water, absorb carbonic acid, and pass to the condition of subcarbonates, and that the carbonate of lime is more soluble in water holding carbonic acid and certain organic acids of the soil in solution than the carbonate of magnesia. At all events, whatever may be the cause of the superiority, it is pretty well established by experience that the cements derived from argillo-magnesian limestones furnish a durable cement for construction in the sea."

In Marshal Vaillant's report to the French Academy of Sciences, from the Commission to which Chatoney and Rivot's paper was referred in 1856, this superiority of the magnesian hydrates is distinctly asserted. A few years ago the French Government Office of Civil Engineers made a series of comparative tests on three samples each of French, English and German cement, in which the results are given in favor of the German cement, which contains magnesia to the extent of 2.4 per cent, against 0.26 in the English and 0.32 in the French, and summed up thus: "A great value partly due to the higher percentage of magnesia contained in it." Gillmore further says that magnesian limestone furnishes nearly all the hydraulic cement manufactured in the western part of the State of New York. At East Vienna it has been used for cement, and at Akron, Erie County, N. Y., a manufactory of some extent is in operation. Vicat says: "Having analyzed several old mortars, with the view of discovering, if possible, to what their superior durability might be attributed, I found, in some excellent specimens of very old mortar, magnesia to exist in considerable proportions." The limestones, therefore, from which these mortars were prepared must have contained the silica and magnesia as constituent ingredients; and it is to be remembered that it is the presence of these substances which communicates the property of hardening under water. Professor Scorgie says of carbonate of magnesia: "Magnesium carbonate is a substance very similar to carbonate of lime; it loses its carbonic acid in burning, combines with silica, etc., and behaves generally in the same way; it does not slake, however, on being wetted, but combines with the water gradually and quietly sets to some extent in doing so. Magnesium carbonate combined with lime, reduces the energy of slaking, and increases that of the 'setting' process; when other substances are present, its behavior and combination with them are similar to those of lime. When carbonate of magnesia is present in sufficient quantity, say about 30 per cent., it renders lime hydraulic independently of and in the absence of clay." Colonel Pasley also, by experiments, demonstrated that magnesium limestones are suitable for hydraulic mortars.

The foregoing assertions that magnesium carbonate, combined with lime, reduces the energy of slaking and increases that of the "setting" processes are satisfactory and conclusive. Many such evidences showing the value of magnesia in hydraulic mortars might be quoted, but perhaps these are sufficient.

Effects of Salt and Frost in Mortar.—Few experiments have as yet been made to test the general effects of salt in mortars, though as a preventive of the effects of frost it has been tried with varying results.

In some experiments, designed to ascertain the effect of frost upon hydraulic limes and cement gauged with and without addition of salt to the water, cubes of stone were joined together with cement mixed with water ranging from pure rainwater to water containing from 2 to 8 per cent. of salt. Before the cement was set the blocks were exposed in air at a temperature varying from 20 to 32 degrees Fahr., after which they were kept for seven days in a warm room. At the end of this time the samples were examined. The cement made with water was quite crumbled, and had lost all its tenacity. The cement made with water containing 2 per cent. was in better condition, but could not be described as good; while that containing 8 per cent. of salt had not suffered from its exposure to the lowest temperature available for the purpose of experiment. It is suggested as possible that the effect of the salt was merely to prevent the water in which it was dissolved from freezing at the temperature named, and so permitted the cement to set in the ordinary way. But it must be allowed that in practice, salt dissolved in the water for mixing mortar has been successfully used to resist the effect of frost. A solution of salt applied to new plastered walls in the event of a sudden frost will protect the work from injury. The addition of a small portion of sugar will improve its adhesion, and increase the frost-resisting powers.

Salt takes up the vapors from the atmosphere, causing the work to show efflorescence, and in some instances to flake, especially in external work. That some engineers believe there is virtue in salt water is beyond doubt, because salt water has been named in their specifications for the gauging of concrete. Salt in Portland cement seems to act somewhat differently; as regards efflorescence it shows more in this material than in lime mortar. Salt should not be used in Portland cement work that has to be subsequently painted. According to the results of tests of mortar used for the exterior brick facing of the Forth Bridge piers below water they show a good average tensile strength. One part of Portland cement and one part of sand were slightly ground together in a mill with salt water, and briquettes made from this gauge gave an average of 365 lbs. per square inch at one week, and 510 lbs. at five weeks after gauging. It would be interesting to note the condition of this mortar a century hence, time being the trying test for all mortars.

A solution of commercial glycerine mixed with the setting stuff, or used as a wash on newly finished lime plaster work, is a good preventive of the evil effects of frost. Glycerine solution may also be used for the same purpose on new concrete paving. Strong sugar water mixed with coarse stuff has some power in resisting frost. The quantity depends upon the class of lime, but the average is about 8 lbs. of sugar to 1 cubic yard of coarse stuff or setting stuff. The sugar must be disselved in hot water and the stuff used as stiff as possible.

Sugar With Cement.—Sugar or other saccharine matter mixed with cement has been tried with varying success. It is well known that saccharine is used with mortars in India. According to some experiments made in this country, the results obtained were that the addition of sugar or molasses delayed the setting of the mortar, the retardation being greater when molasses was used. When certain proportions were not exceeded, the strength of the mixture was that of the pure cement. Less than 2 per cent. of sugar must be added to Portland cement, and less than 1 per cent. to Roman, otherwise the mortar will not hold together. The sugar appears to have no chemical action on the other materials, crystals of it being easily detected on the broken surfaces, the increased binding power of the cement brought about by the addition of sugar being due more to mechanical than chemical causes. In my own experiments with sugar added to Portland cement for casting deep undercut ornament figures and animals out of gelatine moulds, the results at first were very irregular, some casts attaining great hardness, while others crumbled to pieces. The time of setting also varied considerably. Three different brands of cement were used, and it was found that the cement containing the most lime required more sugar than the lowest limed cement, but the average is about 1½ per cent. of added sugar. The sugar must be dissolved in the water used for gauging. The setting and ultimate hardness is also influenced by the atmosphere. The casts should be kept in a dry place until set and dry, before exposing them to damp or wet. Portland cement has a tendency (especially if over limed) to "fur" gelatine moulds, but the sugared cement leaves the moulds quite clean.

In experiments by Austrian plasterers, mixtures of 1 part of cement and 3 parts sand, and 10 per cent. of water, and of pure cement with as much water as was necessary to give the mass plasticity, were prepared. From 1 to 5 per cent. of powdered sugar was well mixed with the dry cement. The cement used was of inferior quality, the sand being ordinary building sand, and not the so-called "normal" sand, which is of a superior quality. They were left to harden in a dry place, and not under water. For each series of samples made with sugar a comparative series without sugar was prepared, all the samples being made by the same man, under the same conditions and with the same care. The tenacity was ascertained by Kraft's cement-testing machine. The strength was far below that prescribed and generally obtained. It should be mentioned that the samples with sugar (especially those of pure cement) showed a strong tendency during the first twenty-four hours to combine intimately with the smooth china plate on which they were placed to swell, and the results of the trial showed that with mixtures of cement and sand, and by hardening in a dry place, the binding effect may be increased by the addition of sugar, which reached its maximum with from 3 to 4 per cent. of sugar added. With pure cement the binding effect was not much increased. If the sugar used for gauging had been dissolved, and not mixed dry, the results would have proved better.

Sugar in Mortar.—Most writers have supposed that the "Old Roman Mortars" contained strong ale, wort, or other saccharine matter, and it is probable that the use of sugar with lime passed from India to Egypt and Rome, and that malt or other saccharine matter was used in their mortars. The addition of sugar to water enables it to take up about 14 times more lime than water by itself. The following is an extract from the Roorkee: "It is common in this country to mix a small quantity of the coarsest sugar, 'goor,' or 'Jaghery,' as it is termed in India, with the water used for mixing up mortar. Where fat limes alone can be produced their bad qualities may in some degree be corrected by it, as its influence is very great in the first solidification of mortar. This is attributed to the fact that mortars made of shell lime have stood the action of the weather for centuries owing to this mixture of Jaghery in their composition. Experiments were made on bricks joined together by mortar consisting of 1 part of common shell lime to 1½ of sand, 1 lb. of Jaghery being mixed with each gallon of water. The bricks were left for 13 hours, and after that time the average breaking weight of the joints in 20 trails was 6½ lbs. per square inch. In twenty-one specimens joined with the same mortar, but without the Jaghery, the breaking weight was 4½ lbs. per square inch."

The Madras plasterers make most beautiful plaster work, almost like enamelled tiles, the shell lime being mixed with Jaghery. The surface takes a fine polish and is as hard as marble, but it requires a good deal of patient manipulation. Dr. Compton has made some experiments with sugar gauged with cements and mortars, and says, "That in medicine there are two kinds of lime-water, one the common lime-water, that can be got by mixing lime and water, and it is particularly noted that, add as much lime as you like, it is impossible to get water to dissolve more than half a grain of lime in one ounce, or about two teaspoonfuls of water. But by adding 2 parts of white sugar to 1 part of lime, there is a solution obtained which contains about 14½ times more lime in the same quantity of water. Here it is to be observed—and it is a most important point—that there are hot limes, such as Buxton, which if they be incautiously mixed with them, will burn the sugar, make it a deep brown color, and convert it into other chemical forms, and possibly destroy its value in mortar."

The Jaghery sugar used in India is sold in the London market at about a penny a pound. Treacle seems to be the most promising form of saccharine matter; beetroot sugar is not good for limes or cements. There is a rough unrefined treacle which is very cheap, and it is supposed would have an excellent effect.

Herzfeld states that he used coarse stuff, consisting of 1 part of lime to 3 of sand, to which about 2 per cent. of sugar had been added, to plaster some walls in the new building of the Berlin Natural History Museum, and on the day following he found the lime plaster had hardened as if gauged with plaster. He also found it useful in joining bricks, and recommends the coarse stuff to be fresh made, and not with a great proportion of water; and states that good molasses will yield as good results as sugar.

Lime Putty.—This material is prepared in a similar way to run lime intended for coarse stuff. It is run through a finer sieve into a box or pit. If the latter is used the interior should be plastered with coarse stuff to prevent leakage and keep the putty clean. For good work the best class of lump lime should be used. The putty should be allowed to stand for at least three months before it is used. For common work the lump lime for making coarse stuff, putty and setting stuff is often run into one pit. The putty at the end farthest from the sieve, being the finest, is retained for putty and for making setting stuff, and the remainder, or coarser portion, being used for coarse stuff. In many instances the putty is left for months in an unprotected state during the progress of the building, which is wrong. It may be kept for an indefinite time without injury if protected from the atmosphere, and therefore it should be covered up to resist the action of the air, as it absorbs the carbonic acid gas and thus becomes slightly carbonated and loses to a certain extent its causticity, and consequently its binding and hardening properties.

Pliny states that the old Roman limes were kept in covered pits. If a small portion is taken off the top of the putty it will be found not only dry, but scaly, short and inert; whereas a portion taken from the middle, or up to the part carbonated, will be found to be of an oily and tenacious nature. A cute plasterer always selects the putty furthest from the sieve for mitring purposes, as it is the finest.

Setting Stuff.—This material is composed of lime putty and washed fine sharp sand. The proportion of sand varies according to the class of lime and kind of work, but the average is 3 parts of sand to 1 of putty. The various proportions are given where required for the different works. Setting stuff is used for finishing coat of lime plastering. It is generally made on a platform of scaffold boards, and sometimes in a bin. The putty and sand are thoroughly mixed together by aid of a larry. The sand should be sized by washing it through a sieve having a mesh of the desired size. In some districts it is made by pressing or beating the putty and sand through a "punching sieve" into a tub. Setting stuff is less liable to shrink and crack, and is improved generally if it is allowed to stand after being made until nearly hard, but not dry, and then "knocked up" to the required consistency with water (preferably lime-water) and the aid of a shovel and larry. While the stuff is firming by evaporation it should be covered up to protect it from dust and atmospheric influences. It should be used as soon as "knocked up." Setting stuff may be colored to any desired tint, and also mixed with various ingredients to obtain a brilliant and marble-like surface.

Haired Putty Setting.—Haired putty was formerly used to a very considerable extent as a setting coat in districts where the local lime was of a strong or hydraulic nature, not very readily manipulated when mixed with sand, as used for setting stuff. This material is composed of fine lime putty and well-beaten white hair. The hair was thoroughly mixed with the putty to toughen and prevent it from cracking. To such an extent was hair added that in some instances the setting coat when broken had the appearance of white felt. This class of setting stuff is now seldom used.

Lime Water.—This water has many medicinal virtues, and is a simple and inexpensive remedy for cuts and bruises. Plasterers are generally healthy and free from any infectious diseases. This may be partly owing to their almost constant contact with lime. Lime water, used as a wash, will harden plaster casts. It is also used when scouring and trowelling setting stuff to harden the surface.

Hair.—Hair is used in coarse stuff as a binding medium, and gives more cohesion and tenacity. It is usually ox-hair (sometimes adulterated with the short hair of horses). Good hair should be long, strong and free from grease or other impurities. It is generally obtained in a dry state in bags or bundles. This dry hair should be well beaten with two laths to break up the lumps, as, unless the lumps are thoroughly broken so as to separate the hair they are only a waste, and worse than no hair at all, since the lumps have no binding power and will cause a soft weak spot in the plaster when laid. Many failures of ceilings have been caused by the hair not being properly beaten and mixed. Human hair is sometimes used for jerry work. Goats' hair is often used here. Hair is usually obtained direct from the tanners' yard, fresh and in a wet state. This makes the best work, as it is much stronger and mixes freely. Hair should never be mixed with hot lime, and with no mortars until nearly ready for using, because wet or hot lime weakens the hair, more especially if dry. Coarse stuff for first coating on lath work requires more hair than for brick or stone work. When coarse stuff is made in a mill the hair should not be added until the stuff is ground, as excessive grinding injures it.

Fibrous Substitutes for Hair.—Manila fiber as a substitute for hair in plaster work has been the subject of experiments in this country. One of the most conclusive of these tests was made by four briquettes or plates of equal size, one containing manila hemp, a second sisal hemp, a third jute and a fourth goats' hair of the best quality. The ends of the plates were supported and weights suspended from the middle. The result showed that plaster mixed with goats' hair broke at 144½ lbs. weight, the jute at 145 lbs., the sisal at 150, and the manila at 195, in the latter case the hemp not breaking, but cracking, and though cracked in the center, the lower half of this plate, when it was suspended, held onto the upper half, the manila securing it fast. The three other plates were broken—that is, the two parts of each plate had severed entirely. Another experiment consisted in mixing two barrelfuls of mortar, each containing equal portions by measure of sharp sand and lime, one of the barrels, however, being mixed with a proper quantity by measure of manila hemp, cut in lengths of 1½ to 2 inches, and the other of best goats' hair. On being thoroughly mixed with the usual quantity of water, the respective compounds were put in the barrels and stored away in a dry cellar, remaining unopened for nine months. On examination the hair mortar crumbled and broke apart, very little of the hair being visible, showing that the hair had been consumed by the action of the lime; but the other, containing the hemp, showed great cohesion. It required quite an effort to pull it apart, the hemp fiber permeating the mass and showing little or no evidence of any injury done to it by the lime.

Sawdust as a Substitute for Hair.—Sawdust has been used as a substitute for hair, also for sand in mortar for wall plastering. It makes a cheap additional aggregate for coarse stuff. Sawdust mortar stands the effects of rough weather and frost when used for external plastering. The sawdust should be used dry and put through a coarse sieve to exclude large particles. I have used it with plaster for both run and cast work. It proved useful for breaks of heavy cornices by rendering the work strong and light for handling. Some kinds require soaking or washing, otherwise they are liable to stain the plaster. Several patents have been issued in America for the use of sawdust in place of hair and of sand. One of these is for the use of equal parts of plaster, or lime and sawdust; another is for the use of 4½ parts each slaked lime and sawdust to 1 part of plaster, ¼ part of glue and 1-16 part of glycerine, with a small part of hair.

Kahl's patent plaster consists of 35 per cent. of saw-dust, 35 per cent. of sand, 10 per cent. of plaster, 10 per cent. of glue, and 10 per cent. of whiting.

Sand.—Sand is the most widely distributed substance in nature, not only in the mineral but also in the animal and vegetable kingdoms. Clay contains no silica (the chemical name for sand). Sand is the siliceous particles of rocks containing quartz, production by the action of rain, wind, wave and frost. Some kinds of sand are also found inland; the deposits mark the sites of ancient beaches or river beds. Sand is classed under various heads, viz., calcareous, argillaceous and metallic. Sand varies in color according to the metallic oxides contained in them. Few substances are of more importance than sand for plastic purposes. Its quality is of primary importance for the production of good coarse stuff, setting stuff, and for gauging with Portland or other cements used for plaster work. Its function is to induce the mortar or cement to shrink uniformly during the process of setting, hardening or drying, irregular shrinkage being the general cause of cracking. Sand is also a factor in solidity and hardness; while being of itself cheaper and used in a larger proportion than lime or cement, it decreases the general cost of materials. There are three kinds—pit, river and sea sands. They generally contain more or less impurities, such as loam, clay, earth and salts, necessitating their being well washed in water, more especially for the finishing coats of plaster or cement work. Pit sand is sometimes found quite clean; it is generally sharp and angular. River sand is fine grained, not so sharp as pit sand, but makes good setting stuff. Sea sand varies in sharpness and size, and for plastering it should be washed to free it from saline particles which cause efflorescence.

Regarding the use of sand in mortars, it may almost be spoken of as a necessary evil. Sand is necessary to give body and hardness to an otherwise too soft and plastic material, and the coarser and cleaner the better, as the coarse particles allow the carbonic acid to penetrate further into the body of the mortar, and assist in the hardening process for this reason. In the case of cements of all kinds sand is only good for lessening the cost of the aggregate, and in the case of the majority of sands in daily use in most places the strength is reduced out of all proportion to the saving effected. Brunel, in the Thames Tunnel, was so convinced of this that he used pure Portland cement in the arches; and General Pasley, treating of this, recommends that only pure cement should be used on all arduous works.

As to the quality of sands, they are of very wide variety—so much so, that 1 part of an inferior or soft clayey sand will reduce the strength of mortar as much as 3 or 4 parts of clean sharp granitic sand. This is well exemplified in the sand test, which is made with what is called standard sand, being a pure silecious sand sifted through a sieve of 400 holes to the square inch and retained on one of 900.

Good sand for lime plaster should be hard, sharp gritty and free from all organic matter. For coarse stuff and cement for floating coats it should not be too fine. Good sand for plaster work may be rubbed between the hands without soiling them. The presence of salt in sand and water is found not to impair the ultimate strength of most mortars; nevertheless it causes an efflorescence of white frothy blotches on plaster surfaces. It also renders the mortar liable to retain moisture.

Fine-grained sand is best for hydraulic lime; the coarse-grained is best for fat limes, and coarse stuffs and

Portland cements for floating. Sand should not be uniform in size, but, like the aggregate for concrete, should vary in size and form. A composition of fine and coarse sand for coarse stuff, unless the sand is naturally so mixed, gives the best results, for as the lime will receive more sand in that way without losing its plasticity it will make a harder and stronger material, whether coarse stuff, setting stuff or for Portland cement work. If there is plenty of fine sand and a scarcity of coarse sand, they should be mixed in the proportion of 2 of coarse to 1 of fine. If on the other hand, there is plenty of coarse sand and a scarcity of fine, they should be mixed in the proportions of 2 of fine to 1 of coarse. The proportion of sand varies according to the different kinds and qualities of limes and cements, also purposes. Baryte is sometimes used as a substitute for sand. Silver sand is used for Portland cement work when a light color and a fine texture is required.

Mastic.—Mastic was formerly extensively used for various purposes in which now Portland cement is chiefly employed. It is still used sometimes for pointing the joint between the wood frames of windows and the stone work. Mastic is waterproof, heat-resisting and adheres to stone, brick, metal and glass with great tenacity. Mastic is made in various ways. Some plasterers make their own.

Scotch Mastic is composed of 14 parts of white or yellow sandstone, 3 parts of whiting and 1 part of litharge. These are mixed on a hot plate to expel any moisture and then sifted to exclude any coarse particles. It is then gauged with raw and boiled linseed oil in the proportion of 2 of raw to 1 of boiled oil. The sandstone is pounded or ground to a fine powdered state before being mixed. The surface to be covered is first brushed with linseed oil.

Common Mastic is prepared as follows: 100 parts of ground stone, 50 parts silver sand or of fine river sand, and 15 parts of litharge. These are all dried and mixed and passed through a fine sieve; it then resembles fine sand. This mastic may be kept for any length of time in a dry place. When required for use it is gauged with raw and boiled linseed oil (in equal proportions) until of the consistency of fine stuff. It requires long and frequent beating and kneading—in fact, the more it is knocked up the better it works. Its fitness for use can be ascertained by smoothing a portion of the gauge with a trowel. If there are any separate parts of the different materials or bright spots seen the knocking-up must be renewed until it is of even texture. The addition of 15 parts of red lead is sometimes used to increase the tenacity of the mastic.

Mastic Manipulation.—The walls are prepared for mastic by raking out the joints and sweeping with a coarse broom, and the brick work well saturated with linseed oil. Narrow screeds about 1 inch wide are formed in plaster to act as guides for floating the work plumb and level. When laying the mastic it must be firmly pressed on and the floating rule carefully passed over the surface until it is straight and flush. The screeds are next cut out and the spaces filled in with extra stiff mastic. The whole surface is then finished with a beech or sycamore hand float, leaving a close and uniform texture. Mastic moldings are first roughed out with Medina or other quick-setting cement. The running mold is muffled so as to allow ¼ inch for the mastic coat.

Hamelein's Mastic.—This mastic consists of sand and pulverized stone, china, pottery, shard, to which are added different oxides of lead, as litharge, gray oxide and minium, all reduced to powder, to which again is added pulverized glass or flint stone, the whole being intimately incorporated with linseed oil. The proportions of the ingredients are as follows: To any given weight of sand or pulverized pottery ware add two-thirds of the weight of pulverized Portland, Bath or any other stone of the same nature. Then to every 550 lbs. of this mixture add 40 lbs. of litharge, 2 lbs. of pulverized glass or flint stones, 1 lb. of minium and 2 lbs. of gray oxide of lead. The whole must be thoroughly mixed together and sifted through a sieve, the fineness of which will depend on the different purposes for which the mastic is intended. The method of using is as follows: To every 30 lbs. of the mastic add 1 quart of linseed oil and well mix together either by treading or with a trowel. As it soon begins to set, no more should be mixed at a time than is requisite for present use. Walls or other surfaces to be plastered with this material must first be brushed with linseed oil.

Mastic Cement.—Mix 60 parts of slaked lime, 35 parts of fine sand and 3 parts of litharge, and knead them to a stiff mass with 7 to 10 parts of old linseed oil. The whole mass must be well beaten and incorporated until thoroughly plastic. This mastic cement assumes a fine smooth surface by troweling. It is impervious to damp and is not affected by atmospheric changes.

TERMS AND PROCESSES.

The following descriptions are suited to most localities, though there are districts in the East and South that vary somewhat from the processes as described: the difference, however, is so trifling that the regular plasterer will have no trouble in reconciling such differences.

Three-Coat Work.—Three-coat work is usually specified by architects for all good buildings, but sometimes two-coat work is specified for inferior rooms, closets, attics or cellars in the same building. Three-coat work makes a straight, smooth, strong and sanitary surface for walls and ceilings when properly executed. The following is the process for three-coat work, which consists of first-coating, floating and setting.

First-Coating.—"First-coating" is termed in the United States "scratch-coating." It is executed by laying and spreading a single coat of coarse stuff upon the walls and ceilings to form a foundation for the subsequent floating and setting coats. Coarse stuff for first-coating should be uniformly mixed or "knocked up," as commonly called. It should contain more hair than that used for floating, so as to obtain a strong binding key on the lath-work and form a firm foundation for the floating coat. Coarse stuff may be tested by lifting some from the heap on the point of a trowel. If it is sufficiently haired and properly mixed the stuff should cling to the trowel when held up and the hairs should not be more than 1-16 inch apart. It should be stiff enough to cling and hold up when laid, yet sufficiently soft and plastic to go through the interstices between the laths. Unless the stuff is made to the proper consistency it will "drop"—that is, small patches where the excess water accumulates or at weak or too wide spaced laths will fall soon after being laid.

When first-coating ceilings, the coarse stuff should be laid diagonally across the laths, a trowelful partly overlapping the previous one, the one binding the other. By laying the stuff diagonally the laths yield less, present a firmer surface and are not so springy as when laid across or at right angles to them. Laying the stuff diagonally and overlapping each trowelful helps to retain the stuff in its place, which otherwise is apt to "drop." The stuff should be laid on with a full-sized laying trowel, using sufficient pressure to force it between the laths and to go sufficiently through to form a rivet and lap or clinch on the upper sides of the lathing. The stuff should be laid fair and as uniform in thickness as possible. The thickness should not exceed 5/8 inch or be less than 3/8 inch. If too thick it tends to weigh down the lath work and is apt to crack; if too thin the subsequent scratching is liable to cut the coat down or nearly to the laths, thus leaving a series of small detached pats which are unstable and form a weak foundation for the floating coat and are a source of cracks and often the cause of the work falling when subjected to vibration. A thickness of 1/2 inch gives the best results.

Scratching.—Scratching is sometimes termed "scoring," also "keying." It is done with a wooden or iron scratch, which may have from one to five points. Scratching is scoring the surface of the first coat to obtain a key for the following coat. The first-coating should be allowed to stand for an hour or two to allow the stuff to get firm before proceeding with the scratching. If scratched while the stuff is soft it is apt to drop, and unless a man is careful and light in his working the scratch will go too deep and weaken the body and the rivets of first-coating. A wide scratch should be slightly angular at the points; if square, it should be drawn across the work in a slanting position so as to give an undercut key. The whole of the surface should be uniformly scratched with a moderately sharp pointed scratch. The surface should be cross-scratched diagonally. Square scratching cuts and weakens the rivets, especially when the scratch is drawn in the same line as the laths. Good work is generally scratched with a single lath. This, like other scratches, should be drawn in a slanting position, so as to give an undercut score. Single scratches is the best way for circular surfaces. First score it diagonally across the laths and then crossways diagonally, keeping the scoring rather square than lozenge-shaped. When too pointed the acute angles are liable to be broken when laying the floating coat. The scores should not be more than 1¼ inch from center to center, or less than one inch from center to center. Close scoring weakens the body of the first-coating, while wide scoring affords insufficient key. Scratching with a single lath requires thrice or even more time than if done with a four or five pointed scratch, but the work is stronger, as the body and the rivets of the first coating are not cut too deep or otherwise weakened. In some instances—such as a thin body of first-coating already mentioned—the scoring is so deep that the body of the work is cut into a series of detached parts. By using a single lath or point the scoring is also more uniform and better undercut, thus obtaining a stronger surface and a better key for the floating coat. The additional time required for "single scratching" should be taken into consideration, and annotated and allowed for when making specifications and estimating. All scratching should be done uniformly, taking care not to miss any parts, especially round door and window frames, wood grounds or where there may be jarring or vibration. On the regular and proper scratching depends the key and stability of the succeeding coats. Scratching with the point of a trowel should not be permitted. The use of a trowel as a scratch is detrimental to the strength of the stuff and the key. The sharp edge of the trowel cuts the hair and thus weakens the stuff. The smooth and thin plate of the trowel leaves a smooth and narrow key; the smooth side of the key presents no attachment for the second coat, while the deep part of the key is too narrow to receive its due portion of stuff to fill it up, thus leaving a space for contained air and a more or less hollow and unsound body.

Rendering.—The first coat on brick, stone or concrete walls is called rendering. Before laying the coarse stuff the superfluous mortar in the joints of brick or stone walls should be cleared off, as the mortar used by bricklayers and stonebuilders often contains live or imperfectly slaked lime, which in many instances is the cause of the plaster work blowing or scaling off. The walls, whether of brick, stone or concrete, should be well swept with a hard coarse broom and thoroughly wetted to correct the suction, which otherwise would absorb the requisite moisture from the coarse stuff, causing it to become inert and dry, consequently weak and non-adhesive. In some cases the joints of brick-work should be raked out and the face of stone walls roughened by picking. The coarse stuff for rendering walls does not require so much hair or to be used so stiff as for coating lathwork. First-coating or rendering is generally looked upon as a simple process, but it should be carefully laid and scratched, as it is the foundation for the other work.

Floating.—Floating or second-coating, termed "browning," is the laying of the second coat of coarse stuff on the first coat when dry to form a straight surface for the finishing coat. If the first coat has been standing for some time it should be well swept to clear off any dust that may have accumulated during the interval between the application of the coats. Where the coarse stuff is of a porous nature a damp brush should be passed lightly over the first coat as the work proceeds to prevent the moisture being sucked out of the second layer, which, if too dry, would tend to crack and fall away. The coarse stuff for floating should be used in a softer state than for first-coating, because when too stiff the extra pressure required for laying is apt to crack the first coat on lath work. It also goes more freely and firmly into the recesses of the scratching. (It may be here mentioned that a mortar called "dogga" is extensively used in South Africa for plaster and building work. Dogga is the ground dug up and tempered with sand, about 2 to 1 for rendering and floating. Heavy ground requires more sand. Lime is very expensive in that country and is only used for the best class of work.) Floating for lime plastering consists of four parts: (1) Plumbing and levelling "screeds" to act as bearing for the floating rule and running mold; (2) flanking or filling in the spaces between the screeds; (3) scouring; (4) keying the surface. These parts are performed as follows:

Screeds.—In good work the wall screeds are plumbed and the ceiling screeds levelled. Wall screeds are plumbed by forming "dots" at the top and bottom of the internal and external wall angles. If there are wood grounds to receive wood skirtings they are used instead

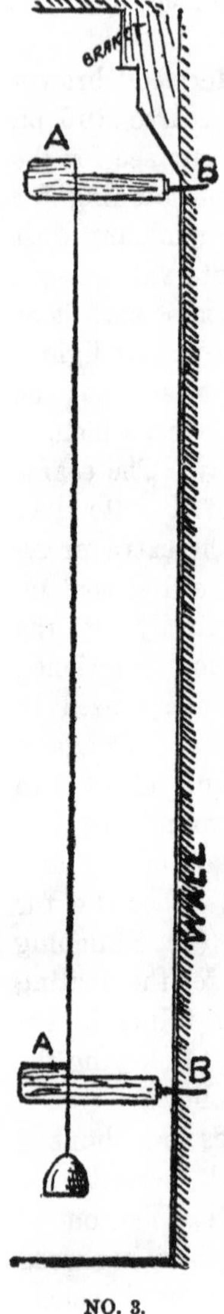

NO. 3.

of bottom dots. The dots are made by driving two nails through the first coat into the studs or joints of the wall, allowing them to project about ½ inch beyond the face of the first coat. The position of the top nail should be immediately beneath the cornice bracket. If there is no bracket the depth of the cornice should be allowed for. The bottom nail is placed in a line with the upper member of the skirting molding. The nails should be placed perpendicular with each other, otherwise the plumb-bobline will not work in unison with the gauges. The dots are plumbed by means of a plumb-rule. If the walls are too high for an ordinary sized plumb-rule to be used a chalkline, with a plumb-bob attached, and two wooden gauges will be required. Illustration No. 3 shows the nails, gauges and plumb-bobline in position. BB are the nails in the wall, one just below the cornice bracket and the other a little above the floor line; AA are the gauges with the line hanging fair with their shoulders, being the correct position when the nails are plumb. The gauges are generally cut out of a strong lath. They must be made exactly to the same length. The plasterer at the top holds the end of one gauge on the top nail, with the chalk-line resting on the shoulder of the gauge, while the plasterer at the bottom holds the other gauge on the bottom nail with one hand and guides the plumb-bob with the other. The nails are now driven in as required until they are plumb. Care must be taken to allow for a fair thickness for the floating coat. This should not be more than 5/8 inch or less than 3/8 inch. When working from a wood ground the top dots should be kept a little inside the plumb-line to allow for the traversing of the cornice screed, because this screed and the gathering at the bottom of the cornice are apt to throw the wall out of plumb unless cut off or allowed for. The dots are completed by laying narrow strips of gauged coarse stuff up to and in a vertical line with the top and bottom nails; the floating rule is then applied and the stuff worked down until flush with the nails. The dots should not be wider than the width of the floating rule, as the rule when bearing on the nails can only be worked with an up-and-down motion, taking in only its own width. The length of the dots may vary from 5 to 7 inches, according to the bearings required for the cornice and skirting running mold. Narrow screeds are easier, quicker and truer made than wide screeds. The latter are apt to have a more or less wavy surface. This applies more especially to "laid screeds"—that is screeds that are simply laid and ruled off without dots or other bearings.

Lath dots are sometimes used instead of nail dots; they are generally used on ceilings and lathed partitions; they are not so liable to crack the first coat as nails. They are formed by laying a strip of coarse stuff and placing thereon a straight lath about 6 inches long and then applying a plumb-rule or plumb-bobline as described for the nail dots. The lath gives strength and resistance while working the floating rule. After the screeds are finished the laths are taken out and the spaces made good. Having finished all the top and bottom dots, the top and bottom longitudinal spaces in a line with the dots, or, in other words, the screeds are laid with coarse stuff. The long floating rule is then applied, bearing on the dots and working up and down in a slanting position, a plasterer working the rule at each end, and working together so as to keep the rule square on edge and uniformly level. Any surplus stuff is taken off the rule and applied to make up any hollow parts in the screed or returned to the gauge board, as the case may be. If the screeds are extra long another man (sometimes more) is required to work at the center of the rule, also clean the surplus stuff off, and make up any deficiencies in the screed. After the screeds are finished, the nails must be extracted to avoid rust discoloring the finishing coat. Large surfaces on walls or ceilings should be divided into bays by narrow screeds placed from 6 to 9 feet apart. This affords more freedom and regularity for laying and ruling off. Gauged coarse stuff is sometimes used for the main screed, i. e., the wall and ceiling screeds on which the cornice is run. In this case the screeds are finished smooth, or so that they only require a very thin or filling-up coat of gauged putty for the cornice screeds. The splayed edges of screeds, especially gauged screeds, should be cut square. A splayed edge being generally smooth, affords little or no key, and also being unequal in thickness, makes a bad joint for the floating coat. If there are any breaks in the room, the screeds must be set off square from the side walls, and the projections at each angle of the breast made equal. The sides are best squared with a large wooden square, and the projections regulated with a gauge.

Flanking.—Flanking or filling in consists of laying

the intervening spaces between the screeds with coarse stuff, and then ruling the surface straight and flush with the screeds, with a floating rule. Two squads of men, two or three in each squad, are required for this purpose—one squad on the floor, and the other on the scaffold. If the height of the room necessitates more than one scaffold, an additional squad is required for each intervening scaffold. In the latter case, the distance between the top and bottom screeds would be too great to allow a floating rule to be conveniently worked. To overcome this difficulty, intermediate screeds must be made at convenient distances. This is done by stretching a chalk-line from the top to the bottom screed, and then forming dots flush with the line, and laying the screeds as previously described. The coarse stuff for flanking should be laid upwards, and in an angular line. This plan is not so apt to spring the lath or crack the key at the deepest, which is the thinnest part of the first coat, as if laid across the laths. After a bay is laid, the surface is straightened with a floating rule. A plasterer at the top and one at the bottom works the rule together uniformly up and down with a cutting motion, and keeping it in a slightly angular position, so that any surplus stuff may not fall on the man below. A rule should not be worked on either of its face edges, as by so doing the face becomes round and uneven, and conducive of unequal screeds. The filling in and ruling off is continued until all the walls are completed. When elaborate ceilings have to be done, involving the expenditure of much time, the top longitudinal screeds are only formed, and the floating of the walls left until three or four days before the setting can be begun, as the setting coat made from some limes adheres better when the floating coat is partly green, or at least not bone dry. As previously mentioned, the whole process of preparing lime plaster and laying it on the walls in thin coats, with a considerable space of time between the coatings, is conducive to the ultimate hardness of the whole, the lime being first slaked and then scoured, all this time being exposed to the carbonic acid of the atmosphere. Again, each coat is long exposed to the same influence before being covered with the next, thus enabling each coat to harden by a natural process before the following coat is laid. All things being equal, it is advisable to allow each coat to stand as long as possible before proceeding with the next. Where the wall surface is irregular, causing extra thick parts in the floating coat, the hollow parts should be rendered or "dubbed out," and the surface scratched before laying the floating coat. The dots for the ceiling screeds are formed close to the cornice bracket. If there are no brackets, the projection of the cornice must be allowed for. Lath dots are best for ceiling screeds. They are formed at all the angles, and made level all round the ceiling. This is done with the aid of a "parallel ceiling rule." When all the dots are made, the screeds are finished, and the surface flanked in as already described.

For common work, the wall screeds are seldom plumbed; but if there are breaks in the room, the external angles, which are more noticeable, should always be plumbed. For this class of work two men generally work together. Working from the floor upwards, one man lays a coat of coarse stuff about 7 inches wide, and as high as he can conveniently reach up on both sides of the internal angles; his colleague follows on with a floating rule and rules them straight. Before finishing the screed, the rule is applied on the portion done, and gradually moved up until one end reaches the cornice line, to see if there is a sufficient thickness for the upper part of the screed. The space between the first-coating and the face of the rule shows the thickness available for the floating coat. The desired thickness is obtained by laying more stuff on the screed, or working it down, as the case may be. As the floating rule cannot be worked close up to the angle, a seam of coarse stuff is formed in the angle.

To allow for shrinkage, and to obtain a firm and square angle, the seams are left until all the floating is done, after which they are cut off square and flush with the floating. This is done with a laying trowel, working it on its flat on the firm floating. Any defects in the angles are made good when scouring the floating. After the vertical angle screeds are firm, horizontal screeds are laid at the highest convenient line, and ruled with a floating rule bearing on the vertical screeds. The intervening spaces are then flanked in by laying with coarse stuff until flush with the screeds. The surface is sometimes ruled fair with a floating rule, but more often straightened with a darby. After the scaffold is erected, the top portions of the vertical screeds are laid and ruled with a floating rule, working it so as to bear on the lower part of the screed previously made, which gives a bearing and guide for the rule. After allowing for the depth of the cornice (if not bracketed), the top horizontal screed is then laid and ruled with a floating rule bearing on the vertical screeds. The intervening spaces are then filled in with coarse stuff, and ruled in or darbied as previously described. The ceiling screeds are made close to the cornice bracket, or (if not bracketed) in a line with the outer member of the intended cornice. A screed is first made at each of the long sides of the ceiling, and when firm the end screeds are laid and ruled, using the long screeds as bearings for the floating rule. If the scaffold is in position before the floating is commenced, the vertical screeds should be formed in one operation. A plasterer on the floor lays the lower part of the screed, while his partner on the scaffold lays the upper part, after which both work with floating rule together in their respective positions. Where practical all screeds should be finished in one operation. In the event of a screed being too long for an ordinary sized rule to take in the whole length and work it in one operation, the screed can be made straight by working the rule backwards and forwards from end to end, testing the straightness by applying the rule on various parts of the screed. The straightness is further proved by lightly stretching a chalk-line from one end to the other end of the screed. After the screeds are firm, the main portion of the ceiling is laid with coarse stuff flush with the screeds, and then made fair with a darby.

When floating large surfaces with a darby, it should be worked in all directions—longwise, crosswise, and diagonally and finishing with a circular motion. For ordinary work a darby is an excellent tool for straightening large surfaces of floating and setting. It also forms a pleasing and easy surface on circular work. For basement and attic rooms a darby properly manipulated will form fairly straight screeds as well as the main surfaces. When floating large ceiling or wall surfaces for plain work, or where it is not necessary that they should be perfectly straight, involving time and material, a hollow surface is preferable to a round surface. A hollow surface is not so noticeable, and is less objectionable to the eye than a round surface. It will be understood that a hollow surface, to be pleasing to the eye if noticed, should flow gradually and regular from the screeds to the center of the surface, and not suddenly or in wavy parts or patches.

There is an inferior kind of floating practiced by piece-workers, in some districts, for cottage work, and even some of the modern jerry-built houses. This is executed by floating direct from the walls in one coat. The surface is sometimes dry-scoured with a "nail hand float," water and proper scouring being unknown in this class of so-called plastering. The ceilings are simply laid with coarse stuff, and the ridges and smooth surface left by the trowel are worked down and roughened by a few rubs with a hand float. This porous and cracked shell is finished with setting stuff, gauged with just as much plaster as will hold the materials together for the time being. The minimum of (or possibly less) trowelling is attempted; a stock brush being found a more easy and speedy tool than a trowel for finishing. The brush is made to perform the trowelling and brushing off in one operation. This shoddy work is unsafe and unsanitary, and ought not to be tolerated.

Scouring Coarse Stuff.—Scouring floated coarse stuff is of great importance. It not only consolidates and hardens the surface, but also prevents cracks in its own body and the subsequent setting coat. For these reasons it should be well and sufficiently done. The straightened coarse stuff should be allowed to stand to permit of shrinkage, evaporation of surface moisture, and a firm surface before proceeding with the scouring. Working a hand float on a soft surface tends to form "water blubs" and hollow parts. When the surface is firm, but not dry, the work is fit to scour. This is done by the plasterer having a hand float in one hand, and a stock brush in the other, with which he sprinkles water on the surface, and vigorously applies the float with a rapid circular motion, using a little soft stuff to fill up any small holes or inequalities that may have been left after the floating rule. Care must be taken that no part is missed or less scoured and that the whole surface is thoroughly and uniformly scoured. The floating should be scoured twice, or for best work three times, and allowing the work to stand from three to five hours, according to the state of the atmosphere, between the first and second scouring, and one day between the second and third scouring. The final scouring should be continued until there is little or no moisture left on the surface. To obtain the same strength and solidity, all other things being equal, coarse stuff composed with a weak lime or containing inferior or an excess of sand, or having insufficient hair, or sparsely tempered and used in an over-soft condition, requires a greater amount of scouring than coarse stuff which is composed with a strong lime, or containing good sand and in due proportion, or with an ample quantity of hair, or well tempered, and used in a moderately stiff yet plastic condition. Even with extra scouring the ultimate strength of inferior coarse stuff is remote and doubtful. This simple matter is a witness to the fact that inferior or insufficient materials require more labor than good and sufficient materials and that the results are somewhat vague and often unsatisfactory.

Keying.—All plastic materials have great adhesive powers, especially to each other. Yet when laying a thin body of fine material on a coarse material which has a more or less smooth, dry and absorptive surface, such as laying setting stuff on floated coarse stuff, the adhesion is partly nullified. Portland cement or hydraulic limes, which set nearly as soon as laid, require no scouring, and being left from the floating rule with an open grained or rough surface, a natural key is obtained for the final coat; but coarse stuff, which only sets or becomes hard by evaporation of its moisture, must be scoured to consolidate the yielding and soft body. Scouring leaves a close-grained and somewhat smooth surface, offering little or no key to the setting coat. The floated coat being often dry before the setting coat is applied, the suction varies greatly; sometimes it is regular, at other times it occurs in patches. Sometimes the suction is so excessive that the setting stuff dries up and peels as soon as laid, and in other instances the reverse occurs, there being no suction at all. In the latter case the setting stuff runs downwards in the form of globules or in rivulets. These defects may to a certain extent be corrected by laying the setting stuff while the floating is still green, or by saturating the surface if the floating is dry. Yet to obtain permanent cohesion in the two coats it is necessary to key or roughen the surface. This is best done by brushing the surface as soon as scoured with a stiff whalebone broom or with a wire brush. A common plan is to dry scour with a "nail float"—i. e., a hand float with the point of a nail projecting about 1/8 inch beyond the sole of the float. When this method is employed the float should be worked in a close circular motion so as to leave a series of close and irregular indents. The usual and careless way of working the float in a wide circular motion leaves the indents too wide apart to give a sound and uniform key; indeed, this method is of little service. A new tool for keying coarse stuff has been recently introduced, which is called a "devil" and is similar to the nail float, with the exception that there are four nail points projecting on the sole, one of which is placed about 1½ inches from each angle. The process of keying the coarse stuff with this is termed "devilling." The work is more speedily and better done with the "devil" than with the nail float.

After the floating is finished the next part of interior plaster work is the running of the cornice, and then finishing the ceiling and walls; but in order to continue the methods of setting, the running of the cornice, etc., are described in subsequent pages, and the setting and other parts of wall work are first described as follows:

Setting.—Setting is the laying and finishing the final coat on floating, termed "finishing," and "hard finish" or "putty coat." In the best work great skill and care is required to make the surfaces perfectly true and uniform in color, smoothness and hardness. The material for three-coat work is generally known as "setting stuff." The mode of making has already been described. Setting stuff should not be applied until the floating is quite firm and nearly dry, to allow for any contraction that may take place in the floating. If the floating should become quite dry during the time required for cornice and ceiling work, or where subjected to strong winds or a warm atmosphere, it should be well wetted a day or two before the setting coat is commenced. This prevents the too rapid absorption of moisture from the setting coat and gives a closer union of the floating and setting coats. Before wetting copiously, a small portion of the floating should be tested with a wet brush to ascertain the degree of suction. In some floating there is no suction, or at least there is none until the surface has been dampened and the glaze and sometimes grease has been washed off. Glaze is caused by slightly hydraulic lime, also by insufficient scouring. Glaze is more noticeable on first-coating which has been left smooth by the laying trowel. Grease occurs through friction, also dirt where the float is left long exposed. These matters of excessive and non-suction, dry, glazed or greasy surface, either singly or in combination, also smooth or unkeyed floating, are the cause of cracked or scaly setting, which one sees more or less in a plaster career. It is therefore absolutely necessary, to insure perfect cohesion of the two coats, that the floated surface should be uniformly keyed, clean and damp before the setting coat is layed. Setting consists of laying the stuff, scouring, trowelling and brushing the surface.

Laying Setting Stuff.—The setting stuff is laid in two coats, the second following immediately upon the first. The laying is best done with a skimming float, which leaves the face of the first coat rougher to receive the second than if done by a laying trowel, which leaves it smooth. The second coat should also be laid with a skimming float, which leaves a more open grain for the purpose of scouring. When laying setting stuff some men take a trowelful or skimming-floatful off the hawk and stoop to spread the stuff from bottom to top with an upward motion, laying the joint with a return downward motion; but a smart man can take a trowelful or floatful of stuff and spread it with a downward motion from top to bottom and lay the joint with the return motion, this saving one stoop in each spread or floatful. This is similar to laying setting stuff on a ceiling. A man who has a thorough command of the trowel hand always lays the stuff in a long even spread outward, and lays the joint with the inward return motion. After one side of a bay or wall is laid the surface is then scoured, trowelled and brushed.

Scouring Setting Stuff.—The importance of good and sufficient scouring of setting stuff with water cannot be too strongly insisted upon. The scouring and the water combined consolidate, harden and render the surface of a uniform texture and evenness. The work must be well and thoroughly scoured, twice with water and an ordinary hand float and finally with a cross-grained float. The hand float is worked with a short and rapid circular motion and sprinkling water uniformly with a stock brush until the surface is uniform in moisture and texture. After a rest to allow the stuff to shrink the scouring is repeated, and then it is ready for the final scouring. This is best done with a cross-grained hand float, which, having sharp square edges, cuts off all ridges and leaves the setting with a uniform and even surface that cannot be so quickly or as well done with an ordinary hand float. Water is more sparingly used for the final scouring, using only as much as will moisten the surface and allow the float to work freely. The scouring is continued until a dense, even and close-grained surface is obtained for the trowelling.

Trowelling and Brushing Setting Stuff.—Trowelling setting stuff is best done by the use of a half worn trowel (commonly called a "polisher"), the edges of which should be perfectly straight and parallel. Some men use an old and worn trowel with the point narrower than the heel. This shaped trowel should never be used for high class work, since, not being parallel, the pressure when trowelling is not equal, and the heel or widest part is apt to score the surface of the setting. The trowel and water should be perfectly clean to prevent any discoloration. The trowelling should be done by one man following up the other, who is finishing the final scouring. This is done by the plasterer having a polishing trowel in one hand and a stock brush in the other, with which he sprinkles water on the surface and works the trowel in long and vigorous strokes, first downwards and upwards, and then crossways or diagonally. This is repeated, using the water more sparingly and finishing or "trowelling off" with an up-and-down motion and leaving the surface free from "fat" or "glut." The work is then brushed with a wet stock brush, first up and down, then crossways, afterwards up and down a second time. The brush is then semi-dried by violent shaking, or rubbing on a clean board, the work again being brushed as before and finished perpendicular.

General Remarks on Setting.—When the work is required for painting the setting stuff is laid on the form of screeds, and when firm the intervening spaces are laid flush with the screeds and the whole surface ruled fair with a floating rule. Should there be any hollow or soft places (the latter being liable to shrink), they are filled in with more setting stuff and ruled over again. This is repeated until the whole surface is true and uniform in thickness and firmness. The whole surface can be scoured, trowelled and brushed in one operation. This method has the advantage of saving joints at the connections between the height a man can lay and finish the setting stuff.

Joints, unless carefully done, are an eyesore, as they are liable to be more or less discolored and uneven on the surface. The best method for making joints and setting stuff, where it is inconvenient to lay and finish the whole surface in one operation, is to leave the edge of the joint untrowelled, leaving a scoured margin so that the adjoining portion can be laid and scoured without spoiling the trowelling of the first portion. For instance, when setting the walls of a room one scaffold high the top parts are laid down to the level of the scaffold, or as far as convenient, and the surface scoured and trowelled. The latter must not extend to the end of the scoured part, so as to leave an untrowelled margin about 4 or 5 inches wide until the scaffold is struck. After the scaffold is removed the lower portions of the walls are laid flush with the untrowelled margin, and then the surface is scoured as before, always going well over the joint. The surface is then finally scoured with a cross-grained float, taking care to moisten and rescour the untrowelled margin to render the whole of the scoured surface equal in texture and moisture for trowelling. The surface is then trowelled and brushed as already described, taking care to go over the trowelled and brushed joint. By this method no joints are visible, and an even surface is obtained. When the suction is slow or irregular, causing the setting stuff to run or be soft in places, float the surface with a darby until sufficiently fair and firm to be scoured. A darby is very useful for forming a fair surface on setting stuff before scouring and trowelling. It forms the next best surface to a ruled surface. A darbied surface is better and truer than a laid surface.

No more setting stuff should be laid than can be conveniently finished in one operation or day. Where practical, one side of a wall should be finished in one piece, and sufficient men should be employed thereon. If the room is not too high, one man or set of men may do the upper part, while another man or set of men does the lower part. The joints are then made while the setting stuff is green. In high rooms, several sets of men work together on different scaffolds, each about 6 ft. 2 in. apart. All angles should be ruled in with a long floating rule. External angles are sometimes formed by nailing a running rule or a straight edged plumb on one side of the wall, to act as a guide, but external angles are generally finished with a run cement bead or an arris.

An average thickness of 1/8 inch of setting coat when finished gives the best result. It should not exceed 3-16 inch, or be less than 1-16 inch in thickness. If too thick, it is liable to crack and flake; if too thin, it is liable to peel. Where extra strength, and cohesion between the floating and setting coats is desirable, the first coat of the setting has a little white hair mixed with it. White hair does not show through the last coat.

Common Setting.—Common setting for wall and ceilings is generally used for second-class work. It is done by laying one coat of setting stuff with a skimming float, and scouring and trowelling once and brushing twice. Where the floating cracks by contraction, or by using insufficient hair in the coarse stuff, or by want of scouring, or where the work is green, the cracks are knocked in with a hammer. The indents are then filled up with gauged setting stuff, and the whole surface laid with a coat of this material, on which a coat of neat setting stuff is laid, scoured, trowelled, and brushed in the usual way.

Skimming.—Skimming is an inferior class of setting, and is only used for the most common work. It is done by laying a coat of fast-setting stuff with a laying trowel. The stuff is skimmed over the floating as thin as possible, using only as much stuff as will whiten and smooth the floating surface. It is trowelled once, and brushed as soon as laid.

Colored Setting.—A beautiful color and brilliant finish for walls is obtained by mixing an equal quantity of sifted marble dust with setting stuff and using this "marble setting stuff" as a final coat. Ordinary setting stuff is greatly improved by substituting a part of marble, or alabaster, or gypsum dust, equal in bulk to half the sand generally used. The marble dust should be as coarse as the sand. Crushed spar is sometimes used in setting stuff to obtain a sparkling surface. Barytes, scoria, and slag are sometimes used as a substitute for sand, for coloring and hardening purposes. Brick dust is also used for coloring, and weather and heat resisting purposes. Ground glass as used by Indian plasterers gives a sparkling surface. Setting stuff may also be colored with the same materials as described for colored stucco. Where marble dust or any of the above materials are used, they should not be added until the setting stuff is required for immediate use. They should not be used until perfect amalgamation has ensued.

Gauged Setting.—Gauged setting is used where the floating is soft, or where the work is required for immediate use, and also for finishing gauged floating. This is performed by one man laying the gauged stuff with a skimming float, while his partner follows up with a darby to lay the surface fair. Another batch of setting stuff is then gauged, and one man lays a thin coat with a trowel, and the other man follows immediately and trowels the work before it is set. The surface is finished by brushing with a semi-wet brush. Gauged setting should never be scoured unless the size water is used in the gauge to delay the setting, as it will kill the plaster and render the stuff useless. Even if size water is used, the scouring must be slightly and quickly done. If a gauged surface is desirable, a fair and hard surface is obtained by simply darbying and trowelling as soon as laid.

Gauged Putty Set.—Ceilings are sometimes set with gauged putty. This is best done by first laying a "scratch coat" of gauged putty with a skimming float, and then passing a hand float over the surface (before the stuff is set) to lay down any ridges, and make the surface more even to receive the second coat. This is laid with a laying trowel, and then trowelled before the stuff is set. The surface is then finished with a semi-wet brush. Trowelling after the stuff is set, or even has begun to set, kills the stuff, and causes it to peel. A little washed sand added to the putty makes a stronger surface, and not so apt to peel.

Putty Set.—In some districts common ceilings are finished with a thin coat of neat lime putty; but unless the putty is made from grey limestone, or is of a hydraulic nature, the work is more or less weak, and in most cases practically useless.

Internal Angles.—The setting coat of internal angles on room walls should be ruled fair and then cleaned out with a feather-edged rule. Before scouring the setting stuff, the angles should be squared and made straight with an angle float. The angle float is a tool now unfortunately seldom used, but it is the best tool for making a true angle. In the absence of an angle float, the angle should be made fair and square with a cross-grained float, and finished with a margin trowel or the heel of a laying trowel. The common way, used in some districts, of finishing an angle with a gauging or pointed trowel, should not be encouraged, as it is impossible to make a true angle with a tool of this shape.

External Angles.—The external angles of room walls and windows are generally finished with a bead, but in some instances with a plain arris, splay, or small moulding. They are formed with Parian or other white cement, and usually run after the floating is done. The floating should be cut square on each side, and down to the brick or lath work. After dusting and wetting the foundation, a running rule is fixed on one side, and then the bead or arris is run. The run edges form bearings for the setting coat. A run arris is more speedily done and truer than a ruled and trowelled arris. In some districts wooden beads are used for external angles. The floating is cut down at each side of the bead, to allow the quirks to be formed when the setting coat is laid. When the setting coat is trowelled, the quirks are formed by applying a large-headed nail on the bead, and drawing it up and down to cut the stuff out. They are then finished by working a laying trowel up and down until smooth and true, and afterwards wet-brushed. The bead quirks are sometimes cut out by aid of a wooden template, also by laying a straight edge on the work as a guide for cutting the stuff out. They are then finished with a trowel and brush, as already described.

Skirtings.—Skirtings or base, are sometimes formed in wood, but are often formed in cement. Cement skirtings are far more sanitary than wood skirtings, as the former connects the wall and the floor in one solid fire-resisting and vermin-proof body, whereas wood skirtings, owing to their nature and construction, afford a ready harbor for vermin, and offer but little or no resistance to damp and fire—indeed, their hollow formation presents a vent in the case of fire. Parian or other white cement is generally used where a fine finish is desirable, and Portland cement where the work is exposed to wet and hard wear. Skirtings are generally run by first roughing out the plinth by aid of a gauge rule bearing on the floating, and then forming a running screed, and fixing a running rule on the plinth. The skirting moulding is then run in the usual way, after which the running rules are taken off, and the plinth set. The mould plate should be cut to form about 1 inch of the top part of the plinth, to form the arris, and a bearing when setting the plinth. The annexed illustration (No. 4) shows the method of forming the core and plinth, and running the moulding. Fig. 1 shows the gauge rule (G) in position to form the core (C). The gauge rule is from 3 feet to 4 feet in length. The plinth is formed by first roughing out with gauged stuff, and then drawing the gauge rule along the floating to form the core, and a fair surface for the running screed. Fig. 2 shows a section to form the core (C). The gauge rule is from 3 (R) fixed on the plinth or core (C).

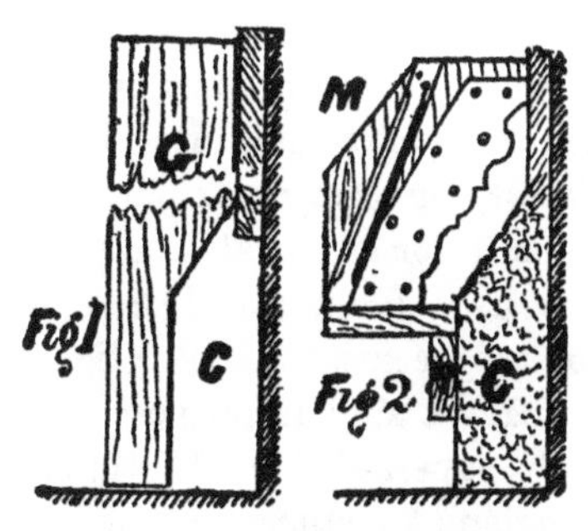

-SKIRTING FORMATION.

NO. 4.

Two-Coat Work.—This is a cheap method of plastering, and only used for common work, such as the walls of factories, warehouses, &c. It is performed by laying one coat of coarse stuff and then forming the surface fair with a darby, after which it is scoured once. It is then finished by laying a thin coat of setting stuff over the surface, and then trowelling once and brushing twice wet and once semi-wet.

One-and-a-Half-Coat Work.—This is sometimes termed "coat-and-half work." It is a species of two-coat work —in fact, it is so termed in some districts. It is done by first laying a coat of coarse stuff fair, and then scratching the surface with a coarse broom, after which a thin coat of extra fat coarse stuff is laid, straightened with a darby, and then trowelled and brushed. The second coat must be laid while the first is green. This permits the two coats to amalgamate better, and the surface to be more easily worked and finished.

Stucco.—Stucco is an Italian term usually applied in Italy to a superior species of external plastering. According to Vasari, Primaticcio "did the first stucchi ever executed in France, and also the first frescos." In the United States stucco is a somewhat indefinite term, used loosely for various plastic mixtures in whose composition lime, plaster, or cements enter. Hydraulic lime was formerly used for external stucco. Roman cement was extensively used for stucco fronts during the first half of the present century. Selenitic lime has sometimes been used for a similar purpose. These materials are now entirely superseded by Portland cement. The adoption in England of stucco externally to give brick houses the appearance of stone is due to Robert Adam. Its plastic nature enables it to adapt itself to most architectural purposes with very considerable decorative effects. The more general use of stone and the improvements in terra cotta have so greatly decreased the use of stucco for fronts, that stucco has become a synonym for a sham, and its real usefulness for certain works and places has been greatly overlooked. When properly prepared and manipulated it makes excellent work, and in the near future a large use may be predicted for its use.

Old Stucco.—It has already been shown that stucco was largely employed by the ancients for plain and decorative purposes. The temple of Apollo at Delos, and even the first Parthenon under the Ægis of Pallas herself, were plastered with stucco. Vitruvius in his seventh book mentions stucco under the name of opus albarium, sometimes written album opus. Tectorium opus (from tector, a plasterer) was a name given by the Romans to a mortar used for plastering. According to Vitruvius, Palladius, and Pliny, there seems to have been a difference between tectorium opus and that called albarium or album opus. Vitruvius says tectorium was composed of three coats of lime and sand, and three of lime and marble. According to Winckelman, the united thickness of these coats was not more than one inch. The first coat was of common, but old, lime and sand, and when it was nearly dry a second coat of lime was laid, and on this drying a third coat of fine lime was laid and made fair. The work was then laid with another two coats of lime and marble, and finished with a coat of fine marble powder. The marble mortar was frequently beaten to render it tough and yet plastic, and it was judged fit for use when it would no longer stick to the trowel. When the lime mortar was dry, the marble mortar was laid, each successive coat of marble mortar being laid before the preceding one was quite dry. The first coat of marble mortar was composed of coarse ground marble and old lime, the second of fine ground marble and lime, the finishing coat being neat marble ground to a fine powder, and laid before the second coat was dry, and worked with a wood float until the surface was consolidated and straight. When dry it was polished with lime and chalk or with marble until like marble itself. Old stucco has been found so hard and highly polished that it has been used for looking-glasses and tables. In time it became hard and not liable to crack, and formed an excellent ground for the painting with which the Greeks and Romans decorated the walls of their houses. According to Vitruvius, this painted plaster could be detached without fear of injury, and detached slabs were carried to Italy and inserted in the walls of Roman houses. To prevent the cracking of the work done on wood, it was strengthened by two layers of reeds, one layer crossing the other at right angles. To insure dryness, and allow the plaster to attain its proper hardness, the walls were perforated at suitable places. The tectorium was then decorated with brilliant colors, which were applied on the last coat while it was fresh; and to heighten the brilliancy and endurance of the colors the surface was rubbed over with wax and pure oil. When marble was used with lime in place of sand it was termed martmoratum. The alburium or album opus was what we term plaster or stucco. The Greeks named tectorium and alburium, koniama and kalachrisis.

Slabs of tectorium from the walls of Pompeii and Herculaneum are now in the Museum of Portici, and specimens are also in the South Kensington Museum. In the Museum of Practical Geology, London, there are several pieces of old plaster, taken from the ruins of Pompeii, some of which show that the decorative colors were not applied *a la* fresco, but subsequent to the polishing. Stucco and plaster are really two very different things. Stucco has for its base carbonate of lime, generally burnt limestone or chalk, with which putty lime and coarse stuff is mixed with sand, &c., and used for plastering walls and ceilings. Plaster has for its base sulphate of lime, being made from gypsum, and is used for cast work and gauging with lime putty, &c. The best kinds of stucco will resist the action of weather, and can be washed. Plaster, unless specially prepared or indurated, perishes by exposure. at least in our climate, and cannot be washed. Stucco is a superior kind of mortar, and it may be used for plastering or for modelling. The admixture of various materials with lime and with plaster to form stucco is referred to by many ancient writers. Pliny mentions fig juice as being mixed with stucco. The Egyptians mixed mud from the Nile with plaster for some of their work. Elm bark and hot barley water was mixed with the stucco for Justinian's Church of the Baptist, Constantinople. We find bullocks' blood employed for this purpose as well in mortar for Rochester Cathedral in the latter part of the ninth century. Bishop Gundulph (1077-1108) is stated to have mixed blood with lime to make it hard. Hot wax mixed with lime was used at Rockingham Castle in 1280. White of eggs and strong wort of salt were mixed with lime used for Queen Eleanor's Cross at Charing Cross in 1300. Pitch and wax were mixed with the lime used for Edward II.'s works at Westminster in 1324. Mediaeval builders habitually used beer, eggs, milk, sugar, gluten, &c., for mixing with mortar for cathedrals. Frequent entries found in the archives prove this. One reads, "For beer to mix with the mortar." Bess of Hardwicke's masons used beer in their mortar, having to melt it in the cold winter of her death. Old plaster is found to have rye straw mixed with it for binding, and was very strong. A brown substance somewhat like plaster, but full of fibre, was in use in the sixteenth century. The accounts for the repairs of the steeple of Newark Church in 1571 contain an entry, "6 strike of malt to make mortar to blend with ye lyme and temper the same, and 350 eggs to mix with it." During the building of the Duke of Devonshire's house at Chiswick, the exterior of which was plastered with stucco, the surrounding district was impoverished for eggs and butter-milk to mix with the stucco. Peter le Neve's mention of rye dough stands not alone, as Sir Christopher Wren's "Parentalia" (1750) records the use of "marble meal" as the old and still the modern way of stucco work in Italy. "Marble meal" simply meant marble dust ground as fine as meal. This dust was used for fine work. Sugar and the gluten of rice are used in Ceylon and India. The Chinese use a rich unctuous earth in combination with lime. In some parts of France urine was used with plaster in the sixteenth century. Nearly all these admixtures are to retard the setting, to allow more time for the manipulation of the stuccos. Some are to accelerate the setting, and some are to increase their ultimate hardness.

Many of the ancient buildings in various parts of the universe, which were built of mud, clay, or sun-dried bricks, had their surfaces decorated with hand-wrought stucco. During explorations in Peru, South America, Dr. Le Plongeon found some interesting specimens of ancient plaster work in a number of the ruins of the early Peruvian houses and cities, which date back to remote antiquity. At Chenni Concha he found the fragments of some ancient ornamental stucco on the adobé (or clay-built) walls, covered with bas-relief decorative designs, while the material is after many centuries still in good preservation. The design and the execution are of considerable merit, and it seems wonderful that a people ordinarily held to be but little better than savages could have conceived ornamentations so æsthetic, and have executed them with such high technical ability.

Cav. M. Geggenheim, who has had much stucco work done in the Palazzo Papadopoli and elsewhere, gives the following formula for the stucco duro which is still used in Venice: It is old stone lime, slaked for three years at least, mixed with Carrara marble dust, ground as fine as flour, into the consistency of paste. This of course is for the finishing coat, the rough modelling being executed with a coarser material.

There are four kinds of so-called stuccos which are used in this country. They are known as common, rough, bastard, and trowelled. The methods of working these species of plastering are embodied in the description of three-coat work—in fact the only difference between these stuccos and three-coat work lies in the setting coat, the first-coating and floating being the same for all. Some of the above terms are now only used by workmen, and the use of stuccos is to a great extent superseded by Portland cement for exterior work, and Parian and other white cements for interior work. The following is a summary of the materials and methods used for the various stuccos.

Common Stucco.—Common stucco was principally used for exterior work. It is composed of 3 parts of coarse sharp sand to 1 of hydraulic or grey lime, to which a small portion of hair is added. It is laid in a similar way to ordinary rendering in one coat, and the surface finished with a hand float.

Rough Stucco.—This is generally used for plastering churches, corridors, and entrance halls to imitate stone. The work is floated with ordinary coarse stuff, and then set with stuff composed of 3 parts of washed sharp sand and 2 of grey lime putty, not chalk. This is laid with a trowel, and then ruled in with a straight edge until the surface is full and fair. After this it is scoured with an ordinary hand float, and finished with a "felt float," not to raise the grit, but to keep it down. The felt float is an ordinary hand float with an unplaned sole, on which a felt sole, about ¼ inch thick, is fixed with gauged plaster. This tool before using generally requires to be rubbed on a straight stone to obtain a uniform face. Great care must be exercised when laying and finishing the surface, so that no joints are shown, or else they will never dry out. When wanted to represent ashlar masonry, the surface is set out with lines to the size of the required stones, and then the lines are indented to form the joints with a jointer or the ring end of a key. The grain of the stone can be better imitated by patting the surface with the hand float as a finish. The staining of stucco to represent the color of stone is done by diluting sulphuric acid (oil of vitriol) with water, and mixing with it the liquid ochres and other colors to the required tints. The setting stuff may also be mixed with the ochres before using. A small portion of the colored stuff should be dried to ascertain the tints before laying the whole surface.

Bastard Stucco is somewhat better in quality than ordinary setting. The final coat is composed of 2½ parts of washed sharp sand and 2 parts of chalk lime putty. It is laid in two coats with a skimming float, scoured up once and then trowelled off and brushed.

Trowelled Stucco is generally used for work that has to be subsequently painted. The stuff for the finishing coat is composed of from 2½ to 3 parts of washed sharp sand to 2 parts of chalk lime putty. The sand is not so fine as that used for ordinary setting, being washed through a sieve having about 12 mesh to the inch. The stuff is laid on, and then traversed with a floating rule in all directions, up and down, across and diagonally. The surface is then scoured up without water, and after a rest to admit of shrinkage, the surface is scoured up three times with water; the trowel to immediately follow the third scouring up. This trowelling is continued until the work becomes so hard that no impression can be made on the surface; it is then brushed off with a soft damp brush (not wet), first horizontally, then diagonally, and finally perpendicularly, leaving a brilliant face. When dry, the gloss goes off, and leaves a fine surface for paint.

Colored Stucco.—The Italians execute lime stuccos in colors, mixing in the lime various oxides—i. e., blacks are obtained by using forge ashes containing particles of iron; pearl greys are made by mixing ashes with the marble; greens are obtained by using green enamel, with a large proportion of marble powder, worked up with lime-water; browns by mixing ashes with the lime and marble in proportions varying with the tints desired; reds by using litharge, or the red oxide of lead; blues by mixing 2 parts of marble powder and 1 of lime, and ½ of oxide, or carbonate of copper. Stucco may also be colored with the same materials as described for colored setting, also for sgraffito and concrete.

Method of Working Keen's, Parian, and Martin's Cements.—When describing the technique or practical manipulation of Parian and the other white cements which have been invented in the nineteenth century, it is only natural that one should feel animated by a peculiar pleasure, because in these cements, our industry, aided by modern science, has, as far as is known, equalled, if not excelled, anything of the kind produced by the ancients, tested by any experiment, whether for strength, solidity, or durability. With these a great saving in time can be effected, as work can be begun and finished in one operation, without waiting for the different coats to dry, as in ordinary lime plastering. For sanitary purposes they are unequalled. This, combined with their chemical properties, which enables them to be painted, papered, or distempered as soon as finished, renders them the most valuable of all plastering materials in this go-ahead age. They are free-working, sanitary, durable, and practically fireproof. They are the very best materials for plastering walls, dadoes, or in similar exposed positions. For skirtings they are invaluable, as they offer an effectual resistance to fire, vermin, and dust. When properly manipulated, they can be worked to a porcelain-like surface. They are nearly perfection, and constitute perfect plasters for most interior work. Their only drawback is that they will not resist the effects of moisture. It is therefore imperative that damp walls should be floated with Portland cement, where a white cement finish is desirable. By the aid of the hard and sanitary white cements plastering has become a tangible reality, instead of a comparative makeshift, which it has hitherto been. The object aimed at in the invention of white cements for internal use is to produce a material of which plaster is the base, which shall set sufficiently slow to be easily manipulated, become dense, hard, non-porous, and may be painted as soon as finished. Before the introduction of these cements, all making good, as it is technically called (i. e., patching holes in old plaster work), used to be done with neat plaster, plaster and sand, or lime gauged with plaster. Keen's was first introduced, then Parian, and lastly Martin's. Parian being most in demand, claims priority in description. Parian and other white cements are uniformly reliable in quality, but through the rapacity of some contractors the cements are often adulterated with plaster to lower the cost, and hasten their setting. This adulteration causes the cement to swell, and in many instances to peel or fall off. Even if it does adhere, it never attains its due hardness, and thus is no better than ordinary plaster. Unfortunately adulteration brings discredit on the cement and the trade. The only remedy is proper supervision by a plasterer who possesses a thorough knowledge of plastic materials and the methods of using them. If plasterers were awarded certificates of competency, adulteration would be prevented, and good work ensured. Honest employers would find this beneficial, for scampers can only thrive where there is a lack of knowledge of the technique peculiar to plastering, and which only plasterers of experience really possess.

In using Parian cement on lath-work, exceptional care must be observed that all the lath nails be galvanized, or painted over, or coated with shellac, to prevent rust. For this same reason all nails used for plumbing and levelling purposes must be extracted after the screeds are set. For first-coating and floating ceilings with this material, the proportions for best work are 1 part of cement to 2 of clean sharp sand, adding about the same quantity of hair as for lime plaster. Walls are generally floated with Portland cement in the proportion of 1 part of cement to 3 of sand, and finished with neat Parian. This system is adopted as a matter of economy, as Portland cement is cheaper than Parian; and where time is no particular object, makes equally as good work. For walls intended to be painted or polished immediately, it is necessary to mix the materials in the same proportion as for ceilings, with the difference that more sand may be used—say 2 parts of cement to 5 of sand. The reason for this is, that when floated with Portland, and finished with Parian an efflorescence invariably appears on the finished surface, and until it has time to dry out, it is inimical to successful painting or polishing. Gauging is an important point; it must be carefully and quickly done to insure success and obtain the full strength of the cement. For first-coating or floating ceilings, empty a sackful, or half a sack according to requirements, in a clean banker; then add the sand in the proportions already given, and thoroughly mix the cement and sand while yet dry; then form a ring, and pour in the water, taking care not to pour in too much, as it must be gauged, and used as stiff as practicable. There will be no difficulty in thus using it, as it will take some hours to set, according to the season of the year (quicker in summer than in winter). When the water is in, add the hair (which must previously be well beaten and soaked), and gauge the whole mass together. Then begin the first coating, scratch it in the usual manner, and so on, until the whole ceiling is first-coated. It should stand for twenty hours before starting to float. Hair is generally omitted for common work, or where the laths are close.

Parian cement ceilings should be dead level, and have a uniform and straight surface; therefore the screeds should be levelled, made narrow, and the sides cut square, and when firm the whole ceiling should be ruled in with a floating rule, sufficiently long to reach from screed to screed. The floating stuff is gauged moderately stiff, and laid diagonally across the line of laths, so as not to spring the lath-work, or disturb the key of the first-coating. After the ceiling has been laid, the floating rule is applied, a man holding each end (and one at the center if extra long). It is then drawn gently and steadily along, filling up hollow places, until the whole surface is straight and true. When the surface is firm, it is brushed with a coarse broom to form a key for the finishing coat. If there is a Parian cement cornice to be run, the usual mode for plaster and putty is adopted for the running rules. The screeds should be made sufficiently smooth to run on, without forming an extra thickness or traversing screed. The cornice is roughed out with the same kind of material as used for the floating, employing a muffled running mould for running the rough stuff. It may not be practical to rough out all the cornice at once, as this stuff does not set quick, therefore it may be necessary to leave it for a time until the stuff stiffens. No definite directions can be laid down in this matter, as the suction is greater in some seasons and rooms than in others. A little extra hair, also extra stiff gauging, is of service to make the stuff cling together, thus allowing the work to be roughed out sooner. The running moulds must be made of strong zinc or copper (no iron to be used on any account). Where the work is in cornices, skirtings, achitraves, &c., the mould should be muffled with a zinc or copper plate. If there is only a small quantity to be run, a plaster muffle may suffice. After the cornice is roughed out, it is finished with neat Parian, and then the mitres formed in the usual way.

In preparing to finish a large space (ceilings or walls) it is absolutely necessary that no more should be laid than can be finished the same day, therefore as many men should be put on the job as will accomplish that object, as no sign of a joint should be shown on the surface. In the case of large or high walls, the scaffold should bé so arranged that the men can work the whole wall from the cornice down to the skirting in one operation. If a wooden skirting has to be subsequently fixed, one end of the rule bears on the fixing grounds; but if a Parian skirting or base is specified, it is generally run before the walls are finished, and allowed to get thoroughly hard, so as to bear the end of the rule used for the finishing coat. The lower end of the rule is cut to fit the upper member of the skirting. Another way is to nail a board onto the end of the rule, so that it bears well on the plain plinth and clears the members of the skirting. The cornice screed must be keyed with a drag before the finishing coat is laid. For large cornices it is often desirable to traverse the running screeds. In this case they must be cut down to the floating, leaving only the margin formed by the running mould. This margin forms a bearing for the top end of the rule. In some instances a special margin or bearing is cut at the outer members of running moulds for cornices and skirtings, and when run they form a bearing for the floating rules.

When ready for the finishing coat, empty as much as required of neat Parian cement into a clean banker, and gauge it smooth and stiff; then soften it down to the desired consistency, always bearing in mind not to make it too soft, as sloppy stuff for any purpose is ever to be avoided. The gauging should be so arranged that when one batch is in use another one is ready, which prevents delay in laying the whole space, thereby ensuring similarity of texture and results. The thickness of the finishing coat should not exceed 1/8 inch. When there are about a dozen yards laid, two men must follow on and rule the surface fair from screed to screed on ceilings, and top and bottom on walls. The greatest possible care must be observed that the whole surface is ruled in fair and uniform, otherwise the surface will be imperfect.

White cements, owing to the suction of the walls or ceilings, have a tendency to shrink more or less, according to the stiffness of the gauge and the section, therefore they must be ruled in twice. When the coat already laid is firm, then some more cement, gauged softer than the first, should be laid thinly all over, and ruled as carefully as before. Having done this the whole surface is nearly ready for scouring. It is allowed to stand for an hour or two, or until quite firm. If scouring is attempted before, it will work into hollows, and a bad job will be the result. If the finger cannot make an impression upon it easily, it is sufficiently firm, and then all hands begin to scour the work, using very little water, and working the hand float with a circular motion. The hand float must not be worked long on one spot, but kept moving over all the surface within reach, and working back again until the whole surface has an even grain or texture. The whole work must be scoured twice to bring it up to a fine solid surface. When there is about half of the wall scoured, two or more plasterers can continue the scouring, and the remainder of the men go back and start the trowelling. This must be done with good long strokes, using very little water, and taking care not to dent the surface with the trowel. After the men have finished the scouring, they come back and start at the beginning with the second "trowelling off" or final trowelling. This is done both vertically and horizontally, and when the work begins to harden, the trowel is laid on the near edge and worked with a cutting motion downwards. This is repeated all over the work until every particle of glut or "fat" is cleared off the surface. If the work has to be polished, the cutting action with the trowel must be followed with a 9-inch joint rule and a damp brush, but the work must be hard before this last can be attempted. Work carried out on the above plan will reflect credit on the material and the workers. The same methods apply equally to Keen's and Martin's. Martin's is preferred by some plasterers for running cornices because it sets quicker than Keen's. For plain surfaces, such as walls and ceilings, it sets too quick, and has to be "killed" (that is working the stuff again and again with water until the initial set is stopped or "dead") before it can be conveniently used. Although it finally sets fairly hard, it never attains the same degree of hardness as Keen's or Parian.

Several other white cements and plasters have been introduced during the last two decades. They will be noticed later on.

White Cement Efflorescence.—For work that has to be painted, care must be exercised in the selection and manipulation of the materials used for the plaster work, so as to avoid as far as possible subsequent efflorescence. In the manufacture of Keen's, Parian, and Martin's cements, Keen's original process is doubtless the best. It requires, however, great care in carrying out, the chemicals used and temperature employed requiring to be suited to the peculiarities of the gypsum. The desired result is extreme hardness, combined with non-efflorescence. Keen's cement is practically non-efflorescent, as if applied on a dry wall containing no soluble salt, in itself there would be no efflorescence that would spoil paint. Perhaps one should not say that Keen's cement, or at least all brands of it, are absolutely non-efflorescent, as there is generally a powdery coating comes on the surface, just enough to whiten a colored handkerchief, something like the coat of puff powder used on some female faces. On no account should Keen's cement be used on walls as a preventive of damp, as it is useless for this purpose. If used on a damp wall, or in places exposed to atmospheric influences, it will effloresce more or less, as its base is gypsum, which always remains soluble. In damp situations the walls should be rendered or floated in Portland cement before the finishing coat of Keen's cement is laid. The same remarks apply to Parian and Martin's cements. The

Keen's cement manufactured by Hunkin's and Willis, St. Louis, Mo., is practically non-efflorescent.

Cornice Brackets.—Brackets or cores are used to decrease the amount of materials and weight, and also to form a foundation and support for cornice or other mouldings. For large exterior work they are generally formed with stone, and for small work bricks, tiles, or slates are used, which are built into the walls as the work proceeds, and roughly fashioned to an approximation to the profile of the intended cornice or other moulding. For interior work the brackets are sometimes constructed with metal lathing, also with spikes and tar bands, termed "spike and rope brackets," but the oldest and most general way for cornice mouldings are "lath brackets." The "brackets" on which the laths are subsequently nailed are cut out of boards from 3/4 inch to 1 1/2 inches thick, according to the size and form of the cornice. The section of the brackets should be about 1 inch less than the profile of the proposed cornice to allow for a thickness of lath and plaster. The thickness of the plaster should not exceed 1 inch, or be less than 1/2 inch. If too thick it is a waste of materials, and the undue weight is apt to pull or spring the laths from the brackets, and if too thin the stuff is apt to crack. The profile of the bracket need not follow closely that of the cornice, but a general or approximate outline of the most salient members followed. Any thin projecting members may be subsequently strengthened by means of projecting nails and tar-strings similar to a spike and rope bracket; also by using extra hair and plaster in the roughing out stuff. Brackets for enriched cornices require special notice. Unless a due allowance is made for sinkings for the thickness of the cast enrichments and a correct form of bed, there will be unnecessary trouble in cutting and hacking the lath work and brackets when the running of the cornice is commenced. There is a marked difference between the section of a running mould for an enriched cornice and that of a plain cornice, even if the profile of both are the same. To avoid mistakes of this nature the plasterer should supply the carpenter with a section of the brackets, taken after the bed of the enrichments are set out on the tracing of the proposed cornice.

Skeleton brackets is a term applied to a method sometimes used for coring out angles, to save materials where there are no brackets, and for small mouldings. This is effected by placing the mould in position and then fitting a piece of lath in a vertical position, and allowing a space of about ¾ inch from the face of the lath to the nearest part or most prominent member of the mould. A mark is then made on the ceiling and wall at the top and bottom of the lath. Similar marks are made at the other end of the wall and ceiling, and then a line is struck on the marks, from end to end of the ceiling and wall, by means of a chalk line. The stuff which forms the parts of the screeds inside the lines is cut away, dusted, wetted, and then a narrow strip of gauged coarse stuff is laid along the lines where the ceiling and wall screeds are cut, and the laths which have been previously cut to the length of the first or trial one are fixed vertically into the gauged stuff, keeping them apart as in ordinary lathing. They are further secured by laying strips of gauged stuff on the outward surfaces at the top and bottom ends. After the stuff is set, the cornice is run in the usual way.

Cornices.—Cornices, either plain or enriched, are formed with a running mould cut to the profile of the intended cornice. The formation of cornices consists of constructing the mould, making the running screeds, fixing the running rules, running the cornice and mitring the angles, with the addition of fixing the cast ornament for enriched cornices. Cornices were formerly run in short lengths and in sections. Two, three, and even four moulds were employed for cornices that are now done with one. For large cornices, where the mould is difficult or sluggish to run, or apt to jump, the bearings should be greased or brushed with soap or dusted with powdered black lead or French chalk. Running moulds are run in some places with the left hand, from left to right, and the mould plates are also fixed to the left hand side, having the bevelled part of the stock to the right or running side. In America the plates are fixed on the running or right side, and the mould is run with the right hand from right to left. The way of running from left to right with the left hand allows more freedom, especially in small mouldings, for the right or trowel hand to assist in feeding the cornice with the stuff that gathers on the mould. It also gives more freedom to his partner who is laying on the stuff, as with the hawk in his left hand and his trowel in his right he is able to work in a natural position, namely, from left to right, as in laying coarse or setting stuff on walls, whereas, when the mould is run with the right hand, and from right to left, the worker has not so much power or freedom in assisting to feed the mould with his left hand. His partner, who is laying the gauged stuff, is working backhanded, and if using a laying trowel, can only work from its heel instead of from the point as is usual; and if using the large gauging trowel for laying on every trowelful used must be put on with a backhanded turn. It may be a matter of opinion as to which method is better, and depends a good deal upon which way the man has been taught, but the manner of running the mould and laying on of stuff from left to right, the same as in writing, is the most natural. Running screeds are used as bearings for running moulds. They are composed of gauged stuff, and made straight with floating rules. Screeds for cornices are formed with raw or with gauged coarse stuff. They are next traversed. The line of the screed is got by placing the running mould in its true position or at one end of the wall, and making a mark on the floating screeds at the outside of the nib and the bottom of the slipper. The same operation is repeated at the other end of the wall, and a continuous line from one mark to the other made on the ceiling wall by means of a chalk line. A narrow strip of gauged putty and plaster is now laid on the lines by one man, while his partner follows on with a traversing rule, working the rule with a slanting motion, and moving backwards and forwards until the screed is just and true. Where the walls are very long, running screeds are done by two men working a long straight edge or floating rule. The screed is afterwards further fined by drawing a cross-grained hand float three or four times over it in a longitudinal direction. Where the coarse stuff screeds are not gauged, the running screeds are made in a similar manner, but the putty is mixed with an equal proportion of setting stuff before gauging. The addition of sand gives more resisting power to the wear of the nib and slipper of the running mould. The running screeds are made on the long sides of the room, and when set they give a bearing for the end screed in its true position at one end of the wall.

Fixing the running rules is the next operation. This is done by placing the running mould in its true position at one end of the wall, taking care that the mould is "square," that is, that the perpendicular parts of members are plumb with the wall. This may be tested with a plumb bob hanging over the side of the mould, and by seeing that the line of the plumb bob hangs properly over a marked line which has been previously made by squaring off from a square member or by extending a parallel line from an upright member of the mould. When the mould is plumb and square, a mark is made on the ceiling screed at the outside part of the nib, and another made on the wall screed at the bottom of the slipper. The same operation is repeated at the other end of the wall, and the line extended from mark to mark by using a chalk line. The line in this case should be blackened by means of charcoal or burnt stick, as it shows better than a white line on the light-colored screeds. As the chalk line may sway when striking the wall line, this line should not be trusted for fixing the running rules to. This may be proved by placing the mould every 3 or 4 feet apart in the length of the wall, taking care to keep the outer edge of the nib at the ceiling line; then marking with a gauging trowel at the bottom of the slipper. Nails are now driven into each of these marks and left projecting as a guide for fixing the running rules. The running rules should not be less than 2½ inches wide or more than 3½ inches wide and ½ inch thick, being made out of good redwood or pine planed on both sides and edges. The rules are now fixed into the wall screed either by nailing them to the studs or into the joints of the walls. They are also fixed by wetting one face of the rule and laying dabs of gauged putty and plaster about two feet 6 inches apart. The rules are now pressed on the wall while the stuff is soft, taking care not to force the guide nails out of position. The rules are further secured by laying patches of gauged stuff underneath the rule partly on the wall and rule where the dabs are. When the rules are fixed by nailing, it is apt to crack the first-coat of floating, and the joints of the wall are not always easily found. The coarse stuff for the first-coat of cornice brackets should be extra haired and carefully scratched to give a strong foundation for the following coats of gauged stuff, which in many instances is extra thick at bold or projecting parts of the mouldings.

For large moulding and wire lathing it is best to leave the brackets uncoated when first coating the general work until the cornice running is commenced, and then to rough out the whole cornice from the lath work with gauged coarse stuff. This gives uniform suction and strength. If the brackets are lathed with wood, they should be first-coated with gauged coarse stuff and scratched before the screeds are formed, so as to allow time for the lath work to settle before the mouldings are roughed out. Weak laths frequently twist by moisture from the first-coating, and gradually settle or resume their original form during the drying of the first-coating. Leaving the lathed brackets uncoated also forms a vent for the moisture from the wall and ceiling first-coating, thus allowing it to dry sooner. The coarse stuff for roughing out the cornice should be gauged uniformly in strength and consistency, as unequal gauging tends to cause unequal swelling in the material, consequently the mould is more difficult to run true. The coarse stuff should be laid regular in thickness, taking care to gradually build up and form all thick parts and projecting members with the trowel to prevent the stuff from dropping and the mould from dragging it off, as generally happens if the stuff is laid in thick and irregular coats. When roughing out large mouldings with coarse stuff, the members of the mitres should also be filled in and ruled fair before the running with gauged putty is commenced, because when mitring, it will be more easily and quickly done, materials will be saved, and when finished, the whole will be more uniform in color.

When all the mouldings are roughed out, the plaster muffle or muffle plate, as the case may be, is taken off, and the running with fine gauged putty commenced. The gauge board and all tools should now be cleaned to free them from grit. A ring of putty is formed on the gauge board, leaving the bottom of the board clear; water is put in the ring and the plaster quickly and evenly sprinkled over the water, taking care not to sprinkle it on the putty ring. The plaster and water are mixed together by stirring with the point of a trowel. The putty is then quickly mixed with the gauged plaster by using the trowel and turning it over with the hawk. It is put on with a large gauging trowel, or if the members are large, with the laying trowel, following the form of the mouldings. The mould is then run along by one man, who also feeds the moulding with any stuff that may gather on the side of the running mould. This operation is continued until all the members of the mouldings are filled out. A thin gauge of fine putty, having less plaster than the previous gauges, is lightly drawn over with a trowel, or brushed over the flat members, and thrown with a brush for small or dry members. This mould is then quickly and steadily run along the cornice from beginning to end and finished. If the moulding is extra large in girth, or a long length of moulding has to be run, extra men are required to lay the stuff, while two may be necessary to run the mould.

When running small mouldings, say of 10 or 12 inches in girth, one man can run and feed the mould while his partner is laying on. When all the mouldings are run around, the running rules are taken down, the screeds cleaned and scraped, and any holes or defects caused by nails or patches used for the rules made good by filling up with gauged putty. If soap, black lead, or any other materials already mentioned are used to aid and ease the running of the mould, they should be scraped off with a drag as soon as the cornice is run off, otherwise they will prevent the finishing coats for wall and ceiling from adhering to those parts.

To Set Out and Construct Corinthian Entablature.—To enable the plasterer to set out a full size or working drawing from the architect's design, also to comprehend the cornice and the architrave, which are sometimes used alone or as separate mouldings, their proportions with that of the entire entablature are given. The entablature and the details of the enrichments of the coffers and modillions are shown on plate.

The whole height of the entablature is divided into ten parts, giving three to the architrave, and three to the frieze, and four to the cornice, as shown by the first upright scale at Fig. 1. This figure shows the combined section and elevation of the entablature. The height of the architrave is subdivided into five parts to form its members, as shown by the second upright scale. Projection is taken from the lower fascia, and is equal to one-fourth part of its height. As the cornice of the Corinthian order is frequently used alone as a separate moulding, an enlarged view with figured details is given, see illustration Fig. 4. It is necessary that the details of the cornice should be mastered before proceeding with the entablature. See Plate 1.

With regards to the enrichments of the entablature, as shown in Fig. 1, the whole must be set out and so disposed and arranged that the centre of each will be in line with each other, or, in other words, that they are regularly disposed perpendicularly above each other, as shown from A to B (Fig. 1) where it will be seen that the centres of the modillion, dentil, egg, and other bedmould enrichments are all in one perpendicular line. Enrichments set out in this way are said, in plasterers' parlance, to "principle." Nothing is more careless, confused, and unseemly than to distribute them without any order or principle, as they are in many buildings. The centre of an egg answers in some places of the cornice to the edge of a dentil, in some to the centre, and in others to the space between, all the rest of the enrichments being distributed in the same slovenly artless manner. The larger parts must regulate the smaller. All the enrichments in entablatures are governed by the modillions, or mutales, and distribution of these must depend on the interval of the columns, and to be so disposed that one of them may come directly over the centre of the column, as shown in the present example at C (Fig. 2), the axis of each column.

The enrichments must partake of the character of the order they enrich. When the frieze is enriched, and the enrichment may be characteristic of the order, or it may serve to indicate the use of the building, the rank, qualities, profession, and achievements of the owner. Having set out the profile and the enrichments, making the running mould and the running mouldings now claims attention. For large work the cornice and the architrave are run separately, the cornice being run from the slipper screed made on the frieze and a nib screed, and the architrave from a slipper screed made on the wall and a nib screed made on the frieze. Sections of the cornice and architrave running moulds are shown at Fig. 4.

It may be here remarked that the nib and slipper bearings of the cornice and architrave running moulds are made for work on ceilings and walls; but if the entablature projects or is independent, and supported by columns, the nib of the cornice mould must be cut so as to bear and run on a nib running rule fixed on the weathering of the cornice, and the slipper of the architrave running mould cut so as to bear and run on a running rule fixed on the soffit of the architrave. The frieze, if plain, is set by hand; and if enriched, a bed for the enrichment must be made by running a small part of the bed at the top and bottom of the frieze when running the cornice and architrave mouldings. In this case the screed on the frieze must be set back to allow for the plate or ground of the ornament, and the nibs and slippers of the running moulds extended at these parts. In setting out the mould plates an allowance must be made for the bed of the various enrichments, as previously described.

The profiles of the three largest enrichments are indicated by the dotted lines. The angles of the beds of these enrichments are splayed, as shown, to save fine plaster used for the cast work. This also strengthens the top member of the architrave while it is being run. It will be seen that an in-dentil is used in this cornice, as shown by the dotted line at 1 on the elevation. This is the space between the face or main dentils. The in-dentil is run with the mouldings, and the dentils are cast and planted. The in-dentil and the dentil may also be cast together in short lengths, and then planted. In this case the running mould must be cut to form a bed for the combined dentils, as indicated by the dotted line on the outside of the section of the running mould. The dotted line on the section of the running mould shows the section of the main dentil. In some examples the external angles of the bed of the dentils are filled in with an ornament fashioned like a cone or pineapple, instead of using an angle dentil. An enlarged view of this class of ornament fixed in position is shown at Fig. 11. The bed of the small enrichments is made square as shown.

When setting out the mould plate, the profile of the soffit of the corona must be taken through the centre of the sunk panel, as shown by the shaded part at Fig. 3, thus forming the raised part of the mould as shown at Fig. 4.

The most intricate part in the construction of a Corinthian cornice consists in the formation of the coffers, as shown at Fig. 2. This is a plan of the cornice at an external angle. F is a coffer, and M is a modillion or "block," as it is commonly called. The coffer consists of a sunk panel, with an enrichment on the four sides, and a rose or patera in the centre as shown. A section of the coffer is shown at Fig. 3. The coffers are formed by fixing a "style," as from S to S (including the side enrichments), on the sunk panel, so as to connect the two run plain sides of the soffit and form two sides of the coffer. The lines in the front and back of S and S indicate the joints of the style before they are stopped. It will be understood that the style is fixed before the block is fixed. A plan of the complete style is shown at Fig. 5. When making the model of the style, the side enrichments must be set out mitred and fixed on the plain part of the style, and a perforation made in the centre to act as a key for the fixing stuff used when fixing the block. A mark must also be made in the centre of the front of the style to act as a guide when fixing the styles. The model of the style is moulded in wax, taking care to splay the back and front edges and the centre perforation, also the mitres of the enrichments, to allow the mould to draw in one piece. These parts are trimmed square after the styles are cast. Having fixed two styles, the front and back parts of the coffer enrichments, as shown at Figs. 6 and 7, are fixed; then the patera (Fig. 8) is fixed; and then the joints of the styles are stopped, which completes the coffer. This done, the block (Fig. 9) is fixed, and then the small enrichment (Fig. 10) is fixed, thus completing a part of the soffit of the corona. The other parts are of course made and fixed in a similar way, but the positions of the coffers and blocks must be set out on the whole length of the cornice before the fixing is commenced.

Setting out coffers and blocks is a simple matter, yet it requires care to ensure accuracy. First fix a coffer and a block in each mitre, as shown at the external mitre (Fig. 2); then from the centres of these blocks set out the whole length of the cornice. This is best done by measuring the full length of the cornice from the mitre blocks, and dividing the total by the combined width of one modillion and a coffer, and if there is no remainder, the combined width is marked on the soffit; but if there are a few inches over, they are divided among the given number of blocks. The marks are proved by going over them with a compass or a wood gauge. When the exact positions of the centres of each coffer with the block is ascertained, the marks are extended across the corona and down the plain member on which the back end of the block rests on by the aid of a square. These extended marks or lines give the centres for fixing the styles of the coffers and the blocks. Fixing the coffers and the blocks is the next part of the process. This being done, as already described, taking care to use the centre mark on the coffer as a guide for fixing it fair with the centre lines on the soffit, and using a wood square to prove the square of the style, also using the edge of the square to prove the level of the coffer with the run sides of the soffit, then clean off any excess stuff that may exude at the keyhole and edges of the style. After this the back and front side enrichments are fixed, as already mentioned. Before fixing the paterae a keyed or undercut hole must be cut in the sunk panels to give a key for the stuff that is used for fixing the paterae. A corresponding keyed hole must also be formed on the back of the paterae. This is best done by making the desired size of sinking in the model of the paterae before it is moulded. These sinkings must be undercut after the paterae are cast.

The model of the paterae is generally moulded with a front and back waxed mould. For large paterae, or those having a deep projection a piece of twisted galvanized or copper wire, sufficiently long to enter the keyed holes in the paterae and the soffit, should be inserted in the fixing stuff when fixing the paterae. This method should always be adopted where the bedding surface of the paterae is small, so as to enable it to resist the weight of a brush while being painted or gilded. If the paterae are extra deep, and project below the line of the soffit, they should be fixed first, otherwise they are liable to get disturbed when fixing the blocks and other enrichments.

The modillions should be fixed with stiff gauged stuff for the keyed holes in the styles, and the corresponding holes in the blocks (which are made while being cast), and using softer gauged stuff for the bedding surface of the block. After the fixing stuff is laid, place the block in position, and work it gently but quickly from right to left, so as to force the excess stuff out, and obtain a true and solid bed, taking care that the centre of the block is linable with the centre mark on the soffit, and using a square to prove the squareness of the block, and then clean off the excess stuff. The small enrichments (Figs. 6, 7, and 10) are fixed with soft gauged stuff, so that they can be easily and quickly fixed. Small cast work of this kind should always be fixed with soft gauged stuff, as there is very little weight to carry until the stuff is set. The suction alone between the two bodies is often sufficient to support the cast until the stuff is set. These small enrichments are moulded with a face or front wax mould.

Modillion.
NO. 5.

Modillions or blocks were formerly cast in three parts, namely, the body, the main part of the leaf, and the tip or curled end of the leaf; the body being cast in a wax piece mould (sometimes a plaster piece mould), and the leaf and its tip in a front and back wax mould, but now the complete block is generally cast in one piece in a gelatine mould. The body of the block may be cast in a gelatine mould, but where the back section of the leaf is clear or away from the block near the scroll end, as shown in the accompanying illustration, and seen in fine old buildings, the leaf should be cast and fixed separately. An enlarged view of the plan and side elevation of a modillion is shown in illustration No. 5. The bed moulds and the other small enrichments in the entablature are generally cast in wax moulds.

When fixing the enrichments in an entablature, take special care that they all "principle" with each other as already mentioned, thus forming a pleasing and artistic finish, which is characteristic of well-designed mouldings.

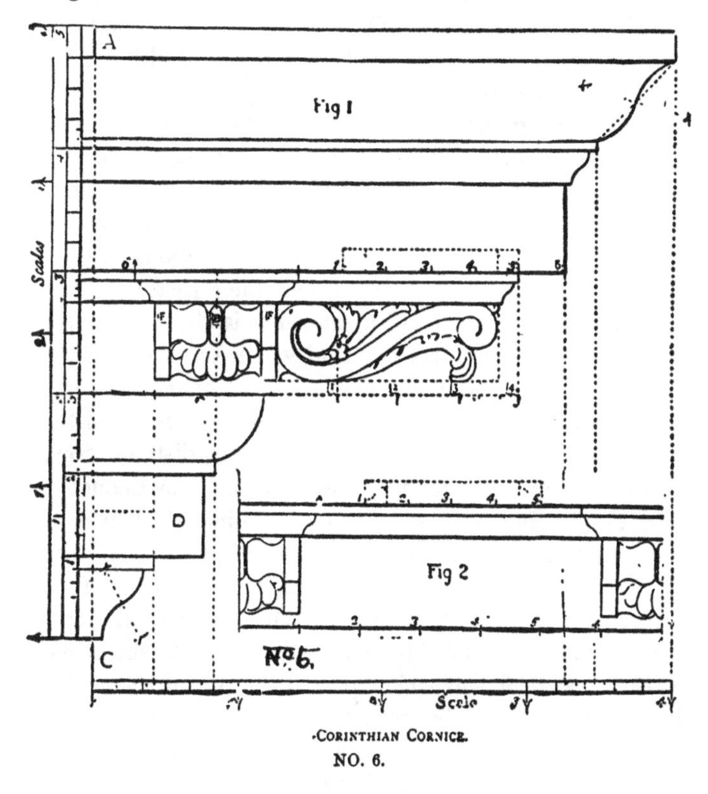

CORINTHIAN CORNICE.
NO. 6.

To Set Out a Corinthian Cornice.—The members which are enriched in the cornice, shown in the preceding plate, are drawn as plain members on this cornice so as to show the profile and method of setting out more clear.

The combined elevation and profile of the cornice shown at Fig. 1, in the accompanying illustration, No. 6, is an enlarged view of the cornice of the Corinthian entablature. The first upright scale contains four parts of the ten into which the whole entablature is divided, as on the preceding plate. The second scale is divided into five parts, the third of which goes to the modillion, the fourth to the corona, and fifth to the cymatium; the first and second together are divided into three parts, the first for the reversed cyma at the bottom, the second for the dentils, and the third for the ovolo. The smaller members are in proportion to the greater, as shown by the smaller divisions on the scale. The modillions are 1-6 of the diameter of the column, and their distances two-sixths and a half. Half a diameter is divided on the corona at Fig. 2 into six parts, of which the width of the modillion is two, and the length of it is four. The cap projects 1-3 of those parts, and the distance between the modillions is five. By this rule the exact distance from centre to centre of the modillions is 7-12 of the diameter. The dotted line A C answers to the diminished part of the column, from whence the cornice is projected; the projection being equal to its height, is divided into four parts, as shown by the scale at the bottom of the cornice. One-fourth of this scale is divided into six parts, as shown at C, five of which gives the width of the modillion. The distance between them is in proportion to it as figured at Fig. 2. The fillets, F F, of the modillion are 1/8 of its width, and so is the bead, B. The position and size of the sunk panel are indicated by the dotted lines in the corona at Figs. 1 and 2, the size being obtained as shown by the figures in the dotted spaces. The width of the dentils, D, is obtained by dividing the semidiameter of the column marked on the corona at Fig. 2

into fourteen parts, two of which gives the width of the dentil, and one the space between them. This space of course is also the width of the in-dentil, the height of which is one-fourth of the height of the main dentil, as indicated by the small division on the inner side of the second upright scale.

The centres and radius for describing the profiles of the cymatium or cymarecta, the ovolo, and the inverted cyma or ogee members are indicated by small crosses and dotted lines.

Mitring.—Mitring is looked upon by the generality of plasterers as a test of speed and ability. As they generally work in pairs on other portions of the work, their individual ability is not easily seen, but when mitring a man carries the operation through alone. Mitring being done by hand, is a near approach to modelling, and is an operation of which a dexterous and good plasterer is naturally proud. The quality and time required for mitres greatly depend upon the degree of hardness of the run cornice, also upon the suction. A mitre can be more freely worked and more expeditiously done on a hard cornice surface, and where there is a suction. The extra absorbing powers of brick walls as compared to lath partitions cause the gauged stuff to get firm sooner, and enables the mouldings to be more readily blocked out before the stuff is set. A common error when mitring is gauging the stuff stronger than that which has been used for the running of the cornice, causing extra swelling and difficulty of ruling the members over, and cutting the run part of the cornice with the joint rule, especially if the stuff sets before the plasterer has had time to rule all the members over, and then being stronger, and consequently setting quicker, he has not so much time for forming the members. Ordinary sized mitres can be done with one gauge by using less plaster than in the gauge for running the cornice, and stiffening the greater portion with dry plaster, and using this for roughing out the mitre; then using the soft portion left for brushing over the members and filling up all holes, and afterwards working the joint rule over the metal to take the superfluous stuff off. Should the mitre not be fine enough, the gauged stuff can be further softened on the hawk by adding water, and working it with the gauging trowel, brushing the soft or creamy stuff all over the mitre again, then working the joint rule again. Small members, and those at the top and bottom of the cornice, where there is most absorption, should be worked by the joint rule first, leaving the large members, drips or coves, or where there is a large body of stuff, to be ruled over last. The joint rule should always be worked horizontally, especially when dealing with beads and carvettos. Drips and large members should be worked with the joint rule with an upright motion, because if worked down, the stuff may be pulled down. Mitres should not be worked, fined, or tooled with small tools, as they can and should be brought to a good and straight surface by the proper use of the joint rule. Small tools should only be used for laying the stuff when required, and cleaning out the intersections of the mitres, quirks, and for stopping. A square-ended small tool may be used for smoothing flat, straight surfaces. Returned mitres and short breaks are "run down," then cut to the required lengths and planted. They may also be mitred by hand.

Mitre-Mould.—Various attempts have been made to construct a running mould that would form the mitres simultaneously with the cornice running. Most plasterers will have heard of, and some may have tried to make and work a mitre-mould to save hand labor. Those who have tried it will have found the results far from satisfactory. The subjoined illustration, No. 7, shows the method of setting out and constructing a mould intended

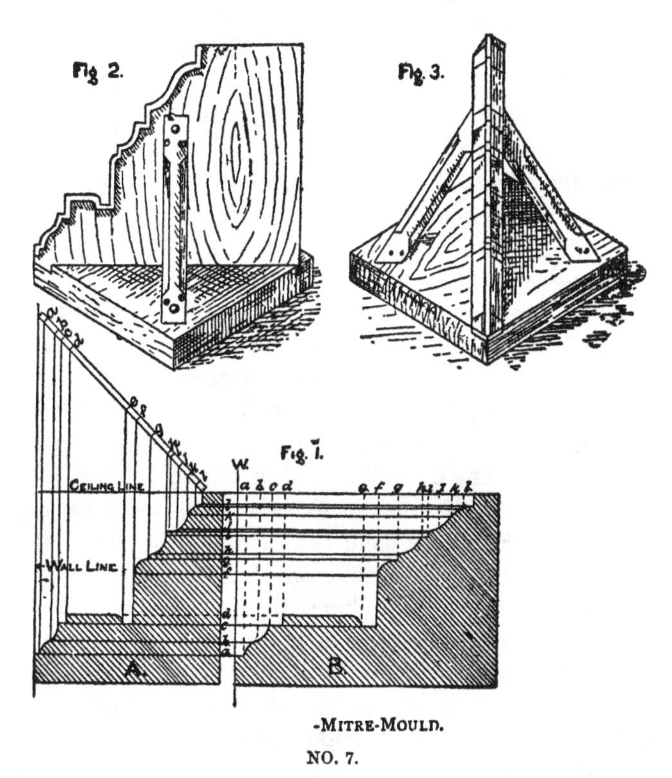

-Mitre-Mould.

NO. 7.

for forming the moulding and mitres in one operation. The mould is made by fixing the metal plate at an angle of 45 degrees on the slipper, or in other words fixing the iron plate at one angle of a square slipper, which allows the mould to run nearly up to the angle, one face of the slipper being used for one side of the wall, and the other face at right angles being used for the other side of the wall. Fig. 1 shows the method of setting out the profile of mould. A is a given section of a moulding, and B is the section of the moulding at the mitre. To obtain this, first draw the moulding A full size, and then extend the ceiling line and draw another wall line. Then from the projection of the top member draw an angle line at 45 degrees. Carry up the projections of the various members to the angle (or mitre line) and then draw horizontal lines from the various members; also centre lines of large members as from a to 1 (the vertical letters). Take off the lines a to 1 (diagonal letters) on the angle line, and set them on the ruling line from a to 1 (horizontal letters), and then laying them down to the horizontal lines, the intersections give the profile for the mitre-mould. Fig. 2 shows a side elevation of the mitre-mould, and Fig. 3 shows a front elevation. It will be seen that the mitre-mould is an expensive and unsatisfactory fad. The time expended in setting out the elongated members, making an extra mould, and cleaning out the intersection by hand (as the mould does not leave a finished mitre), also making good the parts broken by drawing out the mould from interlocked or undercut members in the moulding, is not repaid. An average plasterer would put in all the mitres of an ordinary sized room while the mould was being made. The mould will only run into every second angle, and must be taken off and reversed to fit the next. It may seem a waste of time and space to describe and then show the utter uselessness of a mitre-mould, but having met many plasterers who stated that they had used or had seen a mitre-mould that worked wonders, I am constrained to give a description, not only to save future futile controversy, but to show that in this book the much-debated trade subject has not been omitted. In concluding this subject, it may be stated that not any one of the mitre-mould plasterers would or could practically explain the modus operandi of this mysterious mould.

Fixing Enrichments.—Enrichments should be fixed straight, square, plumb, and firm. Cornice enrichments, such as bed moulds, friezes, &c., for which a bed or sinking to receive them is formed by the running mould, do not require such strong gauges stuff as soffits, medallions, or other hanging casts. For light enrichments the gauged putty and plaster should never be stronger than that used for the cornice, and clean strong size water should be used. This gives more time for fixing a number of casts, and improves the cementing force. The bed for the cast work should be scratched, dusted, and wetted before the cast work is applied. A small portion of fine plaster (the same as used for casting the enrichments) should be gauged with clean size water, to be used for the joints. The gauged fixing stuff should be spread evenly over the back of the cast and over the scratched bed of the moulding. No more should be laid on than will fully fill up the scratches. Then place a small piece of the white or joint gauge on the point, and press the cast into position by gently but quickly sliding the cast twice or thrice backwards and forwards to expel the air and incorporate the two bodies. It is a mistake to dab a lump of gauged stuff at random on the back of the cast and press it on the bed, as the stuff does not properly enter the scratched part of the bed, and the contained air prevents proper cohesion and solidity. When too thick a coat of stuff is laid on the coat, straight and even fixing is more difficult. The excess stuff oozes out at the sides, and unless time and care be taken in cleaning it off, the moulding, or cast, or both, get damaged. A small portion may also ooze out in the first method, but it will be so thin that it can be brushed off while soft. When fixing medallion blocks or trusses, a dovetailed hole should be cut in the vertical and horizontal parts of the bed, and similar holes in the blocks (which are made when being cast) are filled in with gauged stuff and applied in position. If the cast should be very heavy, or of Portland cement, it is further secured by inserting a slate or iron dowel while the stuff is soft, allowing a portion of the dowel to project to enter into the body of the cast. Heavy casts should be temporarily supported by wood props until the fixing stuff is set. When fixing heavy casts the plain surface of the plaster work should be cut as far as the lath to obtain a better and stronger key. The putty in the fixing stuff should be mixed with long strong hair or tow, as described for rib mouldings or ceilings. Hair or tow may also be used advantageously in fixing Portland or other cement work. Cast work, when extremely heavy, should be further secured by means of long screws or bolts, placed so as to pass through the cast work and into the timber, the casts being bedded with gauged haired stuff and temporarily propped up. The screws or bolts should be fixed before the stuff is set to avoid the probable disturbance of the gauged bedding. Before fixing any cast work they should be placed in position to prove their correct fitting. Centre, side and end lines should be made on the surface of the bed to give a guide for fixing. It may be necessary to fix nails at intervals in the lines to give a further guide.

Mitring Enrichments.—Before fixing continuous or space cast work, the length and width of the panel or room should be set out to prove that the mitres are equal-sided, balanced and have flowing lines. Nothing looks so slovenly or unworkmanlike as a mitre in an ornament cut haphazard, with the leading stem disjointed or springing out of a flower or tendril. If the design is vertical, say a bed mould or frieze with an alternate leaf and husk, what can be more offensive to artistic taste than a part of the leaf on one side and a part of the husk on the other side of the mitre! There is no excuse for this want of taste and wanton treatment. A little time expended in setting out the work will obviate these defects. Where there are no shrinking and stretching casts the mitres can be eased by stretching or shrinking the cast work at the joints. Stretching or shrinking are evils, and it depends on the design of the enrichments which of the two is the lesser, but in most instances shrinking is the greater evil. Shrinking does not require so much labor to make the joints good. Stretching does not show quite so much, especially if the joint is well modelled and of the same color. It also gives greater scope and freedom. It has already been mentioned that in good shops the breaks or other short lengths are set out in the shop and that there are stretching and shrinking casts and mitres modelled and made to facilitate the formation of good mitres. This latter method is certainly the cheapest and most satisfactory in the end. The setting out is best done by cutting a lath as a gauge to the length of the cast and marking the length of each cast temporarily on the bed of the cast work from mitre to mitre. When the mitre has been determined on and the casts set out to come in, the marks are made more distant to give a guide for fixing each separate cast as required. It is better to measure thrice than alter twice. Space ornaments should also be set out accurately, but there is no difficulty in the mitres, as the intervening space between each cast can be increased or diminished as required.

When fixing medallion blocks, dentils or paterae, the mitres should be fixed first and then the spaces and positions set out. Special care must be taken when mitring enrichments with distinctive vertical parts, such as figures, or pendants of flowers, or fruit in friezes, that the cast work is not unequally or irregularly scratched so as to enable them to come to an equally balanced mitre at the angles. Where there are no stretchers the cast work should be cut between the main vertical parts, so that the joint on each side will be equal, or, in other words, that the vertical parts will be equidistant from the main or other parts when fixed. The same remarks apply to shrinking. The mitres of running enrichments, such as soffits, etc., are made up with bands or ribbons, which are cast or worked in situ by hand. The latter way is the quickest and most artistic. Another plan is to fix paterae or drops at the internal and external mitres. The scroll work of the enrichment is then formed to spring from the paterae and finish at the patera at the next mitre. Sometimes the inner member at each side of the soffit is worked across at right angles at each mitre, thus forming a small square sinking or panel, which is then filled in with a patera or drop.

Bed moulds, such as an egg and dart, have internal and external mitre leaf modelled and cast. This is a neat and quick way of forming mitres. A good cornice, with well-modelled and effective ornament, may be disfigured and spoiled by careless mitring, yet it is as easy (and in many cases more so) to make good and satisfactory work. It is therefore best to set out correctly and make sure of a correct finish before beginning to fix. Illustration No. 8 shows the method of mitring various forms of fret enrichments.

Pugging.—Pugging or deafening is a body of plastic materials laid on boards fixed between the joists of a floor, or lath and plaster partitions. It is intended to prevent sound and smells from passing from one room to another. Pugging is generally performed by laying a thick coat of coarse stuff on a foundation of rough boards on fillets, which are nailed on the sides of the joists. Chopped hay, straw or ferns, mixed with lime, is

FRET ORNAMENTS, SHOWING THEIR MITRES.

NO. 8.

sometimes used for the plastic coat. Coarse plaster with and without reeds is also used in some districts. Sawdust is sometimes substituted for reeds. Pugging may be done by forming a foundation with thick rough lath wood. On this a coat, about $1/2$ inch thick, of coarse stuff is laid, and when dry a layer about 2 inches thick of dry ashes or lime riddlings is deposited on it. The upper surface is then sprinkled with water and finished with a coat of coarse stuff. This makes sound-proof work, but in the event of subsequent damage or alterations the dry ashes run out, causing further dust and damage. In some instances the dry ashes are gauged with lime. When laid the upper surface is beaten and smoothed with a shovel. This makes sound-proof and durable work, impervious to vermin. Partitions are deafened by lathing between the studding and then laying on a coat of coarse stuff. When dry the partition is lathed and plastered in the usual way. Pugging slabs of fibrous plaster are now largely employed. They have the advantage of being light and dry and are rapidly fixed.

Sound Ceilings.—No lath and plaster ceilings can be made sound and free from cracks unless the joists are well seasoned, firmly fixed and sufficiently strong to carry the overhead weight, as well as sustain the weight of the lath and plaster, and resist jarring. Ceiling joists should never be more than 12 inches apart from center to center. Where double lath is used the joists may be 14 inches from center to center. Good laths, with break joints every three feet, and well nailed, are also imperative. If the above dimensions are exceeded the laths are liable to give or twist on account of the weakness of the laths or the weight of the plaster, or both combined. If the joists exceed 2 inches in the width they should be counter-lathed or strapped to ensure a key for the plaster. Where it is impracticable or inconvenient to fix the ceiling joists so close they should be brandered. This strengthens and stiffens the joists, also gives a free key for the plaster and forms a sound, level ceiling.

Brandered or strapped ceilings are done by nailing wood straps or fillets across the under sides of the joists. The fillets are from 1½ to 2 inches square and are fixed from 12 to 14 inches from centre to centre. The sizes and distance apart varies according to the thickness of the lath and the class of plaster work. Brandered ceilings are largely used in some places and make good sound ceilings.

Cracked Plaster Work.—Cracks in plaster work are due to various causes. They may act individually or in combination. Cracks are often caused by settlement in the building. These cracks may be easily discerned by their breadth, depth and length. They also arise from the shrinkage of bad or unseasoned timber used in the construction or framing of the building, which may cause displacement in the joists or the laths. Cracks are sometimes caused by the laths being too weak, or by too much plaster being laid on weak laths, or too little plaster laid on strong laths. Other causes are the too sudden drying of the work, strong winds or heat, the laying of one coat of mortar on another coat, or on walls that have a strong suction which absorbs the moisture or "life" of the coat being laid, when it becomes short, or crumbly, scaly and apt to peel or fall off. In this last case it does not set, but only dries and shrinks, which gives rise to cracks, and eventually falls or crumbles away. The use of bad materials, insufficient use of lime and hair, or scamping of labor is often followed by cracks. Insufficient labor and unskilled workmanship in the application of the materials is a great source of trouble, but it will be understood that the best quality of labor will not make bad materials good and strong; and, on the other hand, the best materials will not compensate for bad labor. It is only by judicious selection of materials and their skillful manipulation that a high and enduring class of work can be obtained.

Repairing Old Plaster.—Repairing is also termed "patching," "jobbing" and "making good." When repairing or making additions to old plaster work, care should be observed in cutting the joints so that the key of the existing work is not injured or broken. The joints one way should be cut on the studding or joists and in a line with the laths the other way. A joint at the edge of a lath is stronger than at the center. If the lath work is weak the joints should be cut diagonally. Never use a hammer to cut joints on lath work, for the repeated impacts will weaken and crack the old work. If the old plaster is hard, cut the joint with the saw or with a hammer and chisel and finish with a strong knife. Avoid acute angles in patches. Square, round or oval patches not only look better but are much stronger than zigzag ones. Having cut the joints neat and square on edge and then repaired the old lath work, brush the joints and the laths with a dry broom and then wet the joints, but only dampen the lath work, as excessive water tends to warp the laths. The joints are sometimes painted to prevent damp from extending to the old work or causing injury to any surface decoration. Gauged coarse stuff is generally used for roughing out and gauged putty for finishing ordinary work. The coarse stuff is generally gauged with coarse plaster. For small patches the whole thickness is generally brought out in one coat, but for large patches it is best to lay a first coat and then scratch it in the usual way. If time permits this should stand for one day, or even two, to allow the lath work to settle. The stronger and stiffer the gauge, the less power the laths will have to warp. The floating coat is gauged moderately stiff with coarse plaster or with fine plaster and coarse in equal proportions.

When laid, the surface is ruled in with a straightedge, keeping it within the line of the old work to allow for plaster swelling and a thickness of 1-16 inch for the finishing coat. It is often necessary to drag the surface down to allow the finishing coat to be ruled fair and flush with the old work. The surface should be left fair but rough. Gauged work should never be scoured, as it only kills the plaster, and therefore weakens the body of the material. The putty for the final coat should be gauged with fine plaster and a little size water. After being laid the surface is ruled flush with the old work, and when firm it should be smartly trowelled off and finally finished with a semi-wet brush. The joints should be trowelled flush and smooth and the old part brushed to free it from any gauged stuff. All rubbish should be damped as it falls, and removed as soon as possible to prevent further dust and dirt.

Parian or other white cements are used for best work, or where time is a consideration. All white cements having plaster for their basis are manufactured to be non-efflorescent, non-porous, durable, free from liability to unequal shrinkage (which causes cracks), and free in working. They form admirable materials for repairs or additions. When making good old or broken lime plaster work with any of these cements, the joints and lath nails must be painted with red lead, quick drying paint, or with shellac. Galvanized nails ought to be used for the lath work where these cements are to be used. Small holes and cracks are usually stopped with fine plaster gauged with putty, or better still, putty water. Parian cement is also used for a similar purpose. The holes and cracks should be brushed with Parian solution before the stiff Parian is applied. This solution is simply fine Parian gauged to a thin creamy consistency with water. New or damp lime-plastered walls can be painted or papered much sooner, and with greater safety, if brushed with a thin Parian solution. It is also useful for stopping the suction on dry floating and fibrous slabs before laying the final coat. Several of the new patent plaster and white cements are well adapted for repairs, or where time is limited.

Gauged Work.—All gauged work should be regulated in strength according to the purpose required. A brick or stone wall would not require so much plaster as a lath partition. Work not subject to friction or wear does not require so much plaster. If the work is required for immediate use, as with running screeds, or blocking out large mouldings, or fixing large castings much plaster must be used. The amount of plaster required for scaffold work varies from 1/4 to equal proportions for gauging coarse stuff or setting stuff, and from 1-3 to equal proportions for coarse stuff for heavy cornices, and 1-3 to equal proportions for putty and fixing ornament. The amount of plaster also depends upon the quality of the plaster, some of which are much stronger than others. Coarse plaster that is of a dark and sandy nature is generally weak, sets quickly, and becomes soft and useless. Fine plaster should be used for gauging putty when running cornices, also for fixing enrichments. All gauged work should be gauged with uniformity, each separate gauge having the same amount of water and plaster as required for the bulk of stuff being gauged. Unequal gauging causes hard and soft places in the work, and when more plaster is used in one gauge than another there is an extra expansion caused by the swelling of the plaster, which makes the work more difficult to do when floating, setting, running mouldings, or mitring.

A quart and a pint measure should always be kept on the scaffold for measuring the water used for the various gauges. The quantity of water will regulate the quantity of plaster for each gauge. A proper plaster box should also be on the scaffold, made to hold a sack of plaster, and having a lid made in two halves hinged from the centre. This prevents the plaster from getting dirty by falling stuff, and from getting damp by absorption from the atmosphere. Where there is a large quantity or continuous gauging, the box should be placed on a stand (this is called a stand-box) to prevent unnecessary exertion and loss of time by stooping for each handful.

When gauging coarse stuff for large surfaces which require several gauges to complete the work in hand, size water should be used in proper proportions with the neat water used for gauging, so as to allow sufficient time to properly manipulate the material. In the event of gauged stuff setting before the work is laid and ruled off, it is difficult to make the surface strong and fair. This also allows the various gauges to be laid on or against the previous ones while they are in a soft state, thus forming stronger joints and better cohesion between the various gauges. The use of size water in gauged setting stuff and putty enables the work to be freely trowelled and finished. Gauged stuff should not be hand-floated, as excessive working destroys the setting powers of the plaster.

Joist Lines on Ceilings.—Common flat ceilings show in time the precise position of the joists above, and in many instances the position and form of the lath work can be easily discerned. Many theories have been advanced as to the cause of these unsightly lines or marks, which are so distressing to the mind and eye. In my opinion they are due in a great measure to insufficient material and inferior work. The plaster which is between or separate from the joists is more pervious to the atmosphere than that which is in more direct contact. The air in passing through leaves behind it particles of dirt assigned in larger measure to the unattached than to the attached portions. Dust that finds ingress between the joints of flooring boards lies on the unattached portions, consequently the joists show themselves as lighter lines on a more or less dirty background. The same causes apply to the lines on the lath work. Another cause is that the plaster work is too thin. In many instances the floating is brought up from the lath in one coat. This is a most pernicious habit, as it is not only the cause of lath lines, but the ceiling invariably cracks, and develops spontaneously original patterns indicative of rivers, which too often lead like Niagara to a catastrophe in the form of falling plaster. Joists and lath lines on thin ceilings may be partly obviated by laying strong brown paper over the upper side of the lath and plaster and then pasting the edges to the sides of the joists, so as to form a cover to the plaster work. The better and most sanitary way is to lay the work in three coats, allow the first coat to dry, consolidate the floating coat by well scouring with a hand float, and render the setting coat hard, non-absorbent, and impervious to the air by thorough scouring, trowelling, and brushing.

Rough Casting.

Several years ago I was requested by the Editor of "Architecture and Building" of New York to prepare a short treatise on the subject of "Rough Casting" for publication in that magazine. The article was published in almost every architectural journal in the country, and Mr. Kidder embodied it in his excellent work, "Building Construction and Superintendence, Vol. I." I reproduce it here, as the directions given therein have been found to be of the very best, and most workmen in this line of the trade adopt the methods of manipulation herein described.

"Rough casting, or, as it is sometimes called, slap dashing, both of which are synonymous with the French *hourdage,* rough work, and *ravalement,* having a similar meaning, is a method of plastering the outside of a building much used in the northern part of Canada because of its being durable, cheap and well adapted to keep out cold winds during the long winters in that section of the world. The methods of applying rough cast and the mixing thereof do not materially differ from the methods adopted in Northern Europe or even in the Northwestern States, but it is these minor differences, says a writer in an exchange, that make the Canadian rough casting superior, so far as durability is concerned, to much that is done in other parts of the world.

There are frame cottages near the City of Toronto and along the northern shores of Lake Ontario that were plastered and roughcasted exteriorly over 40 years ago, and the mortar today is as good and sound as when first put on, and it looks as though it was good for many years yet if the timbers of the building it preserves remain good. Rough cast buildings are plentiful in every province in the Dominion from Halifax to Vancouver and from Lake Erie to Hudson Bay, and when well built and the rough cast properly mixed and properly applied the result is always satisfactory. It is quite a common occurrence in Manitoba and the Northwest Territories in the winter to find the mercury frozen, yet this intensity of frost does not seem to affect the rough casting in the least, though it will chip bricks, contract and expand timber, and render stone as brittle as glass in many cases, and the effect on iron and steel is such as may prove dangerous if exposed to sudden and unexpected strain.

In preparing a frame or log building for rough casting care must be taken in putting down the foundation. A good stone or brick foundation is, of course, the best, but where rough casting is intended stone or brick foundations are seldom used because of their cost, and the builder is compelled to use posts of wood. The posts are generally made of white cedar, which has a lasting quality of 35 or 40 years if sound when used. The posts are put in the ground from 3 to 5 feet, the deeper the better, as they should be deep enough in any case to prevent frost from forcing them upward. When a sufficient number of posts have been properly placed a line is struck on them a proper height from the ground and the tops levelled off. The sills are then placed—all joints being broken on top of posts—and the whole made level. These sills and all the other timber, scantlings and lumber should be well seasoned, if possible, for the greatest enemy to the plasterer is unseasoned timber; shrinkage of joists, posts and scantling not only breaks the bond of the mortar, but causes great cracks in corners and angles that no amount of pointing or patching can ever make good.

When the frame is up and the rafter on and well secured the whole of the outside should be covered with good, sound, common inch stock pine, hemlock, spruce, or other suitable lumber, dressed to a thickness. If put on diagonally so much the better, but this is not absolutely necessary if the rough casting is to be of the best quality, as will appear hereafter.

When it can be done it is best to get all partitions set in place and lathed, the roof on and all necessary outside finish or grounds put in place and made ready to receive the lath. The carpenter must prepare his finish or grounds for finish to accommodate the extra lath, as the walls will be thickened accordingly.

For the cheaper sort of rough casting in one or two coats the following method of lathing is employed: Nail laths on the boarding—over paper or felt, if paper or felt is used—perpendicularly 16 inches from centre to centre if 4 foot laths are used, or 18 inches or 1 foot from center to center if 3 foot laths are used. The whole surface to be rough cast will require lathing this way. When done lath as is ordinarily done with No. 1 pine lath, breaking joints every 15 inches. Put 5 nails in each lath, driving each nail home solid, coat over with mortar, well haired, and that has been made four or more days; smooth and straighten as well as possible with a darby. When done and while yet soft the rough cast is thrown on it with such force as to drive the pebbles or small stones deep into it. The mixture or dash, as it is called, is composed of fine gravel, clean washed from all earthy particles and mixed with pure lime and water till the whole is of a semi-fluid consistency. This is mixed in a shallow tub or pail and is thrown upon the plastered wall with a wooden float about 5 or 6 inches long and as many wide, made of ½ inch pine, and fitted with a wooden handle. While with this tool the plasterer throws on the rough cast with his right hand, he holds in his left a common white-wash brush, which he dips into the rough cast and then brushes over the mortar and rough cast, which gives them, when finished, a regular, uniform color and appearance.

For this sort of work the following proportions will answer: To one barrel of prepared gravel use a quarter of a barrel of putty; mix well before using. This may be colored to suit the taste by using the proper materials, as given further on. It must be understood that the foregoing is the cheapest sort of rough casting, and is not recommended where more durable but more expensive work is required.

The best mode of doing this work as practised in the Lake district of Ontario is nearly as follows. Have the frame of building prepared as indicated in the foregoing, with partitions all put in and well braced throughout and well secured. Lath diagonally with No. 1 pine lath, keeping 1½ inches space between the lath. Nail each lath with 5 nails, and break joints every eighteen inches. Over this lath again diagonally in the opposite direction, keeping the same space between the lath and breaking joints as before. Careful and solid nailing is required for this layer of lathing, as the permanency of the work depends to some extent on this portion of it being honestly done. The mortar used for the first coat should have a goodly supply of cow's hair mixed in with it, and should be made at least four days before using. The operator must see to it that the mortar be well pressed into the key or interstices of the lathing to make it hold good. The face of the work must be well scratched to form a key for the second coat, which must not be put on before the first or scratch coat is dry. The mortar for the second coat is made in the same way as that required for the first coat, and is applied in a similar manner, with the exception that the scratch coat must be well damped before the second coat is put on in order to keep the second coat moist and soft until the dash or rough cast is thrown in. The rough casting is done exactly in the same manner as described for the cheaper sort of rough cast work.

A building finished in this manner, if the work is well done, possesses many advantages over the ordinary wood covered structure. It is much warmer being almost air tight so far as the walls are concerned. It is safer, as fire will not eat its way through work of that kind for a long time. It is cleaner, as it will not prove such a harbor for insects. It may be made as handsome as desired, for before the rough cast is dashed it may be laid off in panels of any shape by having strips of battens tacked over the soft mortar, which may be removed after the rough casting is done and the coloring finished. It is much superior to the so-called brick veneered house, as it is warmer, more exempt from fire and cheaper.

For 100 yards of rough casting in the manner described the following quantities will be required: 1800 laths, 12 bushels of lime, 1½ barrels of best cow hair, 1¾ yards of sand, ¾ yard of prepared gravel and 16 pounds of hot cut lath nails, 1¼ inches long. The gravel should be sifted through a ½ inch mesh screen, and should be washed before mixing with the lime putty.

To color 100 yards in any of the tints named herewith use the following quantities of ingredients: For a blue black mix 5 pounds of lamp black in the dash. For a buff use 5 pounds of green copperas, to which add 1 pound of fresh cow manure; strain all and mix well with the dash. A fine terra cotta is made by using 15 pounds of metallic oxide mixed with 5 pounds of green copperas. A dark green color is made by using 5 pounds of green copperas and 4 pounds of lamp black. Many tints of these colors may be obtained by varying the quantities given. The colors obtained by these methods are permanent; they do not fade or change with time or atmospheric variations. Many other colors are used but few stand like the ones named. A brick color may be obtained by the use of Venetian red and umber mixed in whisky first and then poured into the dash until the proper tint is obtained. In time, however, like all earthy pigments, these colors fade and have a sickly appearance; they answer better in cements than when incorporated with fat limes.

VARIOUS METHODS OF RUNNING CORNICES, CIRCLES, ELLIPSES AND OTHER ORNAMENTAL STUCCO WORK.

Diminished Columns.—The diminishing of columns is an interesting but somewhat difficult operation. Great care must be exercised not to overdo the entasis or swelling. The swell may commence very gradually from the base to the capital, or the third part of the column may be of the same diameter, and then swell and diminish for the remainder of its height. Two methods are here given to show how this may be done. These are given more to illustrate the method of setting out the diminished floating rules—so necessary to the plasterer—than to define the swell or diminishing of a column, which, being within limits a matter of taste, pertains more correctly to the architect.

The best instrument for forming a diminished column (plain or fluted) is a diminished floating rule, with a cutting edge made to the contour of the proposed column. This rule is used to determine the central position of the astragal and base mouldings (which act as bearings when ruling off the floating stuff and the final coat), so as to obtain a true and uniform diminish, and also to form a fair surface. The appended illustration No. 9 elucidates the method of setting out diminished columns which is also used for setting out the diminished rule for both columns. The method for setting out a diminished rule for a column that diminishes two thirds of its height is as follows: The dimensions of the column

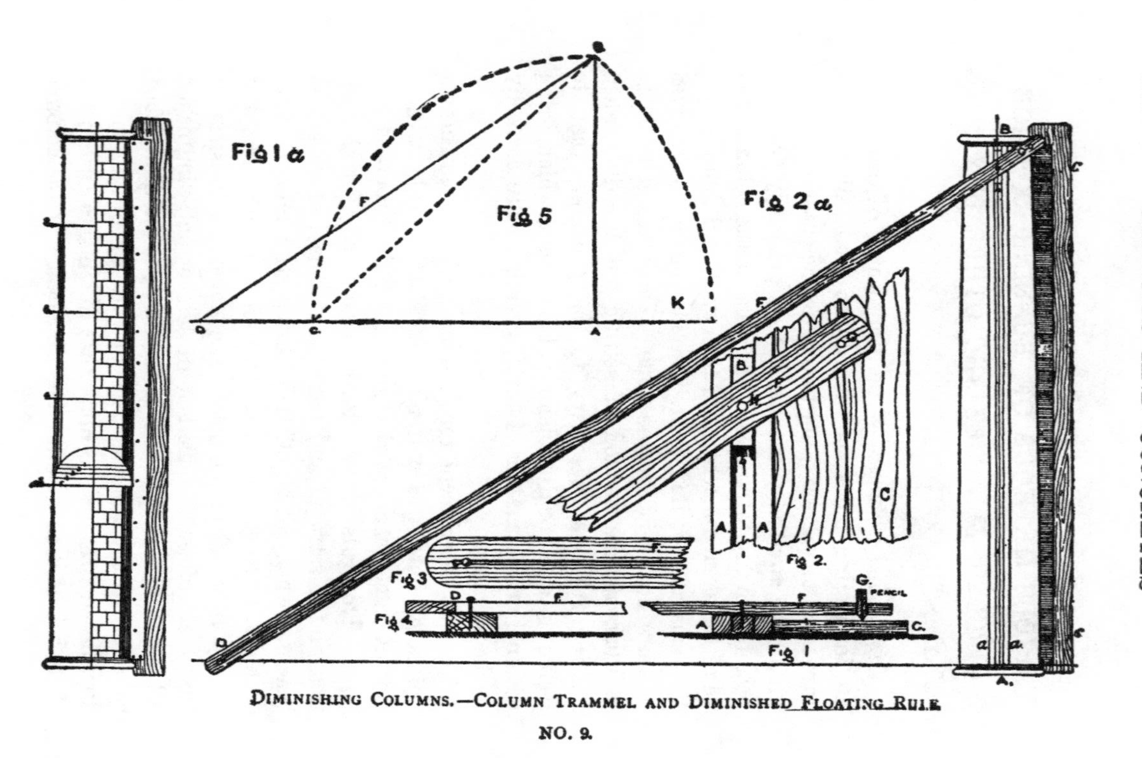

DIMINISHING COLUMNS.—COLUMN TRAMMEL AND DIMINISHED FLOATING RULE

NO. 9.

having been fixed, i. e., the height of the shaft and its upper and lower diameters, draw a perpendicular line which may be taken as the centre line of the column; then set out the upper and lower diameters, as shown in Fig. 1a. This figure also shows one-half of the constructural brick work, and the plaster, which is distinguished by being dark shaded with the floating rule in position. A floating rule for forming the curved and diminished surface requires an iron plate, similar to a mould plate, as shown, so that it will cut the stuff off cleaner and truer, and last longer. The other half of the elevation shows the lines and divisions for obtaining and setting out the entasis.

To diminish the column, first divide the height into three equal parts then at the lower third (5) draw a semicircle equal to the lower diameter of the column. Next divide the upper portion of the column into four equal parts, as shown at 1, 2, 3 and 4, then draw a line, parallel with the axis or centre line of the column, from figure 1 at the top of the column, cutting the semicircle at 1, divide the remainder of the semicircle into four equal parts, which gives the diminishing points. From these points draw lines parallel to the axis of the column, and from the corresponding figures, or from 2 to 2, and so on. In these intersecting points fix pins or nails, and bend a flexible strip of wood or metal round the nails, and draw the curved line. The whole line from top to bottom is then transferred on to the board that is to be used for making the floating rule. This column will have its greatest diameter for one-third of its height, and the upper portion its entasis. This method is so far defective as to require the curve to be drawn by hand, a defect, however, obviated by using a column trammel, which is used for a column that diminishes with a graceful curve from the base to top of the shaft. This trammel is made as follows:

Column Trammel.—A column trammel is simple in construction, and when carefully used gives very satisfactory results, forming a graceful diminished curve from the lower diameter to the upper diameter of the shaft. Before describing the method of setting out and constructing the column trammel, the method of finding the point D on Fig. 2 is given on a separate sketch (Fig. 5) to show the method more clearly.

Fig. 5 illustrates the method of obtaining the point D, on which the centre pin is fixed for the trammel to slide on while working. This point also gives the length of the radius-rod. This sketch is reduced one-half in size to that of Fig. 2a, but the letters correspond to it. Having set out the axis or centre line of the column (A B) and the base line (A C) (extending the latter indefinitely) as described for Fig. 1a, proceed as follows. From A as a centre, and from A to B as a radius, describe an arc, as indicated by the dotted line; then from the intersecting point at C as a centre, and from C to the point at B as a radius (as indicated by the dotted line), describe an arc until it cuts the base line at K. This done add the distance from the point at A to the point at K to the base line, outward from the point at C, which gives the desired point D.

The trammel should be set out on a wall or a clean floor. To set it out, first draw a line to the exact height of the proposed column, as A B on Fig. 2a, then draw a line (indefinitely in length) at right angles to A B, as shown from A to D. This line A B is the axis or centre line of the column, and the line A D is the base line. To construct the trammel, take two rules, each the length of the column, and about 2 inches wide, and 1½ in. thick;

fix one on each side of the axis of the column, taking care to keep them equidistant and parallel to the axis, and forming a grooved space about 2 inches wide, as shown at a, a, the rules, and b the groove. These rules are made thicker than the board intended for the floating rule, so as to allow the trammel pencil to run freely when marking the diminished line on the board. This is shown by the section at Fig. 1. This is as when done in a temporary way on a floor, but a better way is to fix the rules on a board (a flooring board will be found suitable). This makes a permanent groove, and forms an easy ground for the sliding block to work smoothly. It also allows a greater space for a thicker board for the floating rule.

Fig. 2 shows enlarged details of the groove rules (A, A,) the groove (b,) the sliding block (B), with the pin (H), the radius-rod (F), with the pencil (G), and the board for the floating rule (C), with the diminished line. Fig. 1 shows a section of Fig. 2. The letters in all figures correspond with each other. Fig. 2a shows the whole column with the trammel and finished floating rule (C). Make the radius-rod about 2 inches wide, 1 inch thick and in length a little longer than the distance from D to B, and the half diameter of base of the shaft. The sliding block (H) is about 4 inches long and equal in depth and width to that of the sliding groove (b). It should be made smooth, and fit the groove easily, so that it will slide freely from end to end when working. In the exact centre of the block fix a hardwood pin or a round nail (H). This must be fixed exactly over the axis of the column, and so fitted that it will run immediately over it from end to end. Bore a hole in the radius-rod to fit this pin, then from the centre of the pin set off exactly half the diameter of the base of the column on the radius-rod, which will give the point for the pencil hole (G). At this point bore a hole large enough to receive a pencil, which must be tightly held in it. At the lower end of the radius-rod cut a slot just wide enough to receive the center pin at D.

A plan of the radius-rod with the slot and centre pin is shown at Fig. 3 and a section at Fig. 4. The block beneath the radius-rod, in the section is used to keep the rod level with the rules and sliding block, as shown on Fig. 1. To ascertain the length to cut the slot, place the radius-rod along the line A D, and the pencil at the outside of the semi-diameter at the base of the column, and slide it to its place; mark on the rod where the centre pin (D) comes; then place the pencil end of the rod at the top diameter, and mark the rod again at the centre pin; this will give the length of the pin. Having made the trammel, provide a stout board to form the floating rule (cc). This board should be planed on both sides and one edge. Place it near the rules a a, keeping the planed edge outwards, and parallel with the axis or centre line of the column. This allows the planed edge of the floating rule to be used as a straight edge to plumb by when fixing the top and bottom rims or mouldings, which are used as guides and bearings when floating the column. Place the sliding block in position, and lay the radius-rod over the center pin, and the pin of the sliding block, keeping the rod in a line with D A, taking care that the pencil is in its true position; then carefully move it upwards, and pressing the pencil gently upon the board which will give the line for cutting the diminishing floating rule. The floating edge is strengthened by nailing a strip of sheet iron on the board in a similar way to that in which a mould plate on a running mould is treated. This is of special use when floating diminished fluted columns or pilasters, as the thin and sharp edge allows the flutes to be more easily formed. The diminished line on the metal plate can also be formed with the trammel.

A column trammel can also be used for setting out other diminished floating rules for columns less in size than the original one. The only alteration required for this purpose is to alter the point D to suit the size of the proposed column, and the shortening of the radius-rod. It will be seen that the floating rules for both columns are made long enough to bear on the base and necking mouldings, but it is usual to make them shorter so as to bear on cast or run rims or collars, which are fixed at the top and bottom of the shaft.

Constructing Plain Diminished Columns.—Plain diminished columns and pilasters are formed with a diminished rule fashioned at both ends to work on the necking and base mouldings (termed rims), or on collars. The method of making rims and collars, which are used as bearings, is as described for diminished fluted columns.

To Set out the Flutes of Diminished Column.—The annexed illustration No. 10 elucidates the method of setting out the flutes of a column. Fig. 1 shows the half plan of a column; A is the plan of the flutes at the base, and B the plan at the top of the shaft. Fig. 2 shows the elevation of the column, with the various parts marked. Fig. 3 shows the plan and centres for setting out the flutings for the different orders with arrises or with fillets. A fluted column may be divided into twenty, twenty-four, or twenty-six flutes, according to the style or order. There are two different sorts of flutes used. One is worked to an arris, and sunk down in different depths, one of which is described by the fourth part of

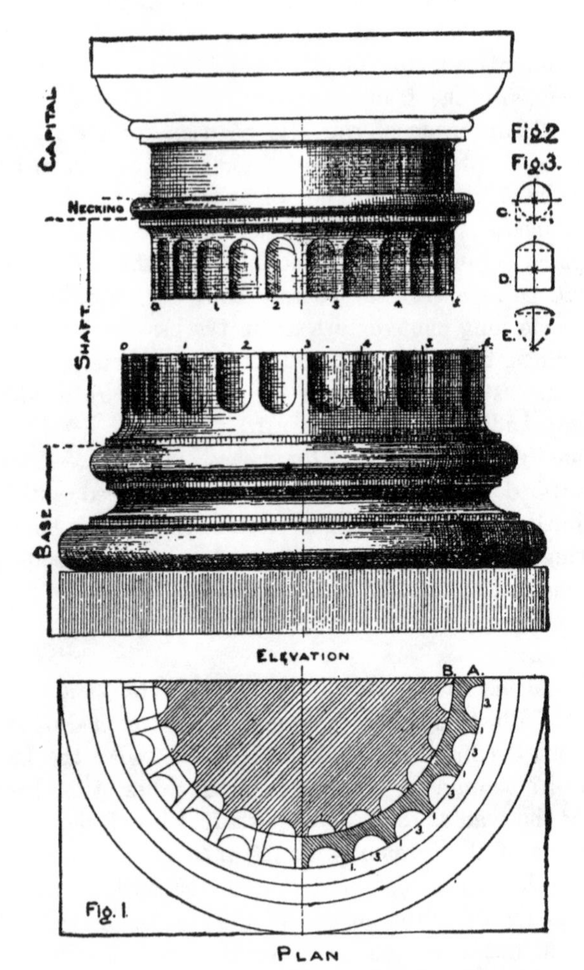

—Diminished Fluted Columns.

NO. 10.

the circle, one by the sixth, and others by the half circle, as shown at C, D, E, Fig. 3.

The square or fillet of the second kind is equal to one-third part of the flute. It will be seen in Fig. 2 that two lines are shown at the top of the flutes. The lower one shows how the flutes finish, when the fourth and sixth depths are taken, and the top line when the half-circle is taken together with the fillets. Flutes that finish with an arris are usually employed for columns in the Doric order, and those that finish with fillets are used in the other orders. The fillets or lists at the top and bottom of the shaft of a column, which serve to divide the shaft from the capital and base mouldings, are commonly called the upper and lower fillets, and sometimes the horizontal fillets, but in architecture they are known as "cinctures." The curved parts at the top and bottom of the shaft which are usually curved into the upper and lower fillets by a concave curve or inverted cavetto, are in architecture termed "apophygis."

Constructing Diminished Fluted Columns.—The formation of diminished fluted columns by means of a running mould is an absorbing and vexed topic among plasterers, and many ingenious plans have been advanced for the construction of hinged and spring running moulds, and diminished running rules. I have known more than one self-improving plasterer who has expended a vast deal of time and lime (not forgetting plaster) to prove by actual practice the possibility of running a diminished fluted column, while others have been content to work them by theory, forgetting that an ounce of practice is worth a ton of theory. Some men thought they had accomplished a feat when they had run a single flute with a hinged mould, between two running rules fixed to form diminution in width, forgetting or not knowing that flutes diminish in depth as well as width.

The difference in depth of flutes, at the base and the top of the shaft, is shown at A, the base, and B, the top, in Fig. 1, illustration No. 10. Running moulds have also been made with springs to regulate the diminish in depth, but their action was uncertain, and they are also too expensive for the purpose. Another form of running mould was made by fixing wire, catgut, or leather on one end of one of the slippers, and on the upper edge of the stock, so that the slipper, when being forced up the diminished space between the running rules, became more angular, or in other words, the slipper on which one end of the wire was attached was higher up the diminished space than the other slipper, and thus caused the stock to cant forward, or be drawn out of an upright, and reduce the depth of the flute. The stock in this case is connected to the slippers not by hinges, but by a pivot inserted at each slipper to allow the stock to cant forward when pulled by the wire. This form of mould also proved to be too erratic in its working to be of useful service. Running moulds having the stock connected to a slipper at each side by means of two hinges (termed a double-hinged mould) allow the mould to assume an angular or slanting form as it passes up the diminished space, thus forming a diminution in the width of flute, but it does not form it with a true arc all the way. On the contrary, it assumes an elliptical form which becomes more and more pronounced as it reaches the top of the shaft.

The nearest approach to perfection in running diminished flute is performed by means of a running mould made with hinged slippers as described, but having the mould plate and stock cut through the centre of the profile, the two parts being then connected by a hinge. This form of running mould (termed a "triple-hinged mould") allows the mould to collapse in the form of a V on plan, and the slippers to run level or parallel with each other, thus forming each half of the flute alike, and at right angles from the centre. Still this has the defect of forming the flute without the necessary decrease in depth.

A method for diminishing the depth of the flutes is to make the running rules with a diminish on face, or rather to make them with an increasing thickness towards the top ends, so that the mould when running up on the increasing thickness will form a corresponding decreased depth of flute. When running a fluted column by this process, the running rules are fixed flush with the face line of the fillets. Only one flute can be run at a time, but twelve may be in band at the same time. As there are generally twenty-four flutes in a column, twelve rules would be required to keep a couple of plasterers going. When the first set of flutes are run, the rules are taken off and fixed to run the remaining flutes. When all are run, the returned ends at top and bottom require to be made good. It will be seen that the running rules for this method must be carefully made and fixed to ensure true lines and forms. It will be understood that a bed or ground must first be formed as a guide for setting out and fixing the running rules on. This is done with the aid of a diminished floating rule. It will also be self-evident that the floating rule would be more profitably employed for forming the entire shaft with the flutes, thus dispensing with running rules and hinged moulds. This method of running the flutes is slow and tedious, but the worst part is that the flutes are not true segments; in fact, the whole of the methods mentioned are more or less a rule of thumb, uncertain and inaccurate.

A knowledge of the rudiments of geometry will prove that the true form of a diminished and swelled fluted column cannot be run with a mould, however ingeniously made. This may be proved by cutting a plaster or cardboard disc to the former radius of a single flute, and describing a line round it on a board. This would be the form the mould, when at right angles at the bottom of the shaft, would give the flute. Then place the disc in an oblique position (the same as the hinged mould would be at the top), and project the plans by means of a set square on to the board. It will be seen that the mould would give the flute an elliptical form. It may be further explained by stating that when the mould is square at the base, or at right angles with the vertical running rules, the form of the flute would be a true segment; but when the mould is moved up the diminished space between the rules, it assumes an oblique or slanting position. It gives the flute an elliptical form, which increases and becomes more pronounced as it approaches the necking. It may be said that the pointed or elliptical defects can be filled in and worked fair with circular hand floats, but this plan necessitates a series of hand floats to fit the ever-varying widths and depths of the flutes.

It may seem unnecessary to describe the above methods, and then to point out their defects. However, the methods and defects are given to prevent the rising plasterer falling into the same errors, and to enable him to resist and rebut the arguments that are so often advanced by some men, who persistently assert that their own particular way (generally one of the methods already mentioned) is the correct and only way of properly performing this different but interesting operation.

It is worthy of note, to show the interest taken in this subject that a patent was obtained for a running mould and process for forming diminished fluted columns, in 1878, which obtained a provisional protection for "improvements in moulds or templates for running stucco or cement tapered fluted columns." The following is a copy of the specification in extenso:—

This invention relates to the running of stucco or cement in forming fluted or other columns, pillars, or pilasters, and similar surfaces, in a more simple, economical, and expeditious manner than heretofore; and the nature and novelty of the invention as applied for running or making the body part of a fluted tapered column of stucco or cement, consisting in constructing a short box-shaped template, having two sides joined together by a back plate outside, with a handle upon it, for drawing it up and down the column, and with an open space inside the back between the sides open above and below, equal to any desired section or segment of the column at its base or widest part, into which the column is equally divided by narrow longitudinal strips of wood, against which the inner edge and end surfaces of the sides of the template slide close, so as to prevent the escape of the semi-liquid or stucco. A thin elastic segmental mould plate is hinged or jointed at its ends to the inner faces or edges of the template, formed in its inner scraping edge to correspond to the segmental curve of the base of the column, with rounded projections corresponding to the flutes to be formed on the column. This plate and its hinges are laid at an angle highest at the inner scraping edge, and inclined downwards towards the back, leaving a space between it and the back for the free passage or escape of the superfluous stucco or cement scraped off the column during the ascent of the mould along the column on its longitudinal shaping strips before mentioned.

"The one end or side of the mould is made to slide or contract laterally in slots or other equivalent guides in the back of the mould frame as it ascends along the contracting or tapering longitudinal laths, the thin plate bending or yielding down in a curvilinear form on its end hinges before mentioned, so as to bulge inwards while bending downwards, and so contract the column in a nearly true radical and segmental form from the bottom to the top of the column, the angle at which the scraping mould plate is set on its hinges determining this contraction of the scraping centre edge of its segment radically in a ratio corresponding to the contraction of the lengths of the segment and moving sides of the mould, which, for large moulds and columns, might be carried and drawn up by handles secured to the tops of the ends of the moulds with ropes led up and over pulleys at the top of the column, thence down to the hand of the operators, so that the mould may be raised and lowered at pleasure to form the whole segment of the column from the bottom to the top in nearly as simple and efficient a manner as plain mouldings are at present run by the usual simple edge scraping moulds, one segment being run after the other in succession until the column is finished.

"For plain or other forms of columns the inner scraping edge of the mould plate is made to correspond to the tapered surface of the column to be formed plain, segmental, or fluted as desired; and for flat, square, or polygonal columns, which do not require a segmental mould scraper, this would be made straight, either plain or fluted, as desired on its scraping edge, and set horizontally on its hinges, instead of at an angle as described for the segmental mould scraper for forming round columns; and this mould scraping plate in any case is preferred to be made of thin elastic steel or tempered copper or brass, which would bend and contract the flutes or ridges on the surface of the columns or pillars, equally and proportionally to the several parts of the column over which the mould is traversed. Although the mould or template has been described as made with only one of its ends movable laterally, it is to be understood that both ends or sides may be fitted so as to move in a similar manner to suit different kinds of work.

This patent method would be better understood if it had been illustrated. No provision for diminishing the depth of the flutes is given in this method. The use of flexible metal for diminishing purposes cannot be relied on for accurate work.

Another method for forming diminished fluted columns is thus performed:—Make a single flute in plaster, and use it as a mould for casting reverse flutes composed of fibrous plaster. After casting as many reverse flutes as there are flutes in the proposed column, indurate them with litharge oil or paraffin wax. Casts of the necking and base, each with about 3 inches of the fluted shaft, are fixed on the brick core. The shaft is then laid with Portland cement (or other desired cement) and sand until within about one-third of the line of fillets, and while this stuff is still soft, take a reverse flute (previously oiled) and press it into position, using the cement flutes at the necking and base as guides for fixing, and using a diminished floating rule to prove the outline. Repeat this process until all the flutes in the column are filled with reverse flutes. The intervening spaces or fillets are then filled in with gauged cement until flush with the outer surface of the reverse flutes, and further regulated with the floating rule. When the stuff is set, the reverse flutes are extracted, and any defects in the flutes made good. On the care in fixing the reverse flutes and filling in the fillets depends the success of this method.

Diminished fluted columns are also made by casting two vertical halves, and then fixing them on the brick core. The halves are fixed by means of cement dots, which are laid on the core at intervals. Corresponding dots are laid on the interior of the casts. The casts are then pressed on the core until the dots meet, and both halves are in proper position. The cast work is made solid with the core by pouring a thin and weak solution of cement and sand into an orifice at the necking.

The cement and sand should be mixed in the proportion of one of the former to five of the latter. This gauge has sufficient binding power and strength for this purpose, and is not liable to expand or contract in wet or dry weather. This process is useful for small work, and makes a good job when cleanly cast and neatly fixed. The necking with the capital and the base may be fixed before or after the shaft casts are fixed, according to circumstances. The shaft casts are best formed in a reverse casting mould.

Another method of casting a diminished fluted column is effected by making a reverse casting mould. Fix it round the core, and pour the gauged material in at the top of the necking mould. By using a reverse casting mould made with a plaster face and a wood backing, or a mould made in fibrous plaster, the whole column with the core can be made in one piece. Hollow columns, composed of Portland cement concrete, can be made to carry any weight supported by a stone column, or one constructed with a brick core of equal diameter. Cast hollow columns are made by temporarily fixing a wood or fibrous plaster core tapered to one end to allow it to be withdrawn when the concrete is set. A rough wooden or a fibrous plaster hollow core is used when casting a hollow column in situ. The core in this case is left in.

After many years' experience and observation on this subject, I am of opinion that the true form of a diminished fluted column (composed in Portland or similar cement, and constructed in situ) is best obtained by hand, with the aid of cement rims or plaster collars and a diminished floating rule. Most plasterers will admit that what can be and is done in stone or wood, can be done equally well in cement or plaster. A plasterer has one advantage, inasmuch as he can add as well as subtract when forming circular surfaces, whereas the mason can only subtract. The two methods hereafter given for forming diminished fluted columns by hand are simple, speedy, and accurate. They are on one principal, and each may be used as circumstances require: one is termed the "rim method," and the other the "collar method."

Forming Diminished Fluted Column by the Rim Method.—First make models of the half circumferences of the astragal or necking and base mouldings, each having about 4 inches of the fluted shaft, as shown at Fig. 1, the plan and Fig. 2, the elevation, on illustration No. 10. To make the models, cut a mould plate to fit each of the full-sized mouldings, and the required size of the shaft, and "horse" them with radius-rods, and run a little over one-half of each circumference in plaster, and then cut them to the exact half circumference. This done, set out the flutes, then cut them out and form the returned ends. The method of setting out the flutes on the ends of the models is shown on the plan at Fig. 1. A is the plan at the base, and B the plan at the top of the shaft. The returned ends of flutes are shown on the elevation, Fig. 2. Add the square plinth to the base, as shown on the plan at Fig. 1, which completes the models. Piece mould the models in plaster, and then cast as many half astragal and bases as required. The materials used for the casts must be of the same kind as intended for the shaft. The brick or core of the column is now cleaned and well wetted, and then the astragal and bases are fixed in position, using the diminished floating rule to prove if they are central, and the fillets linable with each other. Apply a plumb rule on the back edge of the floating rule to test if the astragal and base are concentrical and parallel with each other. When these half casts are fixed together on the shaft they are termed "rims." The intermediate space on the shaft is then filled in and ruled off with the diminished floating rule, using the rims as bearings and guides for forming the fillet line of shaft.

The methods of forming a diminished fluted column by the "rim method" is further elucidated by the annexed illustration, No. 11. This shows an elevation of the brick core of a shaft with the astragal rim, A and the base rim, B, fixed in position. D is the diminished floating rule in position for floating the main or fillet line of the shaft. The method of using a diminished flute rule for the flutes is illustrated in the "collar method."

A second diminished floating rule is required to form the back surface of the flutes. This can be quickly made by laying the first rule flat on the floor, and from this, with compasses, describe the back line of the flute on another board, which is afterwards cut to the desired

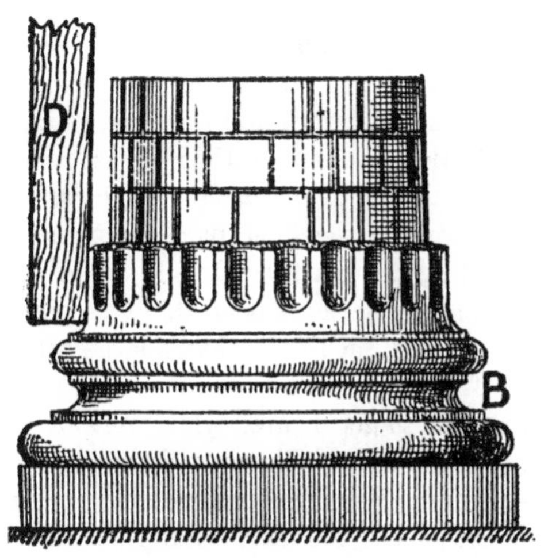

FLOATED FLUTED COLUMNS, RIM METHOD.

NO. 11.

line. This rule is used as a long joint rule to form the flutes. The rule should be worked with uniform pressure, the man at the top working in unison with the man at the bottom, both working the rule with a circular cutting motion. The flutes are fined down by the aid of a small float semicircular in section. For extra large columns three floats should be used—No. 1 cut to the top section, No. 2 cut to the middle section, and No. 3 cut to the bottom section. The length of the floats may vary from 5 inches to 7 inches, according to the height of the column. If the columns are required with a smooth surface, the flutes are worked as above, but the floats are covered with fine felt, leather, or rubber, and the surface finished smooth with short joint rules or with pieces of flexible busks. The cast parts of the shaft, to the fillet members of the astragal and the base, should be keyed with a drag, so that the whole shaft, from arris to arris of the astragal and base fillets, can be fined, thus giving a uniform texture and color, and avoiding a surface joint of the cast work and the fined work.

A modification of this method is as follows:—The lower horizontal fillet of the shaft and the base mouldings are cast separately, the fillet part being used as bearings for floating the shaft, as already described, and the base is fixed after the shaft is fined. This plan is useful for some purposes, such as for extra large columns, as it gives more freedom for working the shafts and the bases are not so liable to get injured while working over them.

Running Diminished Fluted Column by the Collar Method.—Run a plaster collar about 1½ inches wide to the diameter of the top horizontal fillet of the shaft. The thickness must be regulated according to the space between the brick core and the line of fillet. Cut this collar in halves and fix them on the brick core, keeping the under side in a line and level with the top of the proposed fillet of the shaft. Run another collar to fit the horizontal fillet at the base of the shaft, and fix the upper side of this one level with the bottom edge of the fillet at base of the shaft. This done, make two plaster models of the flutes, one for the top and one for the bottom of the shaft, each about 3 inches wide, and in thickness according to the brick core, the diameter being taken about 1 inch above the returned ends of the flutes at the top and bottom of the shaft. These models are set out and made as described for the first method, but using plaster instead of cement for the casts. The plaster casts are fixed in position, and then the brick core is laid and ruled off, using the main diminished floating rule (and the plain collars as bearings) for forming the main contour or line of the vertical fillets, including the horizontal or top and bottom fillets of the shaft, and using the diminished flute floating rule (and the plaster models of the flutes as bearings) for forming the flutes. This done, the fluted collars are cut out, the spaces filled in and ruled off, and the returned ends of the flutes are formed, and then the whole shaft is fined while the work is green. The fillet collars are then cut out, and the astragal and base mouldings are then fixed, thus completing the column. It will be seen that this method entirely dispenses with joints between cast and floated work on the shaft, and allows it to be fined in one operation.

The method of running diminished fluted columns with the aid of collars is further elucidated by the annexed illustration No. 12. A C is the top fillet collar, B C the bottom fillet collar, and F C and F C are the top and bottom flute collars fixed on the brick core of the column. D R is the main diminished floating rule in position for forming the main contour or fillet line of the column. This rule is rebated at the top to allow for a bearing on the top as well as on the edge of the collar. This rule also forms the profile of the top and bottom horizontal fillets, and the curved parts of the shafts below the top fillet and above the bottom fillet. F R is the flute

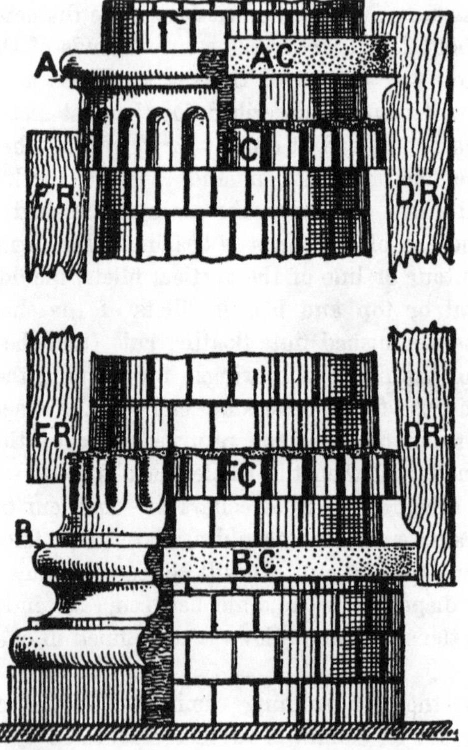

FORMING FLUTED COLUMNS—COLLAR METHOD.

NO. 12.

floating rule in position when forming the flutes. The ends of this rule as shown bear on the back surface of a flute as indicated by the dotted lines. A portion of the astragal moulding, A, with a part of the shaft is shown so as to indicate the position to fix the fillet collar, A C; a portion of the base moulding, B with a part of the shaft, is also given to show the position of the bottom fillet collar, B. C. It will be seen that these collars form fair bed for the astragal and base mouldings, and when taken off they leave true joints as indicated by the arrows at A and B.

A modification of the above methods for forming the fillets and flutes is effected as follows:—Fill in the spaces on the shaft between the collars in this method—or the rims in the former method—and rule them off with a main diminished floating rule as already described and when the stuff is firm but not set, the positions and forms of the fillets and flutes are set out on the floated surface, then the flutes are cut out by hand by means of gouges and drags, and afterwards fined as already described. This system is specially useful for small columns.

For extra high columns it will be found difficult to work a floating rule to form the whole height of the column in one operation, in fact, for some columns to be seen in cities, which are 20 feet to 30 feet high, and even higher, it would be impossible to form them with one floating rule. It is therefore necessary to divide the column into two or more sections, and cut the floating rules accordingly. In this case two or more plaster collars about 3 inches wide, and made to the exact circumference of the column at the point of division, are required. These collars are then temporarily fixed in position to act as screeds, and after the whole surface of the column is filled in and ruled off, the collars are cut out and the spaces filled in, and then the whole surface fined in one operation. Three or even more floats, as already described, are required for the fining of high or massive columns.

Having now briefly reviewed the more or less useful methods, and described some of the most useful and practical methods, the conclusion to be drawn is, that diminished fluted columns are best done by working them by hand, with the aid of diminished floating rules and cast or run bearings. This first or rim method will be found useful for many purposes; but the collar method, with the addition of intermediate collars for extra high columns, is the best for general use.

Diminished Fluted Pilasters.—Pilasters are said to be a Roman invention. They bear an analogy to columns in their parts, have the same names and standard of measurements, and are diminished and fluted on the same principals. When pilasters are placed behind columns, and very near them, they should not project above one-eighth of their diameter; but if they are from 6 to 10 feet behind the column, as in large porticoes and peristyles, they should project at least one-sixth of their diameter. When they are in a line with columns, their projection should be regulated by that of the columns. When pilasters are used alone as principals in composition, they should be made to project one-fourth of their diameter to give regularity to the returned parts of the capitals. The process for forming pilasters is the same as for columns.

Panelled Coves.—Large coves, segmental or elliptical on section, having their surfaces panelled with mouldings which spring from the back or above a wall or main cornice, and finish at or intersect with a beam or other moulding at the top or crown of the cove, require to be carefully set out and screeded. The floating is done from two horizontal screeds made at the top and bottom of the cove, and from these vertical screeds are formed, and then the intermediate spaces or bays are filled in and ruled off with a floating rule bearing on the vertical screeds. The horizontal screeds are easily made, but the vertical ones require special care to insure all being uniform in section. These screeds are formed with a template cut to the desired section, and about 2 inches thick. For large coves they are made with three or more pieces of wood. The most correct and expeditious way of forming circular screeds is by the "pressed screed" process.

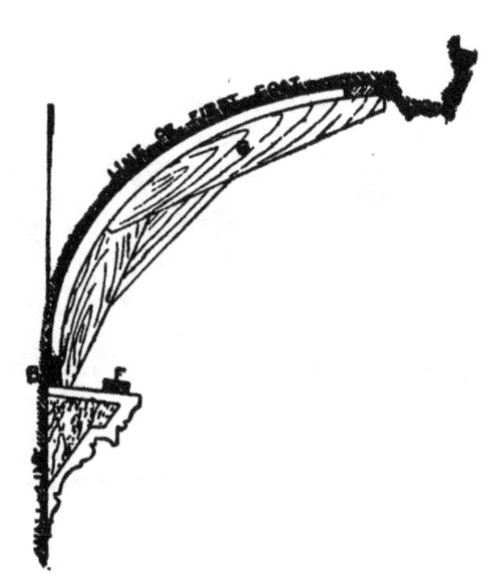

SECTION OF COVE SHOWING PRESSED SCREED PROCESS.

NO. 13.

Pressed screeds are simple and expeditious in construction. They form accurate grounds for floating purposes and for running mouldings on circular surfaces. The method of forming pressed screeds and floating coves is shown in the accompanying illustration No. 13. This shows the section of a cove with the main or wall cornice and the crown moulding. F is a nib rule used when running the main cornice. To float this cove for the running of vertical mouldings, first form the top and bottom horizontal screeds (A and B), then form the pressed screed. This is effected by temporarily fixing the template, G, or by one man holding it on the bottom screed, and another man holding it on the top screed, while a third spreads and presses the gauged coarse stuff until the space between the first coating and edge of the template is filled up, then drawing the trowel down each side of the template clears off any superfluous stuff.

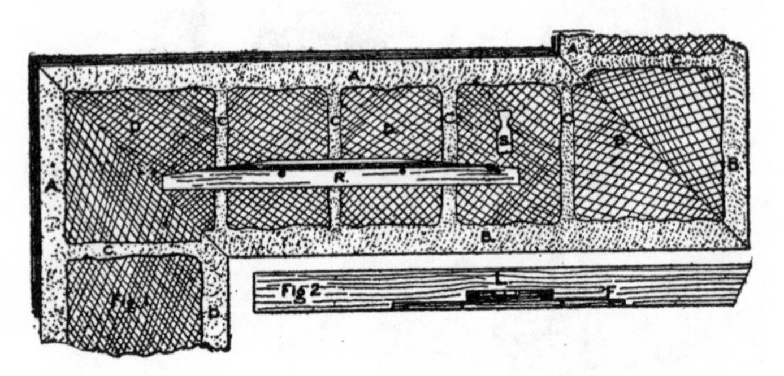

-Fig. 1. Floating Coves. Fig. 2. Levelling Rule.

NO. 14.

The template, which has been previously oiled, is then removed, leaving a narrow, but true and smooth screed ready for working on. This method gives a truer screed, especially in elliptical or long circular screeds, than floating or working with a template, because if the template is not worked perfectly vertical, the curve of the screed is altered and not true.

The subjoined illustration (No. 14) elucidates the method of forming the screeds for floating cove surfaces, also for floating segmental, elliptical. or any other form of interior and exterior angles in coves. Fig. 1 shows a plan of the cove. The letters in this sketch correspond with those on the same parts in the section on illustration No. 13. The first coating and the various bays, after the screeds are made, are indicated by crossed diagonal lines at the D's. The top screed, A, should be levelled from end to end and made parallel in depth with the crown moulding. Their levelness is tested with the aid of a "levelling" rule. The bottom screed, B, should be made parallel with the main cornice, so that the projection of the vertical mouldings will be uniform. The vertical screeds, C, are next formed, making the first two near the internal angles, then two at the external angles. The intervening space is now set out, so that the screeds may be 8 to 10 feet apart. The screeds may be formed farther apart according to requirements. If there are vertical mouldings to be run in the cove, the screeds should be made at the sides of the proposed mouldings. It is always best to have two or three screeds near the angles, so as to give a bearing for the floating rule, R. This shows the position of the rule when floating the internal angle. The external angles on the other side are formed in the same way. The distance between the screeds used for floating the angles can be regulated according to the depth or form of the angle. It will be understood that the floating rule must be sufficiently long to bear on two vertical screeds, and reach to the extreme point of the angle. The floating rule, R, here shown is termed a grooved floating rule. This is grooved on both sides, as shown by the section, S.

Fig. 2 shows the elevation of a levelling rule as used for levelling dots for ceiling, beam, or crown screeds. This is similar to an ordinary parallel rule, but with the addition of a fillet, F, nailed flush with the bottom edge to form a ledge to carry the spirit level, L. The levelling rule is applied on the dots to test if they are level; this is proved by inspecting the spirit-level; if one dot is too full it must be depressed until the levelling rule is level.

Diminished Mouldings.—Mouldings that diminish in depth or projection as well as in width (termed "double diminished mouldings") are not so common as those that diminish in width only. The diminish in width is simple, and is obtained by the aid of a "triple-slippered" running mould and two running rules fixed to form a diminished space, as described hereafter. The formation of a regular and pleasing diminish in depth greatly depends on the profile of the moulding. A moulding having small members, especially at the sides, is more difficult to diminish than one having large members, especially one with plain and deep fillets at the sides. Three methods are here given for running double diminished mouldings on domes, cupolas, or vaulted ceilings, or on lower surfaces. These methods give good results, especially if a little thought for the requirements of the case is bestowed on the designing of the moulding.

Double Diminished Mouldings, False Screed Method — By this method the diminish in depth is obtained by false screeds, and the diminish in width by the aid of a diminished rule, which is fixed on the centre of the profile or bed of enrichment. This method is elucidated in the following illustrations. The annexed illustration No. 15, shows the section of a vertical moulding on the plaster or floated surface of the inside of a dome. C is the main cornice from which the inner line of the dome springs. The D's are dots which are used to regulate the diminish of the false screeds. The various thicknesses and positions of the dots are obtained by setting out the full size of the section on a floor or worked out to a scale. If the section is elliptical, dots should be placed at the points where the transition of curves takes place. When the surface of the dome has been floated, the diminishing dots, D, are placed at each side of the intended moulding and at their proper positions, begin-

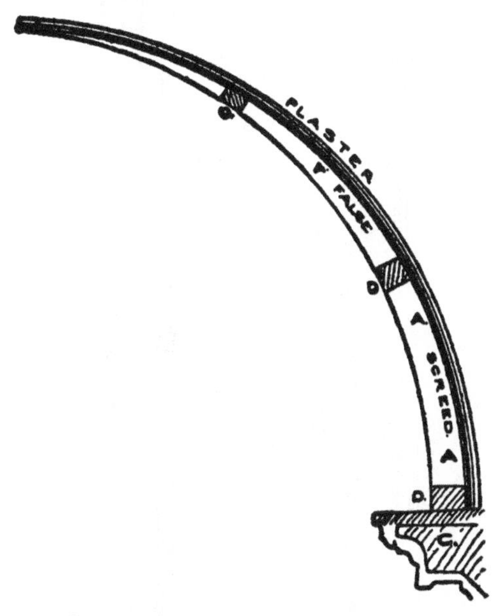

SECTION DOUBLE DIMINISHED MOULDINGS—
FALSE SCREED METHOD.

NO. 15.

ning above the main cornice, C, and going upwards in rotation but having no dot at the top. The spaces between the dots are next filled and ruled in, bearing on the various dots with the curved rules or templates. When ruling the top bay of the screed, the top end of the rule bears on the original floating at the top or ex-

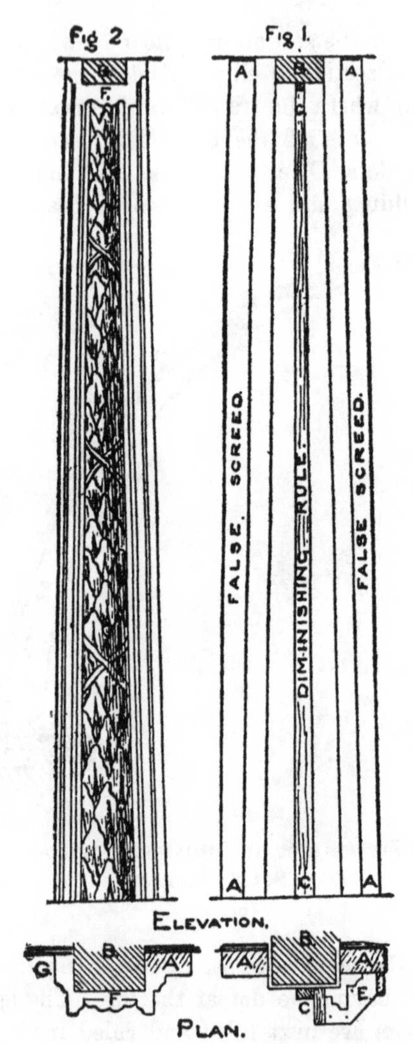

ELEVATION DOUBLE DIMINISHED MOULDINGS—FALSE SCREED METHOD.

NO. 16.

treme point, this point being the true thickness of the screed.

Illustration No. 16 shows the plan and elevation of the work. Fig. 1 shows it in progress, and Fig. 2 when finished. The A's on plan and elevation (Fig. 1) are false screeds, the B's are brackets, while C C indicates the diminished running rule. This rule is made as follows:—First plane one face of a pine board about ½ inch thick, and of sufficient length and width for the desired purpose. On this make a centre line from end to end. From this centre line set off the width at one end, and the diminished width at the other end; then extend the diminished width lines from end to end, and then plane the running edges to the diminished lines. In order to allow the rule to bend freely to the curved surface, make a series of saw-cuts crossways on the back or bed face. The false screeds are made as already described. A centre screed for the running rule is made by the aid of a template. This is made with two slippers, one on each side, similar to a running mould, so as to run on the false screeds, the centre or cutting edge of the template being made to the depth of the proposed screed. The face surface of the bracket is then laid with gauged stuff and finished off by working the template up and down. This done, fix the diminished rule, C, on the centre of the screed. The running mould, E, on the plan is made with the slippers, one to bear on the centre screed and against the running rule, and the other to bear on the side false screed. The slippers are made circular on their running edges, so as to fit the circular screeds. A short slipper at the nib gives more freedom and ease when running the moulding, and the mould is not so liable to cut up the screeds. After the moulding is run on both sides, take the running rule off, then cut the false screeds down to the floating, and make the sides of the fillet good, and then fix the enrichment. Fig. 2 shows the plan and elevation of the finished moulding and enrichment. A, on the plan, shows one side of the moulding before the false screed is cut off, and G shows the screed cut off and the member made good to the floating. The amount of diminish from the bottom to the top of the moulding is shown at the brackets B and B, and by the profiles of the cornice on the plan and elevation. The bed and section of the enrichment is shown at F on the plan. As this enrichment is diminished (in width and projection) the whole length must be modelled.

Running Double Diminished Mouldings, Diminished Rule Method.—This is a method which is introduced, and is somewhat similar to the first method described. It is well adapted for running mouldings, having no enrichment on the centre of the section, the bed of which may be used as a screed and bed for a running rule, as used for the first method. By this method the whole moulding is run in one operation. The diminish in depth is obtained by the use of two running rules diminished on the face, or in other words, diminished in thickness. The diminish in the thickness of the rules is obtained by setting the full size, as described for the false screeds in the first method. A series of saw-cuts must be made on the backs of the rules to allow them to bend to the circular surface of the dome. These rules act in a similar way to the false screed used in the first method, with the addition that they form the fillets of the outside members, thus avoiding cutting the screeds down and making good the fillets. They are also used for obtaining the diminish in width. This is effected by first making a central line on the bed surface of the proposed moulding; then from this line, at each side, set out the half width of the moulding, including the bearing parts of the running mould. This is done at the widest or bottom end of the moulding, and at the narrowest or top end. Then from these width marks, lines are extended from end to end. On these lines, nails are inserted from 2 to 3 feet apart, which act as guides for fixing the running rules. The inner sides of the rule are placed against the outer sides of the nails and fixed, and then the guide nails are extracted, thus forming the diminished space and bearings. A triple-hinged mould with a slipper at each side is used, so that it will close up while being run up the diminished space. The stock is rebated, so that it will run on the tops and inner sides of the rules. The mould plate must be cut to fit the section at the greatest width of the moulding, but care must be taken that the depth at the outer members is the same as proposed for the top. The ends of the inner slippers and the adjoining parts of the stock are cut so as to leave an open space, to allow both parts to work freely when the mould assumes a raking position, as shown on illustration No. 17.

The extra depth of the square of the outside members is formed by the running rules. It may here be remarked that the thickness of the rules at the top should be made about 1/2 inch thicker than the depth of the square part of the outside members. For example, if the depth of the fillets or square part of the outside members is 1 inch, the rules should be 1 1/2 inches thick at the top. This allows for the requisite bearing for the running mould. The ends of the stock that bear on the inside of the rules must be rounded off to allow the mould to run freely when it closes up while being run up between the diminished space.

The various parts of the running mould are shown in the annexed illustration No. 17. Fig. 1 shows the mould

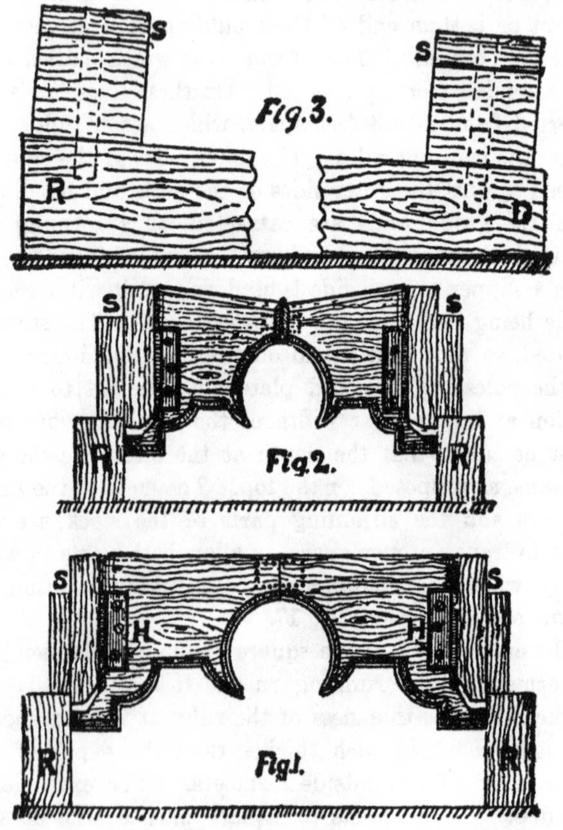

ELEVATIONS AND SECTION OF RUNNING MOULD AND RULES FOR DOUBLE DIMINSHED MOULDINGS—DIMINISHED RULE METHOD.

NO. 17.

in position at the bottom or widest part of the moulding; R, R, are sections of the running rules; S, S, the slippers; and H, H, the hinges which connect the two halves of the stock to the slippers. The hinge which connects the mould in the centre is fixed on the other side of the stock. Its position is indicated by dotted lines. Fig. 2 shows the form of the mould when at the top of the moulding. The letters correspond with those on Fig. 1. The thin seams at the centre and sides of the moulding which are caused by the joint of the mould in the centre and by the joint of the mould and the rules are cleaned off by hand. This method, like the first, has the defect that the actual diminish or the whole depth of diminish lies in the fillets of the outside members of the moulding. The difference between the diminished members and the regular members will be most noticeable on the adjoining members, the vertical fillets of the cavettos. If this defect should prove offensive to the eye, it may to some extent be remedied by working these members down by hand, with the aid of planes, gouges, drags, and joint rules, after the moulding is run, so as to reduce the depth of the fillets, and throw the difference into the cavettos. A line should be set out to the desired diminish on the fillets to act as guides when working the cavettos down.

Running Double Diminished Mouldings, Top Rule Method.—Running double diminished mouldings by the aid of a "top rule" is another method that I have introduced for this purpose. The diminish in width is obtained by fixing two slipper running rules to the desired diminish and a triple-hinged mould as previously described, and as shown at Figs. 1 and 2 on the annexed illustration, No. 18. Fig. 1 shows the running mould, M, and the slipper rules, R, R, at the full-sized or springing end of the moulding, and Fig. 2 shows the running mould and rules at the diminished end. The diminishing depth is obtained by the aid of a "top rule" which is fixed on two blocks, one at each end of the moulding, as shown at Fig. 3. This shows the elevation

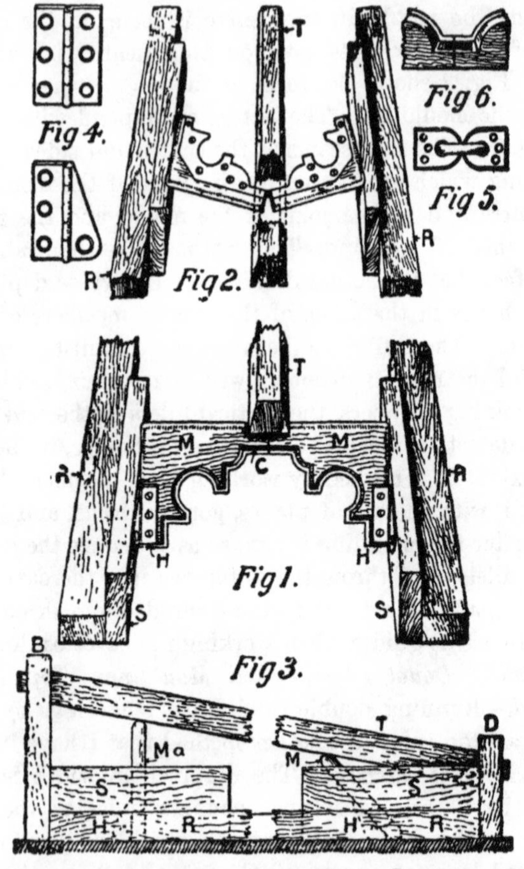

ELEVATIONS, PLAN, AND SECTIONS OF RUNNING MOULD AND RULES FOR DIMINISHED MOULDINGS—TOP-RULE METHOD.

NO. 18.

of one side of the running moulds at the springing and diminished ends of the moulding, also the running rules.

B is the section of the fixing block at the springing end of the moulding, and D is the fixing block at the diminished end, upon which the top rule, T, is fixed. This rule is fixed on the slant, to suit the desired diminish. It must be made sufficiently wide to allow a bearing for a part of each half of the stock, M, M, of the running mould, and also fixed over the joints of the mould, as shown at T, Figs. 1, 2, and 3. The top rule being fixed on the slant, causes the running mould to gradually cant over when it is drawn from its upright position at the springing end of the moulding to the diminished end, as shown at Fig. 3, thus forming the diminish in the depth of the moulding. M a shows the end section of the stock in an upright position when at the springing end, and M is the section of the stock in a slanting position when at the diminished ends of the moulding. The dotted lines in both indicate the parts of the stocks inside the slippers, and the angular dotted line at H, H, indicates the splayed or cut side of the hinge. S S is the outer elevation of one slipper when at each end of the moulding, and R is the slipper running rule. It will be seen that the running mould at Fig. 1 is somewhat similar to the triple-hinged running moulds previously described. But there are two important exceptions, namely, the hinges at the centre and the two sides of the mould.

The side hinges for this mould must be cut on one side and the angles rounded off, leaving only one screw-hole, so as to cause less friction, and allow this part of the hinge to turn on a screw when fixed on the slipper. The use of this will be seen hereafter. An elevation of a hinge, before and after it is cut, is shown at Fig. 4. The lower hole on the cut half of the hinge is used, because the nearer the "turning points" or pivots are to the running ground or screed, as the case may be, the less will the bearing edges of the running mould rise when the mould cants over. For instance, if the "turning points" were made at the centre of the depth of the mould, the bearing edge of the mould would rise from the ground in proportion to the cant of the stock. This would increase the depth of the lower members (those below the pivots or turning points), instead of diminishing them. This hole must be enlarged so as to admit of a short thick screw to give the necessary strength. It will be understood that this part of the hinge works on the plain part at the head of the screw.

Having cut the right and left hinges, they are screwed on to the stock and the slippers of the running mould, keeping the half of the hinge with the three screw-holes on the stock, and the cut part with one screw-hole on the slippers, as shown at H, H, Fig. 1. It will also be noticed that these hinges are fixed at the lower edge of the mould. This is done so as to allow the stock of the mould to cant from its base for the reason already mentioned. When screwing the cut side of the plate to the slipper, allow just sufficient play for the hinge to turn smoothly but firmly on the screw. The centre hinge connecting the halves of the stock, M, M, is formed with two pieces of metal plate. The inner ends are rounded off to allow them to turn and a circular orifice one-third the width of the plate is drilled at the circular ends, and then three or more screw-holes for fixing purposes are drilled on the other ends. The two plates are fastened together with a flat metal ring or with stout copper wire. The thickness of this ring is regulated according to the size of the orifice, but allowing just sufficient play for the plates to turn both ways when the mould assumes a slanting and an angular position, as shown at Fig. 2.

An enlarged view of the centre hinge is shown at Fig. 5. The centre hinge is screwed on the inner side or profile of the stock, as shown at C, Fig. 1. An enlarged view of part of the stock at the joint, when inverted for fixing the centre hinge, is shown at Fig. 6. The top and bottom edges and the ends of the stock must be rounded off, to allow it to cant over easily. The diminish of this moulding, both in depth and width, as shown in the illustration, is a little more than may generally occur in practice, but this is given to show the various parts more clearly, also what to avoid in the amount of diminish when using this method.

The diminishing depth here shown is about two-fifths, and the diminishing width about one-third. The diminishing depth, by this method, should not be overdone, because the running mould assumes an angular position both on plan and section, therefore it forms the vertical parts of the members in a slanting line and the horizontal parts out of a level. These defects become more pronounced at the diminished end of the moulding, as shown at Fig. 2. The top member can easily be made level and fair by hand, but it would entail too much labor to rectify the defects of the other members, therefore this method should only be used for small mouldings or where the diminish in depth is of a slight nature. The seam at the top member, caused by the joint of the mould, is cleaned off and made good by hand.

Cupola Panels and Mouldings.—In order to facilitate the setting out and formation of cupola panels and mouldings, the method of drawing them is given. This will be found very useful in the general setting out and construction of cupolas, whether in "solid" or in "fibrous plaster." Various parts of cupolas and soffits of arches (from designs by J. Gibbs, architect, a pupil of Wren, and a great patron of the plasterer's art), with the method of drawing same, are illustrated on plate 11. To draw an octagonal cupola, as shown by the plan at Fig. 1, take A B (the width of one side of the octagon) as the base line. From the centre of this erect the perpendicular line D C, then draw the lines C A and C B; this will give the triangle A B C, forming the plan of an eighth part of the cupola. The profile (Fig. 2) is made by the quadrant of circle (A B C) directly over the plan. Divide half the base line, A B on plan, into seven parts, as here figured, and six of them will make two panels; the seventh will remain for the border. The same divisions must be marked on the profile over the line A B, as follows:—Take for the border at the bottom four parts, as shown in the plan; place them on the profile from the base line to No. 1, and draw a line parallel to the base line of the plan; measure the length of the two central lines marked 2 2, and place it in the profile for the second panel. From thence draw another parallel line, and measure the length of the two central lines at 3 3 in the plan to find the square height of the third panel, and so on to No. 8, as shown in the plan and profile.

The elevation or upright side of this octagonal cupola (Fig. 3) is made by the following geometrical rule. First draw the base line (A B) on plan even with the base line (A B) of the profile; on this erect the perpendicular line (D C) for the centre of the side; then draw all the parallel lines as shown by G G, etc. Take half the length of each line, figured in the plan, and mark it on each side of the middle line of Fig. 3 until the length of every panel is fixed. From these lines and points the forms or outlines of the panels are taken. The inner divisions are brought over to the number of panels contained therein in the same manner as they appear in Fig. 3. The same rule is used for setting the side shown at Fig. 4.

With regards to the soffits of arches, if they are divided into panels, they must be of any uneven number, as shown at K and L, by having a panel in the centre. The border must not be more than one-sixth nor less than one-seventh part of the whole breadth. The quadrant or profile, E F (Fig. 2), on which the panels of this semi-circular soffit are divided, will be sufficient to explain them. A circular soffit of lesser breadth is shown at M, and one of greater breadth is shown at N. Sections of each soffit are shown at the top of the elevations.

The method of constructing the plaster work of cupolas depends to some extent on the design and size of the panels and mouldings. For example, if the diagonal panels shown in Fig. 3 were sufficiently large to admit of a running mould to run a piece of moulding (on each side of the panels) not less in length than the mitres at each end, the best method would be to run the four sides of all the panels; but if the panels were too small to allow a running mould to run the requisite amount of moulding, it would be necessary to run a part, and cast, or run down, and plant the other parts. In some designs it would be necessary to plant all the mouldings. In some cases the panel mouldings, from the base up to a third or fourth of the height of the cupola, can be conveniently run; but the panels above this which become smaller, and are too small to admit of their being run with economy, should be planted. Another method is to run all the diagonal mouldings that spring from left to right, as from A to a, in one length from border to border, and then run the intermediate parts of the mouldings springing from right to left.

The intermediate parts may also be run down, or cast, and then planted. By this method the intermediate parts only require mitring, and if they are planted the intersections only require to be stopped. If these parts are run, the brackets from right to left must be cut down at the intersections to allow the running mould to pass when running the mouldings from left to right in one length. Whichever method is employed, the surface must be floated true to the various curves to form a ground for the mouldings, whether run or slanted. The surface should also be floated sufficiently smooth to act as screeds without using gauged putty screeds for each moulding. This is done as described for panelled ceilings. The groundwork of the floating is effected by first forming a screed on the base border (A B), and one on the top border (at C), and then from these screeds as bearings, form two screeds on the side or vertical borders, thus completing the main screeds, and from which the panel surface is floated. Owing to the brackets and the form of the panels, it is a somewhat difficult operation to float all the panel surfaces with a uniform depth and curve. It will be seen that a floating rule (cut or so constructed to clear the brackets), whether worked vertically or horizontally, cannot travel into the angles, and float the whole surface. This difficulty is overcome by making dots in each angle, or making narrow screeds from angle to angle of each panel. The horizontal dots or screeds, as the case may be, are ruled off with a gauge rule, which is cut to the required depth, and to bear on the side screeds. The vertical screeds are ruled off with the circular rule, on which pieces of board cut to the desired depth and length of the various panels have been previously fixed. The intervening spaces are then ruled off with short rules cut to the angular curves.

Another and better way is to cut an angular floating rule to fit the curve from A to a, and float all the panel surfaces in a line from border to border in one operation. This angular rule is set out in a similar way as described for angle brackets. The rules for this or the first method must be made to suit the longest line or set of panels. After each set of corresponding panels in the other sides of the cupola is floated, they must be shortened to fit the next set of panels, and so on, until all the panels are floated. The mouldings being diminished in width, are run from a diminished running rule fixed on a centre screed in the same way as described for diminished dome mouldings. The screed for this method is formed by an angular floating rule cut to the angular curve, as already mentioned. For some designs the moulding may be run with a twin-slippered running mould. This form of mould can also be used for forming about one inch of the panel surface. This acts as a ground for floating the panel surfaces. When large paterae are used, the ground panel surface may be cast with them, thus avoiding floating and setting. The octagonal panels shown in Fig. 4 are formed in a similar way to Fig. 1. After the vertical and horizontal mouldings are run, the diagonal sides of the octagons are planted. Where square panels form the design, the mouldings can be run with a radius-rod running mould from a centre pin and block. The sections of the soffits of the arches are run with a radius-rod running mould, fixed on a radius board, and the cross styles or mouldings, as shown at K and L, are planted. A small portion of the arch should be run to form a ground on which the enrichments may be modelled. Fibrous plaster is well adapted for constructing the plaster lining of cupolas.

Panelled Beams.—When panelled beams have mouldings on the lower part of their sides or faces, and on the soffit to form a sunk panel, they may be run in two parts. Screeds are formed on the two sides, and one in the centre of the soffit. If the mouldings on the sides have more girth or are larger than the portion on the soffit, they may be run from rules fixed on the side of the beam, with the nib bearing on the style or on the soffits. If the style and mouldings on the soffit are small, the mould is made to run the face, style, and soffit moulding in one. If the styles are broad, the moulding on the sunk part of the soffit is run from a parallel running rule fixed in the centre of the soffit, thus forming a double rule to run each side of the sunk moulding. The latter way is most generally used. The end or other mouldings required for panelling the soffit are run down and planted.

All beams of any length should always have a camber, not only to allow for any settlement that may take place, but to make it more pleasing to the eye. A beam dead level and straight has the appearance of sagging in the centre. This may be termed an optical illusion.

Trammels for Elliptical Mouldings.—It may at once be pointed out that an ellipse and an oval are not the same. Both ends of an ellipse are similar, and an oval is egg-shaped, one end having a greater curve than the other, therefore the term oval moulding or panel is scarcely correct when applied to the following illustrations. This term, however, is best known and generally used by most workmen in the building trades. The term "elliptical" is generally applied by plasterers when referring to mouldings where the whole ellipse is not carried round, such as for mouldings or elliptical arches, windows, etc.; and the term "oval," where the whole figure is completed, such as panels (elliptical on plan) formed on walls or ceilings. In consideration of the common usage of these terms, they will here be used in describing the setting out or working of same.

Trammels are often used for running oval panel mouldings, and for forming the lines when setting out oval templates. Trammels are made of wood or metal. A simple way to make a trammel for small work is to sink two grooves at right angles in a hardwood board (termed the plate), about 7 inches long, 5 inches wide, and 1 inch thick. The grooves are about 1-2 inch deep and 1-2 inch wide. Two hardwood pins are then made to fit the grooves. They have collars to bear on the surface of the plate. The upper part is made round to fit the centre holes of the rod. The subjoined illustration No. 19 shows a template and various sorts of template pins. Fig. 1 is a view of a template, with the two pins, rod, with the running mould attached in position, and a part of a moulding. Fig. 2 shows various sections of pins. A is the section of the pin as used in Fig. 1. and C is the plan of the pin at the intersection of the grooves. B is the section of a dovetailed pin used for another form of trammel. The rod is made to any desired length, so that it may serve for various sized ovals.

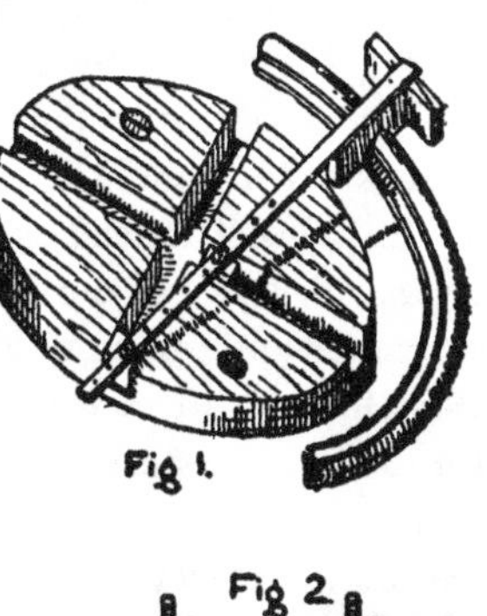

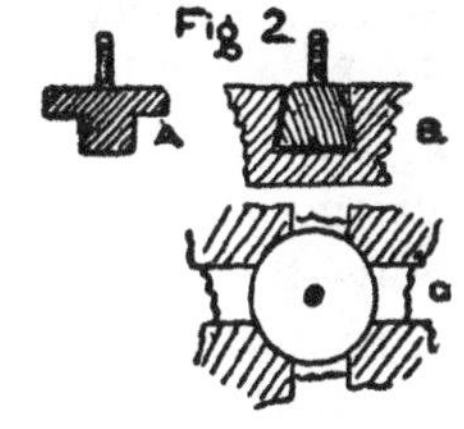

—TRAMMELS.
NO. 19.

The average size for this kind of trammel is about 1 foot 6 inches long, 1 inch wide, and 1-4 inch thick. A series of holes 1-4 inch in diameter (to fit the head of the pin) is made about 1-8 inch apart on the flat side. The first hole is made near one end of the rod, and continued down the centre for about 15 inches, leaving the blank space for screwing on to the running mould. A pin is now laid into each groove, and the size of the desired oval is obtained by regulating the length of the rod at each diameter by means of the holes. The pin in the short groove is the point from which the length of the oval is taken, and the pin in the long groove for the width. The trammel is fixed on the running board by means of two or more screws, as shown. This size of trammel can only be used for oval mouldings from about 10 inches to 36 inches at their longest diameter, therefore larger sizes are required for larger ovals.

A trammel for running large ovals (say from 6 to 10 feet at the major diameter), if made solid, as shown in Fig. 1, would be too heavy and cumbersome for fixing on ceilings where the mouldings are run in situ. A lighter kind termed a "cross" template, is made as follows:—Cut three flooring boards, one a little less in length than the longest diameter of the proposed oval, and two less than the short diameter. Lay them down on a floor in the form of a cross (similar to the grooves in Fig. 1), and fix and brace them together. Four angular braces will hold them together, and allow the whole to be fixed on the ceiling. On the centre of this ground make two lines at right angles to each other, and from these set out the width of the desired grooves at the ends and intersections, and then fix wood fillets, each about one inch thick and two inches wide, to the marks, thus forming the grooves. In order to prevent the pins dropping out of the grooves when the trammel is fixed face downward on the ceiling, the inner sides of the fillets should be splayed so as to receive dovetailed pins, as shown at B, Fig. 2. This may also be effected by fixing running rules on the fillets so as to overlap about 1-4 inch, over the groove space, thus forming rebated or square grooves. The pins are made with shoulders to fit the grooves. In both modes a 1-inch pin must be inserted in the trammel pin to prevent the rod dropping.

A strong, accurate, and permanent trammel can be constructed entirely with metal. To make this, procure a sufficient length of metal tube, about 1-2 inch in diameter, having a slot about 1-8 inch wide, cut longitudinally. Cut the tube into four pieces, mitring the intersections, and fix and brace them together in the form of a cross, as already mentioned. A pin made to fit the slot, fixed in a ball made to fit the tube, completes one of the sliding pins. The rod may be made of metal or wood, but the latter gives more freedom for changing the size for different sized ovals.

Various methods are employed for running oval panel mouldings on ceilings. The most useful are by means of trammels, or wood or plaster templates. A trammel is a good instrument for running oval panels where the mouldings are not wide. Wide mouldings (say over 1 foot) cannot be run true or uniform in width in one operation with a trammel, because the running mould, which is fixed on the end of the rod of the trammel, assumes a raking position when it is between the right angle points of the major and minor diameters of the oval. This raking position takes place at the four joints or change of curves of the oval, and is more pronounced in extra wide mouldings. This difficulty is overcome by running the mouldings in two parts, using a trammel mould for running the first or inner part, and a running mould (horsed to run on the run part) for running the second or outer part. This is effected by dividing the section of the moulding into two parts, taking care to make the joint at the side of a fillet or in the center of a flat member at the outer side of the part to be run with the trammel mould, so as to allow for a good bearing (wide and strong) for the slipper of the running mould used for running the second part. The running mould for the first part is fixed on the rod of the trammel as already mentioned. The running mould for the second part is horsed with a circular slipper cut to fit the curve of the first moulding. If the oval has quick curves, a slipper with two pins will give the best results.

If there is an enrichment in or near the center of the moulding, run the moulding in three parts, using the bed of the enrichment (which is run with a trammel mould) as a center running rule for running the outer and inner parts, which are run with circular or pin-slippered running moulds, as already described. It will be seen that by using either of these three methods, wide mouldings for oval panels can be run uniform on width; the trammel mould giving the form of the oval to the first part of the moulding, or to the center running rule, and the curved slippered running moulds giving the desired uniformity of width to the full section of the moulding. Most forms of oval panel mouldings are best run with templates. When run with trammels, or with radius-rods, the running mould is apt to jump and cause cripples at the junction of the major and minor diameters.

Templates for Running Elliptical Mouldings.—The true form of an ellipsis can only be derived from the diagonal cut from the cone or the cylinder, and the nearest approximation to this curve must be obtained by continuous motion. There is no other instrument so well adapted for effecting this purpose as a trammel. For a true ellipsis, make the distance from the outer end of the rod to the nearest point or centre pin equal to

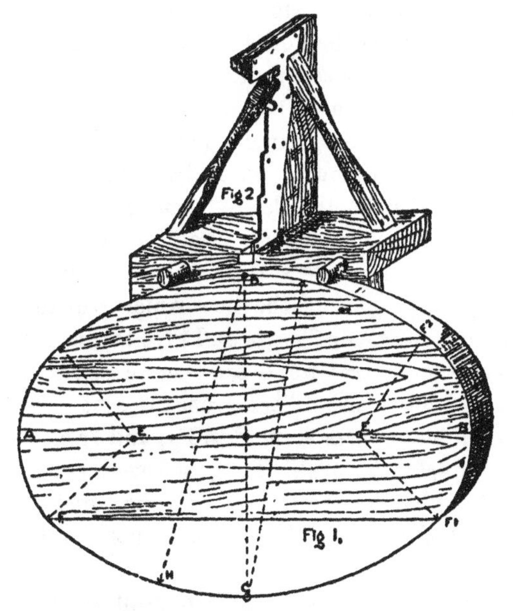

TEMPLATE AND PIN-MOULD FOR RUNNING ELLIPTICAL ARCH MOULDINGS.
NO. 20.

half the shortest or minor diameter of the ellipsis, and from the centre pin to the outer pin equal to half the longest or major diameter. This shows the use of a trammel for setting out the lines to make a template for this form of ellipsis.

The subjoined illustration No. 20 elucidates the method of setting out another form of ellipsis; also an oval having its major axis one-third greater than its minor. This also shows the template and a pin running mould in position for running an elliptical arch moulding. The template (Fig. 1) is made to extend below the springing line of the arch, so as to allow the mould to be run down to the spring of arch and save mitring. The template for running the arch extends to the shaded part; but to utilize the space the curve has been continued round to show a method of setting out a template from which an oval moulding can be run, the oval having its major axis one-third greater than its minor. The method of setting out is as follows: First draw the line AB, the greater diameter, to the desired length; then bisect it, and erect the perpendicular line CD; this being the lesser diameter, is made a third less than the line AB. Then bisect each half of the line, which will divide the line AB into four equal parts and give the centres E, E, which are the centres for describing the ends, as from F to F, and F1 to F2. Then from the centres C and D describe the flat curves from F to F1, and from F to F2, which complete the oval. It is, however, better to set out this template by the trammel, as the junction of the segments of the circles always has a more or less crippled look.

Fig. 2 shows a "pin-mould" in position when running an elliptical arch moulding. This mould is provided with two hardwood pins inserted into the bearing face of the slipper. The pins bear on the edge of the template, and owing to their position, and being apart, allow the mould to take any change of curve without "jumping."

Before running elliptical mouldings on arches or windows, the centres and running rods should be tested, so that the mouldings will intersect accurately, and so avoid jumps at the change of curves. All centre pins should be level with each other, and equidistant from the centre of the arch or window. The outline and intersections of the proposed moulding can be tested by temporarily fixing a pencil on the outer and inner profiles of the running mould, then working the mould over the screeds, so that the pencils will form two lines. I have heard of a three-centered elliptical hood moulding being run over a window with what is called a "bolt radius-rod." This rod is made in two parts and connected with a hinge, and held straight when running the long diameter with a bolt and sockets where fixed at the joint. The running mould is fixed on one end, and a centre plate on the other in the usual way. The long diameter of the moulding is run first, and when the radius-rod reaches the change of curve the bolt is drawn back, and the short diameter of the moulding run with the short part of the radius-rod. A nail is inserted in a board which is previously fixed in the window opening. The nail must be fixed in a line with the change of curve so as to stop the radius-rod, and hold the long part in position while the short part is working. The same operation is repeated for the other side of the work. It is needless to say that this method is far too complicated to be serviceable for general purposes.

Templates are used for running most forms of elliptical panel mouldings. Plasterers may make their own templates or running rules by using fibrous plaster casts as a substitute for wood. This is effected by first setting out a quarter of the proposed oval panel, then cut out or run a temporary plaster running rule to fit the inner line, allowing a space for the slipper of a running mould. Cut a reverse running mould to the section of the proposed fibrous plaster rales (say about 1 inch thick and 3 inches wide), then run the quarter length of the oval, and after making true joints at the ends, cast four fibrous plaster quarters, and then lay and fix them reversely, thus completing the full oval template or running rule. The full oval running rule can also be run in situ and in one operation. This may be done with a trammel or with radius-rods, according to the form and size of the panel. Strong and stiff gauged plaster or a strong white cement, should be used for the running rule, to enable it to resist the friction of the running mould while running the moulding. Radius-rods are more often used for setting out the lines for oval templates than for running the mouldings. Circular mouldings—vertical, horizontal, or angular—run off circular grounds require special running rules, so that they will take or bend to the double curvature. For this purpose, cane, flexible metal pipes, and wooden rules, having series of saw-cuts on the backs and sides, have been used, but cast fibrous plaster rules or a jack template are more suitable for most of these purposes. Template can also be made by means of a plasterer's oval.

Plasterer's Oval.—The subjoined illustration (No. 21) elucidates the setting out of this form of oval to any given size, also the method of forming two oval mouldings from two circle mouldings. The ovals are formed by running two circular mouldings in plaster, the diameter of one being exactly double that of the other. Each circle is cut into four quadrants or quarters. Two of the quadrants of the larger circle form the sides of one oval, and two quadrants of the smaller circle form the ends, the four segments making a fairly good oval. The remaining segments constitute another oval of similar size and shape. The method is simple and speedy, and it can also be employed for the formation of elliptical

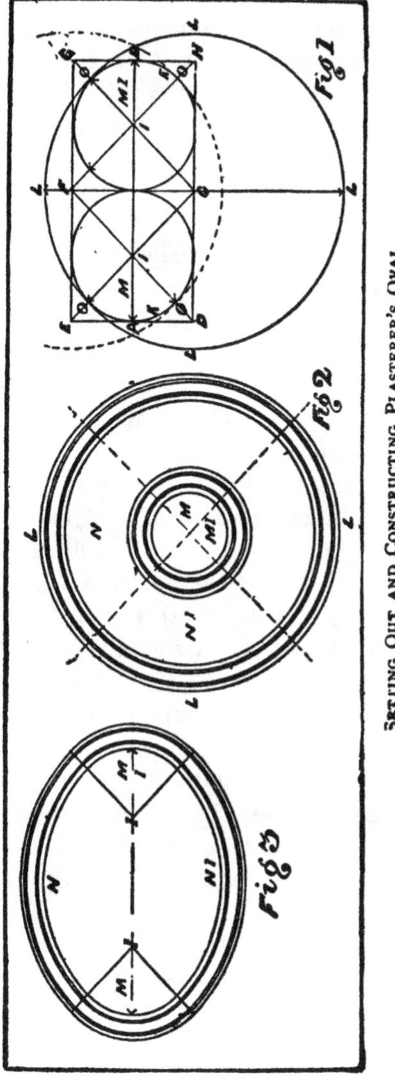

SETTING OUT AND CONSTRUCTING PLASTERER'S OVAL.

NO. 21.

mouldings on arches, doors, or windows as well as for oval panel mouldings. The formation of ovals by this method has been employed by plasterers for generations, but owing to the want of a definite rule for setting out this form of oval to any given size, its use has been somewhat limited. To meet this want, I have invented a method which can be adopted for most purposes, and which I give here for the first time. For want of a better name we have called this a "Plasterer's Oval," for the reason that plaster lends itself more readily than any other material to the formation of circular mouldings. No one in the building trades can form a circle or an oval moulding so quickly and accurately as a plasterer. The method of setting out and of constructing this form of oval is as follows: To set out an oval to a given size, the greater diameter being given. Take this greater diameter as a base to determine the required diameters of the large and small circle mouldings, M and N, Fig. 2. Let the line A B, Fig. 1, be the given diameter, say 3 feet; on this form two squares, each according to their diameter would be 1 foot 6 inches by 1 foot 6 inches, as shown at C D E F and F G H C; then draw diagonals in each square as at C E and D F and C G and F H and at their intersections 1 and 1 as centres draw the circles 1 K and 1 K. The radius in this example would be 9 inches. The quadrants M and M 1 correspond with the same letters in Figs. 2 and 3, and they form the two ends of the oval. After this take C as a centre, and with a radius from C to O at E or G describe that part of the circle L from O L O, which forms the upper side of the oval; now take F as a centre, and with the same radius describe the lower side, joining K K at O and O, thus forming the plan of the oval as shown by the line A L B, and the dotted line below C. It will be seen that the respective centres to describe this figure give the centres and diameters to run the two circle mouldings from which the ovals are formed.

To construct the oval, first make a running mould to the desired profile, using a radius-rod in the usual manner, for running circles on the flat. Before running the mouldings, set out two lines at right angles on the moulding board, taking care to extend the lines a little beyond the outline of the large circle, as shown by the dotted lines (Fig. 2). The extended parts of these lines act as guides for cutting the moulding into exact quadrants. The intersection of them is the centre from which both circles are run. Apply the running mould, and turn it round, so that it leaves a faint mark on the running board to indicate the width of the moulding to be run. The width can also be marked by the aid of a pencil, holding it at the outside member, and turning the mould round, repeating this operation on the inside member. On this space drive in eight tacks, two in each quadrant, leaving the heads projecting about ½ inch. The object of these tacks is to prevent the moulding from lifting owing to plaster swelling, or from moving round while being run. Cover the tacks with clay to allow the moulding to be freely taken up after it is run and cut. The moulding is then run in the usual way, and is cut into four quarters, or quadrants. This is done by applying two set-squares, one inside and one outside of the moulding; and at one of the quarter lines lay a straight-edge over the moulding and against the set-squares. The moulding can then be marked or sawn at the proper place and angle. The dotted or quarter lines divide the mouldings into quadrants, and give the angles for cutting them.

The use of extending the lines beyond the moulding will here be seen. A part may be obliterated while the moulding is being run, but the extended part will afford a correct guide for the outside set-square. If the quadrants are cut fine, square, and clean, the joints will be scarcely perceptible when the four segments are placed together. When this circle is cut and taken off the board, the radius has to be altered to exactly one-half of the large circle, and the small circle is run and cut precisely in the same way as the large one. The four quadrants can now be fixed to form an oval, as shown in Fig. 3. If a quantity of oval mouldings be required, a casting mould can be taken off this oval in which they may be cast. It will be seen that the quadrants M and N 1 form the sides of the oval in Fig. 3, and the quadrants M and M 1 form the ends. It will also be seen that after completing this oval there are four quadrants left to form another oval. If but one oval is required, run only one-half of each circle, allowing a little space beyond the centre line, so that a square and clean joint can be cut. A thin saw with fine small teeth should be used for this purpose.

Fig. 3 shows the four segments of the moulding in position forming the oval. In this figure the moulding is struck on the outside of the setting-out circle line, as shown in Fig. 1, but the moulding in Fig. 2 is struck on the inside of the setting-out lines. This is simply to show that the same centres can be used for mouldings struck on either side of the lines. A mould for casting oval mouldings, also templates, can also be made by the above process. For this purpose a reverse running mould must be used for running the two circles. A plaster piece mould for casting oval mouldings that are undercut may also be formed by this method. In this case the running mould must be made and used as described for "reverse moulds."

Coved Ceilings.—Coves to ceilings are of various heights, as one-third, one-fourth, one-fifth, &c., of the whole height. The form of the cove is generally either a quadrant of a circle or of an ellipsis, taking its rise a little above the cornice, and finishing at the crown or other moulding. If the room is low in proportion to its width, the cove must likewise be low; and when it is high, the cove must likewise be so; by which means the excess of height will be rendered less perceptible. An example of two coved ceilings (from designs by James Gibbs) are shown is the annexed illustration No. 22. Fig. 1 shows the plan and elevation of a coved ceiling, with circular windows between the groins. Fig. 2 shows the plan and elevation of a coved ceiling, the design of which is less intricate than that of Fig. 1. The curve of this cove is a quadrant of a circle, as shown by the section at the side. The plans will enable the section of each design to be understood, and vice versa, and the whole will render the method of constructing coves and circular mouldings on circular surfaces (which is given hereafter) to be more clearly understood. The external and internal angle mouldings in these coves may be formed with a jack template or as described for coves.

Circle Mouldings on Circular Surfaces.—The accompanying illustration, Plate III, is given to elucidate various methods of running circular mouldings on circular surfaces, shows the elevation of a cove suitable for an aquarium or marine hall. The external angle rib moulding, C, and the panel rib moulding, D, spring from the top or weathering of a main moulding, and intersect with a horizontal or crown moulding at the top of the cove. The section of the horizontal moulding is shown

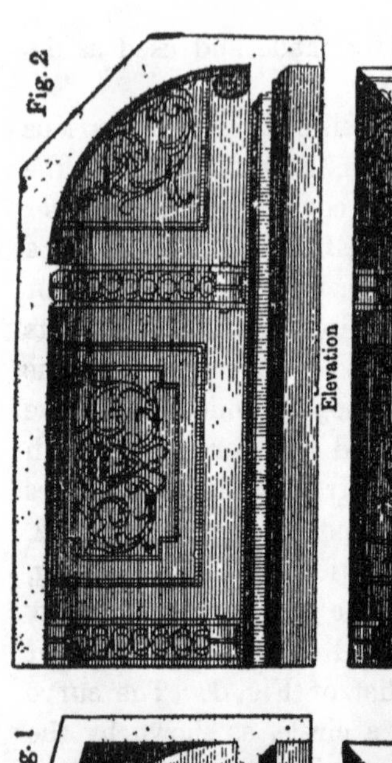

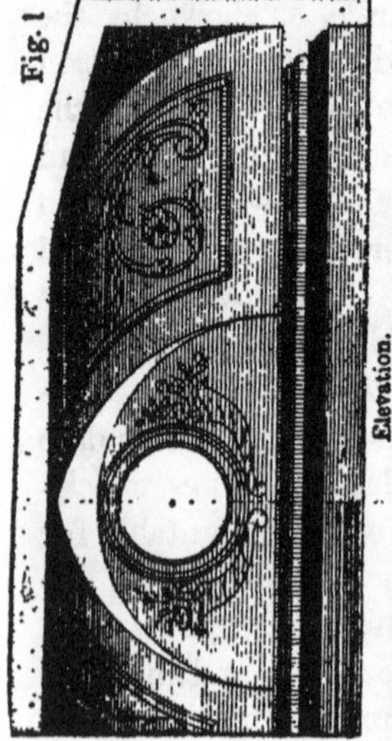

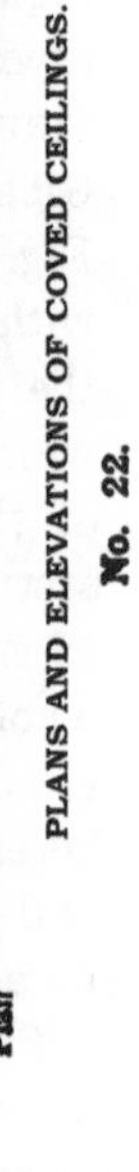

PLANS AND ELEVATIONS OF COVED CEILINGS.

No. 22.

at G, and the section of the panel moulding is shown above D; the section of the external rib being of course double that of the panel moulding. Where circular or straight mouldings intersect with each other, it is advantageous in most cases to run the circular mouldings first, so that the whole of the moulding can be run, and leave the intersection to be mitred on the straight part, which is naturally the easiest part. In some examples it is not advisable to run the circular part first. For example, if the crown or horizontal moulding, as shown at G, Fig. 1, was the lower part of a large crown moulding made to intersect with small cove mouldings, it would be best to run the straight moulding first, and then cut away as much of the straight moulding as will allow the nib of the running mould to pass while running the circular moulding. For the section in this example there would be very little mitring to do, as it would simply be a butt mitre up to the back of the circular mouldings. The external rib moulding, C, is best run with a jack template. The circular panel mouldings (one-half of a moulding is shown at D) can be run by two methods. By the first, the moulding is run in three parts, using a sledge-slippered running mould fixed on a hinged radius-rod, and the two straight parts are run from running rules. By the second method, the whole moulding is run at one operation by using a fibrous plaster template, made as already described.

Forming Niches.—Niches are recesses formed in walls, sometimes for the purpose of placing some ornamental object in them, such as statues, vases, &c., and they are often constructed in thick walls in order to save materials. The plans or bases of niches are generally semicircular, but some partake of all the segments under a semicircle, while others are elliptical, and in a few instances they are square or rectangular. The elevations of niches are generally in accordance with their plans, but variations from this rule are sometimes met with. The crown or heads of niches are generally plain, but they are sometimes enriched with scalloped shells, &c., or panelled with mouldings. With respect to the proportion of niches, there is no fixed rule, but the general one is twice and a half their width for their height. Various methods are employed in the formation of niches. The crowns of circular niches are generally run with a mould, because being circle on circle and small in surface, it is difficult to finish them true and smooth by hand.

The accompanying illustration (No. 23) elucidates two methods of forming semicircular niches with the aid of running moulds. Fig. 1 shows the elevation, and Fig. 2 the section of the crown and a part of the body of niche, with the centre-boards and moulds in position when forming the crown of the niche. Fig. 4 shows the section of the body of the cove, with the mould in position when forming same. By the first method the niche is formed in two operations, and by the second method it is formed in one operation only. For the first method, cut a running mould to the section of the niche, as shown at B, Fig. 1, then fix it on the centre board, A, with two hinges, keeping the upper surface or mould plate level with the top edge of the centre board, as shown on the section of the niche, Fig. 2. This also shows the end section of the centre-board and the mould, with the mould plate and a hinge. The dotted line indicates the distance the mould travels. After this, fix the combined centre-board and mould on the wall, taking care that the top edge of the centre-board is level and ex-

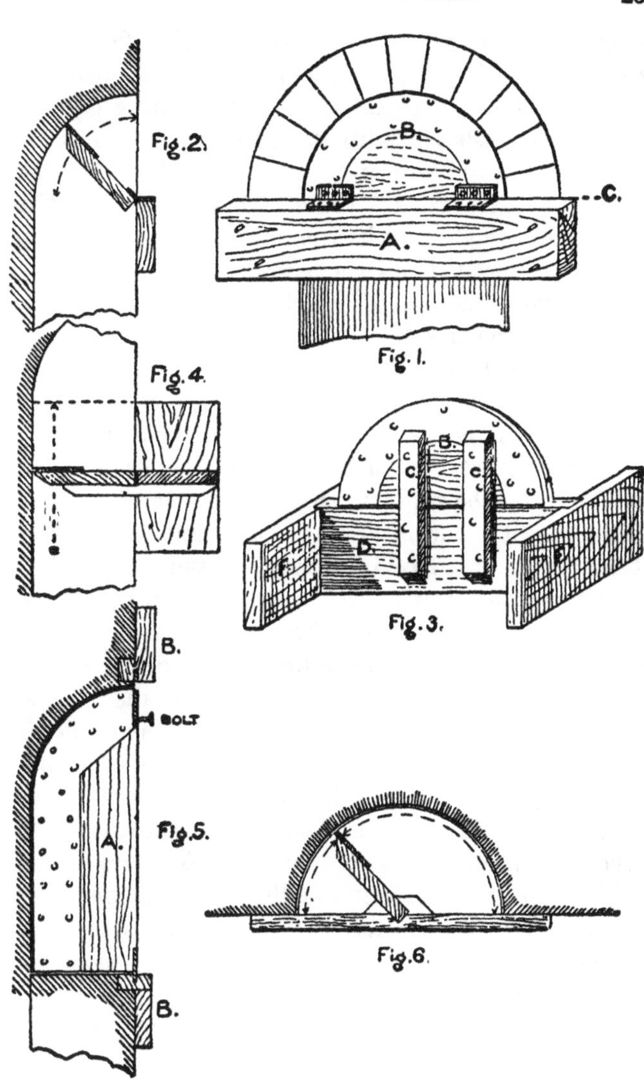

FORMING NICHES WITH RUNNING MOULDS.

NO. 23.

actly at the springing of the crown, C. The face of the wall must be floated plumb, and an allowance made by means of dots for the thickness of the setting coat before the centre-board is fixed. After the crown is finished, the centre-board and running mould is taken off the wall and separated. The mould is then horsed with two slippers to allow of its running the body or vertical part of the niche. The mould works on a running rule fixed on one of two screeds which are formed on the face of the wall, one on each side of the opening. Care must be taken that the screeds are plumb with the centre-board dots. Fig. 3 shows an elevation of the mould when horsed. B is the mould, D is a connecting board on which the mould is fixed by means of the cleats, C, C, and F, F, are the slippers. Fig. 4 shows an end section of the horsed mould in position when running the body of the niche. The base is finished by hand.

By the second method the niche is run in one operation, as already mentioned. This is effected by cutting a running mould to the vertical section of the niche, then fixing a pivot at the bottom and a bolt at the top. A wood block, with a socket to fit the bolt on the mould, is let into the face of the wall at the top of the niche, and temporarily fixed, then another block with a socket to fit the pivot of the mould is fixed at the bottom of the niche. Care must be taken that the sockets are plumb and in a line with the centre of the niche, also that they are in a line with the face of the wall, so as to allow the mould to form a true semicircle with perpendicular arrises. Place the pivot of the mould in the socket, and push the bolt up and secure it, and the mould is ready for working.

Fig. 5 shows a section of the niche with the mould in position. A is the mould with the pivot and bolt, and

B, B, are the socket blocks. A plan of the niche and mould is shown at Fig. 6. This also shows the plan of the pivot block, and a board which is sometimes used to secure the block. The dotted line indicates the distance the mould travels. When there are splays or beads on the angle of the niche, the crown part is run with a radius-rod mould from a centre-board, and the vertical parts with a "twin-slipper running mould" on running rules fixed on the wall screeds, or with a nib running mould on a slipper and a nib running rule.

The vertical parts of the beads or splays may also be run with the mould shown in Fig. 3. For this purpose two plates cut to the desired section must be fixed on the mould, one at each side. The crown part is run with a radius-rod, as already mentioned. The crown surface and the angle moulding can also be run in one operation. This is effected by cutting a mould plate to the section of the moulding, including the section of the crown surface, then horsing it with a slipper to run on the wall surface, and a pivot to fit a socket formed in a centre-board, or with a radius-rod to work on a centre-board. A pivot will be found most suitable for small work and a radius-rod for large work. In either case they must be fixed on the centre of the mould, so as to be in a line with the mould plate. After the crown is run, the mould plate of the crown surface is cut off, and the remaining part of the mould used for running the vertical mouldings.

In some designs a small moulding, such as an impost moulding, is carried round the body surface of the niche, and in a line with the springing of the crown. This moulding can be run in a similar way as shown at Fig. 5, or by fixing a flexible wood or a plaster running rule on the body of the niche for the mould to run on.

The crowns of niches that are parallel with small mouldings are best executed by making a model of the design, then moulding it and casting, and fixing as many as are required. In niche crowns that are enriched with shells, foliage, &c., the enrichment should be cast with the crown surface as a background. Fibrous plaster is well adapted for the construction of niches. For this purpose a reverse casting mould should be employed for forming the casts. This is made by cutting a reverse running mould to the section of the niche, and after a sufficient length of the body is run, cut the mould in half and run the crown. Then fix it on the end of the run body, and then fix rules at the sides and ends to form fences and rims, thus completing the casting mould.

Any of the above methods for forming niches with running moulds can be advantageously used for forming the body and crown of the Ionic niche when such is required.

Running an Elliptical Moulding in Situ.

In No. 24 a method of running an elliptical curve with a trammel is shown. Fig. 1 represents the front elevation of the trammel mounted and in working order, and Fig. 2 is a section of the same.

Take two floor boards, B, long enough to reach to the springing line of the arch, and nail them on the back of two lengths of 5 in. by 2 in., A, which, as shown may be somewhat longer. Fix these up inside the jambs of the opening, taking care to see that they are perfectly upright, and keep them the thickness of the trammel boards (which is 1 in.) back from the face of the opening on which the architrave is to be. Then cut three pieces of

5 in. by 2 in., C, tight in between and secure them in place with 3 in. cut nails, taking care to see that the bottom side of the top one is above the springing line. Then prepare the trammel boards, D and E, 6 in. by 1

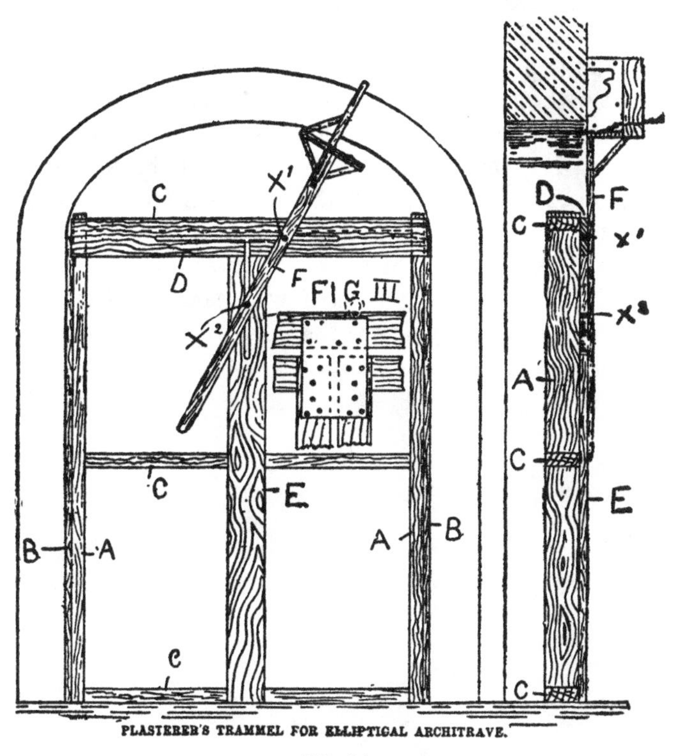

PLASTERER'S TRAMMEL FOR ELLIPTICAL ARCHITRAVE.

NO. 24.

in., and cut the slots, which are ¾ in. wide and of a length which may be easily ascertained by simple geometry. Halve the boards together at the joint and further secure them by screwing a plate of the thickest sheet zinc obtainable on the back, as per Fig. 3. Nail the boards up as shown, keeping the horizontal slot central on the springing line and the vertical slot exactly in the centre of the opening, and be most particular to see that the whole lot is perfectly upright and level. Next prepare the trammel stick, 2 in. by 1 in., and mount the mould on the top in the usual manner, as shown. Then insert the pins in holes bored in the stick and secure by a screw through the edge. Have them just thick enough to work comfortably in the slots, and keep the centre of the pin X1, the distance of the rise, and the centre of the pin X2, the distance of the half span from the bottom member of the architrave. All the timber may be deal except the pins, which must be of some kind of hard wood. If well made and used with care this trammel ought to serve many times; the pins, of course, needing adjustment for arches of different size.

MISCELLANEOUS MATTERS.

Depeter.—This is a sort of a rough-cast, and consists of forming a fair surface with coarse stuff or Portland cement. As soon as laid a hand-float is parred over the surface a few times to give it an even and uniform texture, and while it is soft, pressing in by hand, small pieces of hard coal, broken bottles, pottery, bricks, shells, stones, pebbles, or marble. The design may be varied and enriched by using various colored pieces in forming margins, bands or other ornamentation. On the contrast of colors and the broad bands depends the effect of this class of work. A combination of "Depeter" and rough-cast may be used with excellent effect.

Sgraffitto.—Sgraffitto or "graffitto" is an Italian word, and means "scratched." Scratched decoration is the most ancient mode of surface decoration employed by man. The primitive savage of the flint-weapon period used this simple form of ornamentation. Scratched work, as used by prehistoric man, may be fitly termed the proem of the civilized arts of drawing, modelling and sculpture. The term is now employed for plaster decorations, scratched or incised upon plaster or cement before it is set. It may be used for both external and internal decoration. The annexed illustrations (Nos. 25 and 26) will demonstrate the high degree to which the art of sgraffitto attained in Italy.

Some graffittos are really low relief work rather than the sgraffitto, they being very deep cut with the iron or steel point, which was necessitated by the final coat being plastered on instead of washed on. Deep cutting

SCRAFFITTO FRIEZE FROM ROME.
NO. 25.

gives a hard appearance to the design, prevents the water from running off the walls, and catches the dirt. In executing true sgraffitto, the cut or scratch should be exceedingly slight—in fact, some parts scarcely perceptible.

Sgraffitto decorations do not suffer materially from stubbing it with an old broom, leaving it barely half an inch from the finished face. For internal work, the ordinary pricking up suffices. When this is dry, a thin coat of selentic lime mixed with the desired coloring matter for the background, is floated over it. This background may be black, bone-black being used; red, for which use Venetian or Indian red, or the ordinary purole brown of commerce, singly or mixed, to produce any tone desired; yellow, produced by ochres or umbers; blue, by German blue, Antwerp blue, or any of the commoner blues, avoiding cobalt, and these colors you may use to any degree of intensity or paleness. When this coat is nearly dry, skim over it a very thin coat of pure selentic lime, which dries of a parchment color and generally suffices. If you want a pure white lime, use a moderate quick-setting one, as stiff as you can work it, and as each variety of lime has its own individual perversity, I can give no general direction, and would advise the beginner to stick to selentic, which is always procurable. You have, of course, prepared your cartoon. This is pricked and pounced as for any other transfer process, and then with an old, well-worn, big-bladed knife, for there is no better tool, you can cut round all the outlines, and with a flat spatula clear away all the thin upper coat, leaving the colored ground as smooth as you can. If your plaster is not quite dry enough for the two coats to separate easily, wait a little longer, but not too long, for that is fatal. By the time you have cleared out your background, the plaster will be in a good condition to allow you to cut out the finer parts of the design, such as folds of the draperies, or the finer lines of the faces or of the ornament. Use your knife slightly on the slope, and if you want to produce half-tones, slope it very much; but, as a rule, the more you avoid half-tones, and the simpler and purer your line, the more effective your work will be. Recollect, above all things, you are making a design and not a picture, and you must never hesitate, for to retouch is impossible. Sometimes it may be desirable to gild the background, and you can then carve or impress it with any design you choose. It occasionally happens you want to give some semblance of pictorial character to your work when it is small in scale and near the eye, and then you can proceed as though you were cutting a wood-block.

By cutting out your ground color in places, and plastering it with that of another color, you may vary any portion of it you desire. You can also wash over certain parts of your upper coat with a water-color if you desire, combining fresco with the sgraffitto, both of which manners are often used; but, as a rule, the broader your design, and the simpler your treatment of it, the better. It will be seen that this process is very available for simple architectonic effects; and for churches, hospitals, and other places where large surfaces have to be covered, it is the least costly process that can be adopted. It has also the great advantage of being non-absorbent, and it can be washed down at any time. The artist is untrammelled by difficulties of execution, but he should bear in mind that the more carefully he draws his lines and the simpler he keeps his composition, the more charmed with the process he will be, and the better will be the effect of his work.

A well-known artist records his experience of sgraffitto as follows:

"Rake and sweep out the mortar joints, then give the wall as much water as it will drink, or it will absorb the moisture from the coarse coat, as it will not set, but merely dry, in which case it will be worth little more than dry mud. Care should be taken that the cement and sand which compose the coarse coat should be properly gauged, or there may be an unequal suction for the finishing coats. The surface of the coarse should be well roughened to give a good key, and it should stand some days to thoroughly set before laying the finishing coat. When sufficiently set, fix your cartoon in its destined position with nails; pounce through the pricked outline; remove the cartoon; replace the nails in the register holes; mark with chalk spaces for the different colors, as indicated by the pounce impression on the coarse coat; lay the several colors of the color coat according to the design as shown by the chalk outlines; take care that in doing so the register nails are not displaced; roughen the face in order to make a good key for the final coat. When set, follow on with the final surface coat, only laying as much as can be cut and cleaned up in a day. When this is sufficiently steady, fix up the cartoon in its registered position; pounce through the pricked outline; remove the cartoon, and cut out the design in the surface coat before it sets; then if the register is correct, cut through to different colors, according to the design, and in the course of a few days the work should set as hard and as homogeneous as stone, and as damp-proof as the nature of things permit.

"When cleaning up the ground of color which may be exposed, care should be taken to obtain a similar quantity of surface all through the work, so as to get a broad effect of deliberate and calculated contrast between the trowelled surface of the final coat and the scraped surface of the simple contrasts of light against dark, or dark against light. The following are the proportions of the various coats:

"Coarse coats: One of Portland cement to 3 of washed sharp coarse sand.

"Color coat: One and one-half of air-slaked Portland to 1 of color laid 1/8 inch thick. Distemper colors are Indian red, Turkey red, ochre, umber, lime blue; lime blue and ochre for green; oxide of manganese for black. In using lime blue, its violet hue may be overcome by adding a little ochre. It should be noted that it sets much quicker and harder than the other colors named.

"Final coat, internal work: Parian, air-slaked for twenty-four hours to retard its setting, or fine lime and selenitic sifted through a fine sieve.

"For external work: Three selenitic and 2 silver sand.

"When finishing, space out the wall according to the scheme of decoration, and decide where to begin, and give the wall in such place as much water as it will drink; then lay the color coat, and leave sufficient key for the final coat. Calculate how much surface of color coat it may be advisable to get on to the wall, as it is better to maintain throughout the work the same duration of time between the laying of the color coat and the following on with the final surface coat; for this reason, that if the color sets hard before laying the final coat, it is impossible to get up the color to its full strength wherever it may be revealed in the scratching of the decoration. When the color coat is quite firm, and all shine has passed away from its surface, follow on with the final coat, but only lay as much as can be finished in one day. The final coat is trowelled up, and the design is incised or scratched out. Individual taste and experience must decide as to thickness of final coat, but if laid between 1/8 inch and 1-12 inch, and the lines cut with slanting edges, a side light gives emphasis to the finished result, making the outlines tell alternately as they take the light or cast a shadow.''

Another method which I have used in sgraffitto for external decoration was done entirely with Portland cement. This material for strap-work or broad foliage, or where minuteness of detail is unnecessary, will be found suitable for many places and positions. Three colors may be used if required, such as black for the background, red for the middle coat, and grey or white for the final coat. These colors may be varied and substituted for each other as desired, or as the design dictates. The Portland cement for floating can be made black by using black smithy ashes as an aggregate, and by gauging with black manganese if for a thin coat. The red is obtained by adding from 5 to 10 per cent. of red oxide, the white by gauging the cement with white marble dust, or with whiting or lime, the grey being the natural color of the cement. After the first coat is laid, it is keyed with a coarse broom. The second coat is laid fair and left moderately rough with a hand-float. The suction of the first coat will give sufficient firmness to allow the third coat to be laid on without disturbing the second. The third coat should be laid before the second is set hard. The second and third coats may be used neat, or gauged with fine sifted aggregate as required. The finer the stuff, the easier and cleaner the work, and the cut lines are more accurate and free from jagged edges. The outlines of the design may be pounced or otherwise transferred to the surface of the work, and the details put in by hand. The thickness of the second coat should be about 3-16 inch, and the third coat about 1/8 inch. The thickness of one or both coats may be varied to suit the design. The beauty of effect of this method of linear decoration, aided by two or three colors, depends greatly on the treatment of design, the clearness of the incised lines, and the pleasing color contrasts. It will be seen that in the three methods described there is a similarity, yet the method of using two color coats on a dark floating coat will give more variety and effect. There is a large use for sgraffitto in the future, as it has been in the past, and its use is intimately bound up with the future of cement concrete.

In order that the foregoing examples of high-class sgraffitto may not deter the young plasterer from trying his " 'prentice han' " in this class of work, some simple designs are given in the annexed illustration (No. 27). Fig. 1 shows a design for a frieze in two colors. The ground may be black or red, and the ornament buff or grey. The colored material for the ornament is laid first, and the colored material for the ground laid last. Fig. 2 shows a design for a cove in two colors, one with two shades. The ground is grey, and the band work buff. A deeper shade of buff for the honeysuckle can be obtained by brushing this part with liquid color made deeper than the original gauge, also by laying a black coat first, and in a line with the honeysuckle; then laying the buff stuff for the band work next, and then laying the grey color last. In the latter case the honeysuckle is cut deeper than the band work, so as to expose the black coat.

Different effects can be obtained by changing the colors. Sections of the surface of the frieze and part of the moulding are shown at the ends.

Fresco.—The plasterer is closely allied to the artist painter. He has always to be in readiness to plaster the wall for the artist. Owing to the alliance with distinguished artists, and the various methods of preparing and using the plaster materials, I am induced to give a few notes, also extracts from writers of authority.

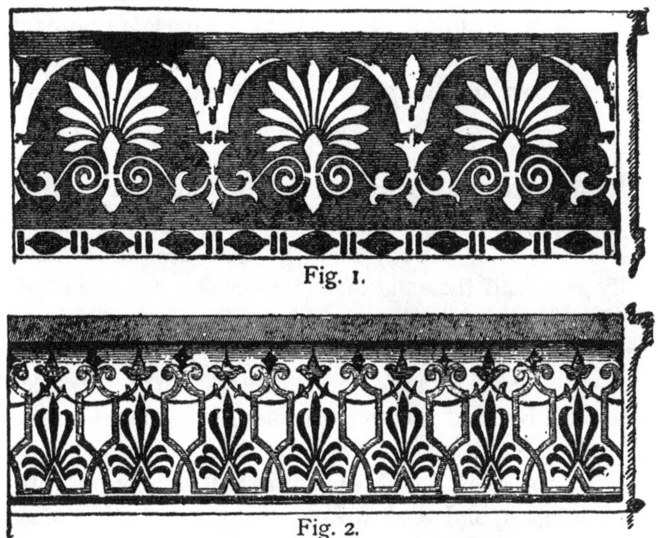

Fig. 1.

Fig. 2.

-SGRAFFITIO FRIEZE IN TWO COLOURS.

NO. 27.

Fresco is a mode of painting with water-colors on freshly laid plaster while it remains naturally wet. It is called "fresco" either because it was originally used on buildings in the open air, or because it was done on fresh plaster. Fresco is an ancient art, being mentioned by

Pliny. Mr. Flinders Petrie found some remarkably fine specimens on floors and walls at Tel-el-Amarna, which reveal the state of the art four thousand years ago. Fine frescoes were discovered in the ruins of Pompeii. In one of the principal houses the plaster walls are adorned with theatrical scenes; in an inner room is the niche often to be seen in Pompeiian houses. The frescoes on the wall consist of floral dados. Above this is a whole aquarium, with shells, plants, birds and animals. They are all executed in their natural colors, and are naturally and gracefully drawn. Michael Angelo's beautiful fresco on the ceiling of the Sistine Chapel in the Vatican is grand both in conception and execution. It measures 133 feet in length by 43 feet in width. Raphael's frescoes in the Vatican, Farnesina Palace, &c., are wonderfully fine, and may be regarded as the high-water mark of Cinque Cento decoration.

For fresco or *buon fresco* the lime has to be carefully run, and the sand should be white, clean, and of even grain, being well washed and sifted to free it from impurities or saline properties. Silver sand is preferred by some artists. The older the putty lime, the better the results. The lime is slaked in a tub, and then run through a fine wire sieve into a tank, and after being covered up, is left for three months. It is then put into the tub again, and re-slaked, or rather well worked, and run through a fine hair sieve into earthenware jars or slate tanks, and the water which collects at the top drawn or poured off, the jars or tank being covered over to exclude the air. Lime putty in this state will keep for an indefinite time without injury. From 2 to 4 parts of sand to 1 part putty is usual. Marble dust alone is sometimes used in place of sand, and also sand with equal parts. Every difference of lime and sand found in various localities should be considered and tested before using. A soft sand is quickly dissolved by a strong lime, and a plaster made of this is fit for use sooner, and will deteriorate more quickly than a plaster made with a less powerful lime and a harder sand, or with marble dust.

The wall surface to be plastered must be well scraped and hacked, the joints raked out and brushed, and the whole surface well scrubbed and wetted. The rendering is done with the best possible prepared old coarse stuff. If the walls are rough or uneven, they should be first pricked up and then floated. In any case, the surface is left true, and with a rough face, to receive the finishing coat. Portland cement or hydraulic lime gauged with sand, also gauged with coarse stuff, has been used where the walls were damp (damp is fatal to fresco), or if exposed to the atmosphere. When Portland cement or hydraulic lime is used, the work should be allowed to stand until thoroughly dry to allow any contained soluble saline efflorescence to come to the surface. This is brushed off with a dry brush, and a few days are allowed to elapse to see if there is a further efflorescence. When this is all extracted and swept off, and the artist is ready to commence, the wall is washed with a thin solution of the fine setting stuff, and then laid about 1/8 inch thick, with well-beaten, worked, and tempered fine setting stuff. It is then rubbed with a straight-edge and scoured with a hand-float (using lime water for scouring) until the surface is true and of uniform grain. Most artists prefer a scoured surface without being trowelled. No more surface should be covered than can be conveniently painted in one day. While the plaster is still soft and damp, the cartoon is laid on, and the lines and details pounced in or indented by means of a bone or hard-wood tool. Should the finishing coat get too dry in any part, it can be made fit for work by using a fine spray of water. The method of plastering and the gauging of materials may slightly vary according to the desire of the painter and the kind of fresco in hand. The following is taken from an old manuscript dated 1699:—

"1. In painting the wall to make it endure the weather, you must grind colors with lime water, milk, or whey, mixed in size.

"2. Then paste or plaster must be made or well-washed lime, mixed with powder of old rubbish stones. The lime must be often washed till finally all the salt is extracted, and all your work must be done in clear and dry weather.

"3. To make the work endure, stick into the wall stumps of headed nails, about 5 or 6 inches asunder, and by this means you may preserve the plaster from peeling.

"4. Then with the paste plaster the walls a pretty thickness, letting it dry; but scratch the first coat with the point of your trowel longways and crossways, as soon as you have done laying on what plaster or paste you think fit, that the next plastering you lay upon it may take good key, and not come off nor part from the first coat of plastering; and when the first coat is dry, plaster it over again with the thickness of half a barley-corn, very fine and smooth. Then, your colors being already prepared, work this last plastering over with the said colors in what draught or design you please—history, etc.,—so will your painting unite and join fast to the plaster, and dry together as a perfect compost.

"Note—Your first coat of plaster or paste must be very haired with ox-hair in it, or else your work will crack quite through the second coat of plastering; and will spoil all your painting that you paint upon the second coat of plastering; but in the second coat that is laid on of paste or plaster there must be no hair in it at all, but made thus:—

Mix or temper up with well-washed lime, fine powder of old stones (called finishing stuff) and sharp grit sand, as much as you shall have occasion for, to plaster over your first coat, and plaster it all very smooth and even, that no roughness, hills, nor dales, be seen, nor scratch of your trowel. The best way is to float the second coat of plastering thus:—After you have laid it all over the first coat with your trowel as even and smooth as possible, you can then take a float made of wood, very smooth, and 1 foot long and 7 or 8 inches wide, with a handle on the upper side of it to put your hand into to float your work withal, and thus will make your plastering to lie even; and lastly, with your trowel you may make the said plastering as smooth as possible.

"5. In painting be nimble and free; let your work be bold and strong; but be sure to be exact, for there is no alteration after the first painting, and therefore heighten your paint enough at first; you may deepen at pleasure.

"6. All earthy colors are best, as the ochres, Spanish brown, terra-vert, and the like. Mineral colors are naught.

"7. Lastly, let your pencil and brushes be long and soft, otherwise your work will not be smooth; let your colors be full, and flow freely from the pencil or brush; and let your design be perfect at first, for in this there is no alteration to be made."

Fresco Secco.—Closely allied with the genuine fresco (fresco buono) is another kind called fresco secco (dry), or mezzo (half) fresco. The plaster work for fresco secco is similar to that used for fresco buono. It is allowed to stand until thoroughly dry. The surface is then rubbed with pumice-stone, and about twelve hours before the painting is commenced it is thoroughly wetted with water mixed with a little lime. The surface is again moistened the next morning, and the painting begun in the usual way. If the wall should become too dry, it is moistened with the aid of a syringe. There is no fear of joinings in the painting being observable, and the artist can quit or resume his work at pleasure. Joinings are distinctly noticeable in the frescos in the Loggia of the Vatican. Fresco secco paintings are heavy and opaque, whereas real fresco is light and transparent. While the superiority of fresco buono over fresco secco for the highest class of decorative painting is unquestionable, still the latter is suitable for many places and forms of decorative paintings. The head by Giotto in the National Gallery, from the Brancacci Chapel of the Carmine at Florence, is in fresco secco.

Indian Fresco and Marble Plaster.—"Fresco painting is a common mode of decoration in Jeypore, and is used in ornamenting walls inside and outside of buildings—also as a dado or border round the wainscot or on the floor—and on any surface where decoration is desired. The beautiful marble plaster on which it is done is common Rajputana, and is used to line the surface of walls or floors, and of baths or bath-rooms. It is admirably adapted to places where coolness and cleanliness are desired, and is very suitable to a warm climate. It would no doubt be more commonly used if pure lime could be obtained.

"To prepare the marble plaster, the process in use in Jeypore is as follows:—Take pure stone lime, mix it with water until it has dissolved, then strain it through a fine cloth. In Jeypore the lime is made from pounded marble chips or almost pure limestone. The substance which remains in the cloth is called bujra, and all that passes through the cloth is called ghole. These should be prepared a few days before they are required so as to allow time to settle, and every day the water should be changed, so as to leave a very fine sediment.

"Jinki, which is also used, is pure marble ground to a very fine powder; kurra is a mixture of bujra and jinki; and jinkera is a mixture of ghole and kurra. These are the materials used, and the names by which they are known in Jeypore. In Madras, where similar plaster is used, it is made, I believe, from shells and the ingredients are probably known by other local names.

"If the surface to be polished is a slab or stone, the kurra mixture consists of 1 part by weight of burja and 1½ parts of jinki. If the surface is a wall or a chunam floor, it must be first thoroughly dry and consolidated—then take equal parts of burja and jinki to form the kurra mixture. Mix the burja and the jinki well together; add a little water and grind them well together, in the same ways as natives mix their condiments, by hand with a stone rolling-pin on a slab, until they form a perfectly fine paste. Wet the surface which is to be polished, and spread over it a layer of this kurra mixture, about ⅛ inch thick. Then beat the surface gently with a flat wooden beater, sprinkling a few drops of clean water on the surface occasionally. Then mix a little ghole with the kurra plaster (described above as jinkera) and lay it on evenly with a brush as if it were a coat of paint; rub the surface over carefully with any close-grained flat stone, called in Jeypore jhaon. The object of this is to smooth down all irregularity and roughness, and to prepare a smooth even surface. Sprinkle a few drops of water and repeat the process, taking care that no hollow places are allowed to remain. Paint it over with fine jinkera (ghole and kurra mixed), increasing the proportion of ghole, and rub it down well with a flat stone (jhaon) as before; then paint it over with ghole only, after each coat rubbing it down carefully with the jhaon stone. After this, rub it all over with a soft linen cloth, called in Jeypore nainsukh, folded into a pad. Then give it another coat of ghole, and now rub it down carefully with a piece of polished agate, called in Jeypore ghinti, until it begins to shine. The surface must not be allowed to dry too rapidly, or a good polish will not be obtained. Care must be taken that the lime has been thoroughly slaked in the first instance, or it may blister; also that the surface, if a floor, is thoroughly consolidated, as the least settlement naturally causes the plaster to crack. The polishing process with the agate cannot be repeated too often; the more it is carefully done, the better will be the polish. Every time the agate is moved backwards it should be made to pass over a portion of its previous course, so as to prevent any mark or line at the edge. Lastly, if the surface is to remain white, take some water which has been mixed with grated cocoanut, and lay it on the surface. Let it dry, and then rub it down with a fine cloth folded into a pad. If any coloring is desired, the same process is adopted until the polishing with the agate is begun. This is only done slightly. If any pattern is desired, it is drawn on paper and pricked out. The paper is placed on the surface, and is dusted with very finely powdered charcoal tied up in a muslin bag. The charcoal passes through the perforations and marks the plaster surface. The paints are mixed with water, and are painted on by hand while the surface is still fresh and moist hence the term fresco. Where a large surface has to be done, it is necessary to employ several men at the same time, in order that the surface might be all painted before it has time to dry; or else the pattern must be so arranged that the connection of one day's work with the work of the next will not be amiss. Immediately after the surface has been painted the colors are beaten in with the back of a small trowel, in such a manner that the color is not rubbed or mixed with the color adjacent. As soon as it shows to the touch that the color has become incorporated with the plaster, the surface is painted over with water mixed with grated cocoanut, and is then polished down with the agate.

"The following colors can be used in process:—Lamp black; red lead; green (from a stone known as hara pathar); yellow (from a stone called pila pathar); brown or chocolate. A little glue is mixed with the two first colors, and gum only with the others. The colors used are mostly earths or minerals, as other will not stand the action of the lime. Vegetable pigments cannot be used for this model of painting, even when mixed with mineral pigments, and of the latter only these are available which resist the chemical action of the lime. The lime in drying throws out a kind of crystal surface which protects the color and imparts a degree of clearness superior to that of any work in tempera or size paint. The process, although apparently simple, requires dexterity and certainty of hand, for the surface of the plaster is delicate, and the lime only imbibes a certain quantity of additional moisture in the form of liquid colors, after which it loses its crystallizing quality, and the surface or a portion of it becomes rotten. It is only after the lime has dried that such flaws are discovered, and the only remedy is to cut away the defective portion, lay on fresh plaster and do the work over again. The colors become lighter after the plaster dries, so allowance must be made for this. The advantages which this process possesses are clearness, exhibiting the colors in a pure and bright state; the surface is not dull and dry as in tempera or size painting, nor glossy as in oil painting; it can be easily seen from any point, and it is not injured by exposure to the air; it will stand washing, and can be cleansed with water without injury."

SCAGLIOLA.

Historical.—Scagliola derives its name from the use of a great number of small pieces or splinters; *scagliole* of marble being used in the best description of this work. It is said to have been invented in the early part of the sixteenth century by Guido Sassi, of Cari, in Lombardy, but it is more probable that he revived an old process, and introduced a greater variety of colors in the small pieces of marble and alabaster used to harden the surface, and better imitate real and rare marbles. It is sometimes called *mischia* from the many mixtures of colors introduced by it. The use of colored plaster for imitating marbles was known to the ancients, although the pure white, or *marmoratum opus* and *albarum opus,* mentioned by Pliny, was more used. The plastic materials used by the Egyptians in coating the walls of their tombs partook of the nature of marble. The ancients also used a marble-like plaster for lining the bottoms and sides of their aqueducts, which has endured for many centuries without spoiling or cracking. In the decoration of their domes the Moors used colored plasters, which have stood the ravages of time. The beautiful *chunam* or plaster of India, as used by the natives, has a hard surface, takes a brilliant polish rivalling that of real marble, and has withstood for many ages the sun and weather without sign of decay. The roofs and floors of many houses in Venice are coated with smooth and polished plaster, made at a later date, strong enough to resist the effects of wear and weather, without visible signs of crack or flaw, and without much injury from the foot. Scagliola was largely employed by the Florentines in some of their most elaborate works. It has been used in France with great success for architectural embellishment. The rooms are so finished that no additional work in the shape of house-painting is required, the polish of the plaster and its evenness of tint rivalling porcelain. Scagliola is the material used. At times the surface of the plaster is fluted, or various designs are executed in intaglio upon it in the most beautiful manner.

Scagliola is one of the most beautiful parts of decorative plaster work, and it is regrettable that there should not be a greater revival of such a charming and beautiful art. Its limited use in recent times is greatly owing to its manufacture being restricted by rules and rigid methods and even prejudices, and being confined to monopolists, who kept the method secret until it was looked upon as a mystery which greatly enhanced its cost. But through the information now at hand, combined with a little practical experience and enterprise, there is no valid reason why architects should not adopt it for second or even for third class buildings. It possesses great beauty, and is capable of affording grand effects and the richest embellishments in architecture. Scagliola, in skilful hands, can be produced in every variety of color and shade, in every possible pattern, in every conceivable form and size, from a paper weight to the superficial area of a large wall. It can be made at a price that would enable it to take the place of the most durable material now in use. Experience has proved that it will last as long as the house it adorns, and with an occasional cleaning, it will always retain its polish and beauty. It has been produced in past days in our own and other lands, and carried to such high excellence, that many of the precious marbles, such as jasper, verd antique, porphyry, brocatello, giallo antique, Sienna, etc., have been imitated so minutely, and with an astonishing degree of perfection, as to defy detection. It will not only retain its polish for years, but can be renovated at much less comparative cost than painting and varnishing marbled wood, or plaster work. It is cheaper and more satisfactory to use scagliola in the first instance than to go to the expense of plastering walls, columns, etc., with Keen's or other kindred cements, used for their hardness and ready reception of paint, which are to be afterwards marbled and varnished. Both are imitations, but painted marble can never be compared with scagliola, which has the look, color, touch, and polish of the more costly natural marbles.

Various Artificial Marbles.—Various patents have been taken out for the production of artificial marbles, having for their bases plaster of Paris. These patents will be briefly mentioned here.

Evaux's Artificial Marble is composed of plaster mixed with albumen and mineral colors, the ground being zinc white. Rowbotham also employed plaster and albumen soaked in a solution of tannic acid. Lilienthal makes an artificial marble with Keen's cement, slaked lime, and curdled milk.

Pick's "Neoplaster."—This composition was patented in 1883, and is composed of 75 per cent. of plaster, mixed with feldspar, marl, coke dust, and pumice-stone. Guleton and Sandeman patented an artificial marble in 1876. It is composed of Keen's cement backed with fibre, and soaked or brushed on the back with a solution of asphalt. The slabs were made in glass moulds. Laroque's patent marble is formed of plaster and alum gauged with gum water, the veining being done with threads of silk dipped in the required colors. The backs of the slabs or panels are strengthened with canvas.

Mur Marble is composed of a mixture of Keen's and Marin's cement in equal proportions, made into a paste, with a solution of sulphate of iron and a small quantity of nitric acid in water. The slabs are dried and tarred at a temperature of 250 degrees F. for about twenty hours, and when cool are rubbed, colored, varnished, or japanned, as required. There is another patent formed of plaster, gauged with a solution containing tungstate of soda, tartaric acid, bicarbonate of soda, and tartarate of potash. Another is composed of Keen's cement 10 parts, ground glass 1 part, and alum ½ part, dissolved in hot water.

Guattaris Marble is obtained by transforming gypsum (sulphate of lime) into carbonate of lime (marble). There are two methods. The first consists of dehydrating blocks of gypsum, and then hardening by immersion in baths containing solutions of silicate of soda, silicate of lime, chloride of lime, sulphate of potash, soda, acid phosphate of lime, etc. The blocks are cut into slabs or carved before being put into the bath. The second method consists in dehydrating the gypsum, and bathing in some of the above chemicals. They are then dried and burnt at a red heat, and allowed to cool. After a second burning and cooling, the products are ground as for plaster. This powder is called "Marmorite". The marmorite is gauged in a trough with some of the water from the baths as above, kneaded into a paste, and the colors added and mixed. The paste is then put into moulds and pressed, and when set they are taken out, dried, and finally polished. Mineral colors are used. Yellow and its tints are obtained with citrate of iron dissolved in oxysulphate of iron, sulphate of cadmium, chloride of yttrium, chromate of lithium, and yellow of antimony. Red and its tints are obtained with dragon's blood, sesquioxide of iron, mussaride red, and sulphate of didymium, and the salts derived from it, which give a rose color. Azure blue is obtained with sulphate of sodium mixed with acetate of copper and tartaric acid and oxide of cobalt. Green and its tints are obtained with verdigris, hydrochlorate of cobalt. Black is obtained by pyrolignite of iron reduced by boiling in gallic acid with sirco black. Black marble is also obtained by immersing gypsum blocks or slabs or the cast marmorite in a hot preparation of bitumen. During this operation the dehydration of the material under treatment is accomplished, and the bitumen not only penetrates the mass, but fills up all the pores and spaces evacuated by the water which was contained in the material treated, and a hard mass of brilliant black is obtained in every way equal to Flanders marble. It is said that the above imitation marbles are largely used in Florence.

Scagliola Manufacture.—Scagliola can be made in situ or in the work shop, according to the requirements of the work; but in either case it is necessary that the work place should be kept at a warm temperature, and the work protected from dust or damp atmosphere. The plaster should be the strongest and finest in quality, and free from saline impurities. It should be well sifted to free it from lumps or coarse grains, which otherwise would appear as small specks of white in the midst of the dark colors when the polishing is completed. Glue water should be made in small quantities, or as much as will suffice for the day, as it deteriorates if kept too long. Glue tends to harden the plaster, and gives gloss to the surface. Unfortunately it is also the cause of its subsequent dullness and decay when exposed to moisture and damp air, hence the necessity of using the best glue, good and fresh glue water. If scagliola is required to be done in situ on brick walls, the joints should be well raked out and the walls well wetted. This gives a good key, stops the excessive absorption, and partly prevents the evil effects of saline matters, that are found in most kinds of new bricks. These saline matters are the principal cause of subsequent efflorescence which sometimes appears on plastic surfaces, and is so unsightly and disastrous to surface decorations. Saline matters are also caused by acids, used in the manufacture of some cements. Saline is also found in mortars made with sea water, or with unwashed sea sand. These impurities can be avoided by carefully selecting, mixing, and working of the materials. Brick walls for scagliola should be allowed to stand as long as possible, and wetted at intervals. This allows more time for the saline to exude and be washed off. The exudation may be hastened or the salts absorbed and killed by brushing the walls with a solution of freshly slaked lime. This is allowed to stand until dry, and then cleaned off by scrubbing with warm water and a coarse broom. If space permits, a wall battened and lathed is the best preventive. Scagliola slabs, screwed to plugs or battens, are protected from saline and internal damp.

Iron columns to support overhead weights, and fixed as the building proceeds, are often covered with scagliola. If the work is done in situ, the iron core is surrounded with a wood skeleton and strong laths, or painted wire lathing. The wood templates are cut, equal to the lower and upper diameters of the columns, and one fixed at the top and bottom of the shaft. The ground work is then ruled fair with a diminished floating rule. This gives a guide and equal thickness for the scag (the trade abbreviation for scagliola stuff).

The floating coat is composed of the best and strongest plaster procurable, and gauged as stiff as possible with sufficient strong size water, so that it will take from twelve to twenty-four hours to set. The floating is generally brought out from the lath in one coat. A tenth part of well-washed hair is sometimes mixed with the gauged plaster, to give greater toughness and tenacity. The surface must be carefully scratched with a singly-pointed lath, to give a sound and regular key for the scag, which is laid on in slices, and pressed and beaten with a stiffish, square pointed gauging trowel, somewhat like a margin trowel. The scag is laid about ⅛ inch fuller than the outline, and when set, the surface is worked down with a "toothed plane." This plane is similar to that used by cabinetmakers for veneering purposes. The irons are toothed in various degrees of fineness, and set at an angle of 70 degrees. If the columns are fluted, a half-pound plane is required for the flutes. As the planing proceeds, the outline is tested at intervals with a rule, as a mason does in using a straight-edge when working mouldings. A planed or chisel-cut surface shows up the grain and figure of the marble much better than if ruled. A rule is apt to work out or otherwise spoil the figure of most marbles. The beating on the slices may disturb the figure of the marble at the outer surface, but if the scag is gauged stiff, the inner portion will be intact, hence the advantage of planing. To obtain greater cohesion between the scag and the floating, the latter is brushed with soft gauged stuff just before each piece of the former is laid. The scratching is also filled up at the same time, so as to obtain the full power of the key with the least amount of pressing on and beating the scag slices in position. When the shaft is planed, the wood colors are taken off; then the base and necking moulding, which has been previously cast, are screwed in position, using plaster (colored the same as the ground of the marble) for the joints. When dry, the whole is stoned and polished. Pilasters or other surface work done *in situ* are executed by similar processes. Cast and turned work should always be supported by strong wooden frames, formed with ribs, and covered with ¼ inch to ½ inch thick sawn laths. The strength of the frames is regulated according to the position and purpose of the intended work. For example, a column with base placed on a square pedestal would not require so strong framing as the pedestal which has to support the column and base. Also being on the floor level, it is more exposed to contact and pressure. Framing is also necessary for fixing purposes, and to allow for the work being-handled freely when being moved from the work shop to the building, and when being fixed. Small work may be made without framing. Turned columns are framed in two different methods, each way being for a special purpose. If it is an "independent column", or in other words a complete column, not intended to surround a brick or iron core, the frame is made lighter and thinner, and in such ways as to admit the column to be cut either in two equal parts, or with one-third out, or just as much as will allow the larger part to pass over the iron core. Care must be taken that the inner diameter of the skeleton frame is greater than the diameter of the iron core. This is to allow for fixing. The outer diameter of the frame is made about 1 inch less than the finished outline of column, to allow ½ inch for the core and ½ inch for the scag. The two parts of the frame are fixed with wooden pegs (not nails), so that they may be sawn when the column is cut into halves. This is not done until the column is polished and ready for fixing. The parts are best separated by cutting with a thin and fine-toothed saw. The thinner the cut the better the joint. The two parts are fixed on the iron core with brass screws or clamps, from 3 to 4 feet apart, and the joints made good with colored plaster as before. Sometimes a zigzag joint is made, the one side fitting the other, to give the marble or figure a more regular and natural appearance. The joints are then stopped with various tints, these being the same gauge as used for the face.

Sometimes the framing is made longer than the shaft, so as to project at each end. These projecting parts are used as fixing points for screws, and binding round with hoop-iron before the plinth and cap are fixed. These parts project the edges of the work while being moved and fixed. Considerable skill and patience is required to make a strong joint, well polished, and imperceptible to the eye. The frames are made with solid ends, with a square hole in each to fit the spindle. The solid ends are cut out of inch deal, and are used to keep the skeleton firm and in a central position when the spindle is turning on its bearings. One of the ends is fixed to flange of the spindle with screws. If a case column is being made, the solid ends are taken off before the column is cut; but they form permanent parts of the framing for an independent column. The mould is fixed at one side, and level with the centre of the spindle, which is the centre of the column's diameter. Care must be taken that the profile of the mould plate to the centre of the spindle is one-half of the required diameter at each end of the shaft.

Vases are generally made without wood framing. They are turned on a spindle with a plaster core screwed to the flange in the form of a parabola, to give the form of the hollow inside. On the core a coat of scag is laid and allowed to set. This is scratched to give a key for the coarse plaster which forms the body of the vase. This is formed to the desired outer profile by means of a mould fixed on the outside, and muffled to allow for a thickness of outside scag. When the core is run, the muffle is taken off, and the scag laid, keeping it about 1/8 inch thicker than the true profile, to allow for turning and stoning. When the scag is set, it is turned, and then the vase is taken off the spindle and plaster core. The spindle hole is used as a key for a slate or iron dowel for fixing the vase on to the square plinth. The vase is then polished. Cheap work is usually run or turned with a mould. This is done to save turning with chisels, but it spoils the true figure of most marbles.

A more recent way of imitating marbles is known by the name of Marezzo, which does not require so much polishing, being made on plate glass or other smooth surface. Keen's superfine plaster is used. The mode of making Marezzo is described later on. Specimens of the real marbles, to give the color and form of veining, spots, and figures, will be of great service to the beginner.

Mixing.—Mixing the colors is an important part of scagliola manufacture, and the following colors, mixing and mode of using, will serve as an index for the imitating of any other marble that is not detailed. Fine plaster (not cement) is used for making the best class of scagliola, gauged with sized water, which is made by dissolving 1 lb. of best glue with 7 quarts of water. (This is known in the trade as "strong water".) The stuff, when gauged will take about six hours to set. All mixing is done on a clean marble or slate slab. One of the principal arts is the mixing, but there are no two men who mix exactly alike, and it is largely a matter of experience. The chopping or cutting into slices with a knife is another important point in the mixing, apart of course from the special colors. Where there are two shades of one color in any given work, the cutting does not affect their original shade. No dry color is used, only ground water-colors. The beginner had better experiment with a small sample of "Penzatti" or Penzance marble. With one gill of size water, gauge plaster middling stiff, then mix thoroughly with the gauged plaster a little red. Do the same with a little black. (See quantities below.) Blend this stuff properly by working it on the bench with the hands (not tools), then roll it out, and cut it into slices about one inch thick. Take up these slices, and part them with the fingers about the size of a walnut, and put them aside, a little distance apart, on a bench.

The veining in this instance is white. Over these little lumps scatter half a handful of crumbs, made by reserving a little of the gauged plaster, and making it crumbly with dry plaster, mixing with it a few small bits of alabaster or marble. Then gauge a little plaster in a basin, with a tooth brush, about 2 inches wide, dip into this gauged plaster, and smudge the little lumps all over with it. Knock these lumps together into a big one, and chop the big lump three times. (This chopping means cutting with a knife into slices once, and knocking up again; cutting with a knife a second time, and knocking up again; and then cutting with a knife a third time, when it is finished.) This lump is then ready to be cut into slices, and applied to any purpose required; but in this case, being wanted for a specimen, it is cut into slices about ½ inch thick, and laid close together flat on a sheet of paper, and allowed to remain until set. It is then planed, and when dry polished. This operation is an embodiment of the principle of "scag" mixing nearly from beginning to end, only submitting one color for another for the various marbles. The mixing is generally known as plain and rich, and may be described thus: Take a Sienna pedestal, for instance. Two shades of sienna, plain mixing; one or two shades of dark with veining, rich mixing, both done on the same principle as Penzatti. They are cut into slices and laid on alternately. All veining of any color is done as described above, only modified by the consideration that if strong veining is wanted the stuff must be stiffish, and for fine veining it must be slightly softer. Various-sized measures for the water and scales for weighing the color should be used. Pats of each gauge should be set aside as test pats to determine when the main portion of stuff is set. It is advisable to number the pats for future reference as to quantity of colors, time of setting, and tints when dry. The various colors and tints are gauged and chopped as previously described, and according to the marble required. The core being laid on the skeleton, and left in a keyed and rough state until dry and expansion ceased, it is ready when set for the scag. The core is now damped and well brushed with the white or other vein that has to be made. The veining is gauged thin, and being brushed and laid in the core, will tend to make the slices adhere better, and fill up the interstices caused by the jagged edges of the cut slices. The slices are then taken and pressed firmly onto the core, arranging in proportion to the figure of the marble. To render the work more dense, beat it with a flat-faced mallet and a large gauging trowel with a square end. Try the work with a rule to see if the surface is fair. The rough surface should not be less than 1/8 inch thicker than the true line of the work, to allow for planing and stoning. When required, pieces of alabaster are inserted before the stuff is set. Metallic ores are used in some marbles, also pieces of granite and real marble. When the scag is laid, the work is left until set and dry. It is then planed stopped, stoned and polished. Columns and circular work are turned on a lathe, and the rough surface reduced to the true profile with long chisels similar to those for turning wood or other materials. This should not be attempted until the materials are thoroughly set.

Colors and Quantities.—The following are the colors and quantities used for various marbles. The proportions of strong water, which is made varies, the due quantity should be tested by gauging small pats of plaster to ascertain the time of setting. As the tints of real marble vary in some species, the mixing must to some extent be left to the ingenuity of the workman. With a little practice and perseverance, a careful and observant man will soon succeed in getting the required tints.

Penzance Marble.—10 oz. of light purple brown to 1 pint. Veining (plain mixing), 2 oz. black to 1 gill; veining (rich mixing) 5 oz. black to ½ pint; veining (rich mixing), 1 oz. black to ½ gill. All liquid measurements refer to strong water.

Egyptian Green.—5 oz. black to 1 pint. Veining, ½ oz. green to ½ pint light shade; veining, ¼ oz. green to ½ gill. White the same, black chopped three times; a few black spots same as brown Belge.

Brown Belge.—Four shades—1 light purple brown (indigo); 2 middle shades (blue black); 1 very dark shade (vegetable black). Veining, burnt sienna with red alabaster spots—4 oz. (light shade) to ½ pint; 4 oz. (middle) to ½ pint; 4 oz. (very dark) to ½ pint; ½ oz. burnt sienna to ¼ pint; ¼ oz. black to ¼ pint; ½ pint for the grey with crumbs, and red alabaster spots.

Dark Porphyry.—Color, light purple brown, with black, and a little ultramarine, blue spots, black, vermilion grey, and a little red.

Green Genoa.—2¼ oz. green to ½ pint (rich mixing); 5 oz. black to 1 pint. Veining, ½ oz. green to ¼ pint. White veining the same, with alabaster spots, and black.

Rouge Royale.—Color, light purple brown, with a little sienna, and umber, with ultramarine, blue or blue black. Vert-Vert.—¼ oz. green to ½ pint; dark green with sienna; dry green plaster.

Devonshire Red Marble.—All sienna work. *Light mixing*—1 shade grey; 1 shade lemon chrome; 1 shade light purple brown; 1 shade flesh color; veining burnt sienna. *Dark mixing.*—1 shade light purple brown, with indigo blue in it; 1 shade dark purple brown; 1 shade middling purple brown; 1 shade grey; 1 shade lemon chrome. Veining, burnt sienna, with small alabaster spots.

Sienna Mixing.—5 oz. sienna to ½ pint, dark shade; 3 oz. sienna to ½ pint, middle shade; 2 oz. sienna to ½ pint, light shade.

Griotte Marble.—10 oz. of light purple brown to 1 pint 5 oz. of dark purple brown to ½ pint, with alabaster spots. Ground with red veins, and small spots.

Spanish Buff.—Burnt sienna, 2 shades, with large alabaster spots. Veining, white and blue black, with small alabaster spots. Ground with red veins, and blue spots.

Light Verd Antique.—2½ oz. green to ½ pint; 1½ oz. black to 1 gill; ½ gill black to 1 gill grey shade.

Dark Verd Antique.—Green spots cut; grey spots cut; black spots with green and grey. Veining 2½ oz. green to ½ pint (rich mixing); 2½ oz. dark green to ½ pint (rich mixing); ¼ oz. black to ½ pint (rich mixing).

Plain mixing, same as above, with small alabaster spots, and small black spots.

Black and Gold.—5 oz. of black to 1 pint. Veining, 2 shades dark sienna to ½ pint (rich mixing); 2 shades light to ½ pint (rich mixing); 2 parts light and grey, with alabaster spots, and crumbs. Veining must be stiff; 3 oz. of black to 1 gill.

Walnut.—2 parts burnt umber; 1 part rose pink.

Verta Alps Marble.—5 oz. black to 1 pint. Veining, 1¼ oz. of green to 1½ gills; ¼ oz. green to ½ gill, with black crumbs chopped three times for the ground.

Rosse De La Vantz Marble.—Rich mixing with indigo blue—1 shade light purple brown; 1 shade dark purple brown; 1 shade Venetian red. Veining, black for the ground, and white and green veining for the mixing, with alabaster spots and crumbs.

Polishing White Scagliola.—White scagliola is often made with superfine Keen's cement. A small portion of mineral green or ultramarine blue is added to improve and indurate the white color. White work requires special care to prevent discoloration or specks. When the work is left for drying purposes, or at the end of the day, it should be covered up with clean cotton cloths to prevent the ingress of dust, smoke or being touched with dirty hands. The tools should be bright and clean. Steel tools should be as sparingly used as possible. When the cement has thoroughly set and the work is hard, it is rubbed down with pumice-stone, or finely grained grit-stone, by the aid of a sponge and clean water, rubbing lightly and evenly until the surface is perfectly true. It is then stoned with snake-water (Water of Ayr), using the sponge freely and the water sparingly until all the scratches disappear. Afterwards well sponge the surface until free from glue and moisture. It is now ready for the first stopping. Stopping is an important part of the polishing process, and should be carefully and well done, to ensure a good, sound, and durable polish.

First gauge a sufficient quantity of cement and clean water in a clean earthenware gauge-pot. The gauged stuff should be about the consistency of thick cream. It is well dubbed in, and brushed into and over the surface, taking care that no holes or blubs are left. When the stuff on the face gets a little stiff, scrape off the superfluous stopping with a hard-wood scraper having a sharp edge. Then repeat the brushing (but not the dubbing) with the soft gauged stuff, and scraping two or three times, or until the surface is solid and sound. The work is now left until the cement is perfectly set. It is then stoned again for the third time with a piece of fine snake-stone, and stopped as before, with the exception that the superfine stopping is not scraped off, but wiped off with soft clean rags. The work is left until the cement is set and the surface dry. It is then polished with putty powder (oxide of tin), which is rubbed over the surface with soft clean white rags, damped with clean water. In polishing mouldings, the stone must be cut or filed to fit each separate member of the moulding.

Polishing Scagliola.—The polishing of scagliola is slightly different. It is rubbed down with a soft seconds (marble grit) or gritty stone, using the sponge and water freely until the surface is true. The glut and glue are cleaned off with a brush and sponge, using plenty of water, until the pores are free from grit. The moisture is sponged off, and the work left until sufficiently dry. It is then stopped in the same manner as white work, but using stiff stopping for large holes and steel scrapers instead of wood. The stopping is made with the same kind of plaster, size water and color as was used for the ground color of the marble that is being imitated. The stopping and stoning is repeated as before, and it is finally polished with putty powder, using pure linseed oil instead of water. The repeated operations of stopping and stoning must not be proceeded with until the previous stopping is perfectly set, and the work dry. A small portion of spirits of turpentine is sometimes added to the gauged colored stuff to facilitate the drying. The work between each combined stopping and stoning will take from one to five days to dry, according to the size and thickness of the work and the state of the atmosphere. Never dry the work by heat. The thorough dryness and hardness of the work are most essential before proceeding to polish with the putty powder and linseed oil, because any contained damp will work out and spoil the polish. Work not perfectly dry may take a high polish, but it will soon go off when the damp comes through. Columns or large hollow work are not so liable to be affected by the damp, as it may escape through the back; but there must be some opening or ventilation to allow it to finally escape.

If the polishing is well and carefully done, the polish produced on scagliola will equal, if not surpass, that on real marble. Tripoli polishing stone, sometimes called *alana*, is a kind of chalk of a yellowish-grey color. Water of Ayr stone is also used for polishing. In large work a rubber of felt dipped in putty powder may be used. Salad oil is sometimes used for finishing. Linseed oil makes the hardest finish, and dries quicker.

Marezzo.—Marezzo artificial marble manufactured from plaster or Keen's cement and mineral coloring matter is made in wood or plaster moulds for moulded work, and on slate or glass benches if in slabs. If thick plate glass is used, the worker has the advantage of being able to look through it to see if the figure of the work requires altering. Glass also has the advantage of leaving a smoother and more polished face. All wood and plaster moulds should be got up with a good face, and properly seasoned, to save stoning and polishing the face of the work. Keen's cement may be used advantageously in making Marezzo, especially for chimney pieces, or other works required for exposed positions. Keen's cement for Marezzo should be of the highest class. If the cement is not of the best, it will effloresce, rendering the work of polishing difficult, if not spoiling it altogether. Keen's cement requires no size water, but in gauging either Keen's or plaster, no more should be gauged than can be conveniently used. The quantities of colors, Keen's cement, plaster, and size water should be measured and gauged pats kept for future reference.

All gauge-pots snould be of earthenware, as they are more easily cleaned out, and do not rust, as is the case with metal pots. All the tools should be kept bright and clean, as when working scagliola.

Marezzo is made in the reverse way to scagliola, as the face or marble is put in the mould first, and the core or backing put on afterwards.

All the mineral colors should be of good quality, in fine powder, and ground in water, known as "pulp." A number of basins should be handy, and there should be a supply of twist silk in skeins varying in diameter from ⅛ to ¼ of an inch, and cut into lengths of 14 to 18 inches. For common work, good long flax fibre may be used. Canvas is also required. One end of the silk or fibre skein must be knotted. These are known as "drop threads."

After the moulds are made, seasoned, and oiled, the young hand may begin by trying to make some easy marble, for a slab or chimney-piece. Gauge Keen's extra superfine cement or superfine plaster, in a large basin labelled No. 1, well mixing it until about the consistency of cream. This is pure white. Now pour a small quantity of this white plup into two small gauge-pots, Nos. 3 and 4. Pour a third of what remains in the No. 1 pot into another gauge pot, No. 2. Take some black-colored pulp, and make No. 1 a blackish-grey. Color in the same way No 2. only very much blacker than No. 1. No. 3 is now slightly tinted with pulp from No. 1. This leaves No. 4 pure white. Then take a skein of twist (or threads), dip into No. 4, the pure white, and well charge it by stirring it about with the fingers; take out the threads, taking each end between the thumb and forefinger of each hand, and with the remaining fingers of each hand separate the threads allowing plenty of "swag," and strike this into the face of the mould, making each stroke at different angles, recharging the threads when necessary. Repeat this process with pulp from No. 3, but in a lesser quantity; then dip your finger ends into No. 2, and fling drops about the size of large peas all over the veining. These drops must be thrown on with considerable force, so as to cut into the veins as much as possible. Dip the fingers into No. 1, and throw on No. 2, using alternately from each gauge-pot until you get a uniform thickness of surface (scag), about 1/8 inch in thickness. Now run a trowel over this to lay down any ridges. Cover the work with a piece of canvas, laying it evenly, smoothly, and without wrinkles. Be careful to put the canvas in the proper place, as moving it would spoil the lines of the veining; then spread a quantity of dry coarse Keen's lightly over the entire surface. This will absorb any superfluous moisture through the canvas. After the canvas and coarse Keen's have lain from ten to twenty minutes, or according to the stiffness of the gauge of the marble, the canvas and coarse cement are easily lifted off. Should any portion of the face of the scag leave the mould, and adhere to the canvas, it is taken off and put back in its place in the mould. The whole surface is now trowelled to render it dense and hard. The moisture should be sufficiently absorbed, or the trowelling may spoil the figure. The proper absorption of the moisture by the dry cement through the canvas, and well trowelling, are most essential to good work, ensuring hardness and density.

The core or backing is now made by using the coarse Keen's previously used for absorbing the moisture from the face, gauging it with some fresh coarse Keen's as stiff as possible. This is laid on as thick as required. If the face of the scag be very dry, spread a thin coarse gauged Keen's, so as to give a perfect cohesion between the marble and the backing. The flat surface of the backing should always be ruled or floated straight with a uniform thickness, so as to give a true bed for the cast when it is taken out of the mould, and laid on a bench ready for stoning, stopping, and polishing. This can be done as soon as it is thoroughly set and hard, and in the same manner as scagliola.

Marbles having long stringy veins require a different method of putting in the veins. Take the skeins, or "threads," by the knot with one hand, and thoroughly saturate them with the veining mixture, and run the finger and thumb of the other hand down the threads to clear them of any excess of veining color with which they may be charged. Then give the end not knotted to your partner, holding the knot in your left hand. Pull the threads asunder, so as to take the form of the veins of the marble you are copying, then lay them in the mould, leaving the knots hanging over the edge of the mould, or at least visible, to facilitate their removal when required. The threads should be arranged on the mould so as to take the form of the veining. The other colored materials are then thrown upon the thread veins, which quickly absorb the coloring matter from them; care being taken that the various colors are thrown or dropped from the finger tips, to form the figure of the body of the marble that is being copied. When the mould is sufficiently and properly covered with the marbling, take hold of the knots and withdraw the threads. These should be cleaned by passing down the finger and thumb for future use, saving the superfluous stuff for filling up any holes in the marbling. The absorption of the use of canvas and dry coarse Keen's, and the filling in of the backing or core, is then proceeded with as before described.

Granites, porphyries, etc., are made in a different manner. For porphyries with white and black specks, make a slab of white Keen's about 1/8 inch thick, and another in black, the same thickness. When they are set and hard, chop them into small pieces, then run them through a sieve, having a mesh to let through the pieces of the required size only. The pieces retained in the sieve can be broken and sieved again. The whole is now sieved again through a smaller mesh, which retains only the size wanted. The refuse can be used for small work or backing up. When the gauged stuff for the facing is mixed of the required tint (a reddish-brown), damp the black and white specks with the gauged color by means of a trowel and rolling, care being taken not to break the edges and faces of the black and white specks. When it is well mixed, lay it onto the face of the mould about 3-16 inch thick, pressing it as firmly and evenly as possible. Then absorb the moisture by means of canvas and dry coarse Keen's, trowel it well to give density, and fill in the backing or core as before. For "Rouge Royale," "Verd Antique," &c., requiring large white patches of irregular size, the sieving can be dispensed with. The white pieces are broken haphazard, and pieces of alabaster can also be inserted in these, and many other marbles, due regard being given to the size and quantity, so as not to produce an unnatural effect. The remainder of the figure is formed with the "drop threads," and the other colors being thrown on.

From this description of Marezzo, the workman will understand that in the case of marbles classed as "Breccias," such as "Rouge Royale," "Black and Gold," &c.,

having patches and rough jagged veins in them, he must have flat pieces of the required color previously made and broken up, or alabaster, as the case may be inserted into them, and the veining done with the "drop threads" and that fine or long veining threads are not required; that unicolored marbles require no veining threads; that the long veined marbles require the long threads, and in some cases the "drop threads" as well, and that granites, porphyries, &c., require no threads; that black is difficult to make owing to the pure white cement requiring so much color; and finally, that in all cases, whether Marezzo or scagliola, the polishing is done in a similar manner, whether using plaster or Keen's cement.

The details given must be carefully followed to produce work artistic in figure and appearance. The directions for making "St. Ann's" so far as manipulation is concerned, apply to all others. A little patience, practice, and perseverance will soon give confidence and expertness in producing sound scagliola and Marezzo.

Granite Finish.—Granite is a peculiar finishing coat of plaster which is sometimes used in this country to imitate granite. For granite finish, first render the walls with hydraulic lime, and when nearly dry lay with a thin coat of the same material but colored light brown. Then while this coat is still moist, splash the surface lightly with white stuff, then with black stuff, using only half as much as used for the white stuff. The red stuff is best applied by dotting the surface with a small brush charged with the colored stuff. After these colored lime stuffs are firm, but not set, the surface is carefully trowelled, using the minimum of water so as not to mix the various colored stuffs. The surface is sometimes left in a rough state, or as left when splashed. After the surface is firm, it is set out and jointed to represent blocks of graite.

Granite Plastering.—Granite plastering is a method, introduced by the author, to imitate granite. This mode of imitating granite is based on the scagliola process. It is also somewhat similar to the granite finish, and gives better and more reliable results.

The method of executing granite plaster work is as follows: First select the most suitable lime or cement for the situation, such as Portland cement or hydraulic lime for exterior work, and Parian or other white cement for interior work. Having decided on the material, gauge three different colored batches, one white, one red, and one black, taking care that the stuff is gauged stiff and expeditiously so as to obtain a hard substance. The material is colored to the desired shades, as described for scagliola or colored stuccos. When gauged the stuffs are laid separately on a bench and rolled until about 3-16 inch thick, and when nearly set they are cut into small irregular cubes and allowed to set and harden. The wall is then floated, ruled fair, and the surface keyed, and when set it is laid with a thin bedding coat of similar stuff used for the floating, but colored light brown. The colored cubes are then mixed together in due proportions, and gauged with a portion of the light brown colored stuff and laid on the thin coat while it is soft. The whole is then firmly pressed with a hand-float until a close, compact, and straight surface is obtained, taking care when pressing the stuff not to break the cubes. After the stuff is set and perfectly dry and hard, the surface is rubbed down and polished, as described for scagliola or for marble plaster. The bedding coat should be sufficiently thick to receive the colored cubes, otherwise the larger cubes will project at parts, and cause extra labor in making a uniform and straight surface. Unless the cubes are fairly level when pressed, the surface will have a spotty appearance, besides being more difficult to polish. Where expense or time is a consideration, a striking appearance is obtained at less cost than polished work, by simply finishing the surface with a cross-grained hand-float, and a semi-polished surface is obtained by trowelling, or by scraping the surface with a joint-rule. Grey or light-colored granites are imitated by altering the colors of the cubes and the bedding coat as desired. Bold and striking effects on wall surfaces can be obtained by a combination of different colored granites, laid out in bands and borders. The effect can be increased by the introduction of borders in sgraffito, with the bands in granite plaster.

PART II

CEMENTS AND CONCRETES, AND HOW TO USE THEM.

It is not necessary to the workman that he should expend a long period of his valuable time in reading up the history of cements and concretes, nevertheless it is proper he should be acquainted with the outlines of the origin, growth, and development of cements, concretes and their uses, and to this end the following brief historical summary is presented, sufficient to give the workman a fair idea of the beginning and growth of the use of cements and concretes:

The word concrete is of Latin origin, and signifies a mass of materials bound or held together by a cementing matrix. The Romans used concrete B. C. 500. They made good use of lime concrete both in the construction of buildings and roadways. "Roads," says Gibbon, "were the most important element in the civilization of ancient Rome; and the cost of the Appian Way was such as to entitle it to the proud designation of 'Regina Viarum' (the Queen of Roads)." The Appian (the oldest of the Roman highways) was commenced by Appius Claudius Caius, when he was censor, about three centuries before the birth of Christ. It extended from Rome to Capua, whence it was consequently carried on to Tarentum and Brundusium. Antonio Nibby, an archaeologist of the highest authority, states that the Appian Way had an admirable substructure, with lime concrete materials superimposed, and large hexagonal blocks of stone laid on the top of all. The Romans built concrete aqueducts, often several miles long, to convey water to the cities. The palace of Sallust, the historian, was built about B. C. 50, and was frequently used as a residence by most of the emperors until as late as the fourth century. It was partly burnt by Alaric in the year 410. This once magnificent edifice was erected on a strange site, partly in the valley at the foot of the Quirinal Hill, and partly on the top of the hill. The latter portion of the palace, which was of great extent, has been almost wholly destroyed by the builders of the modern boulevard. The walls, which were thick and high, were most valuable examples of the Roman use of concrete, unfaced by brick or stone. There is still visible evidence, in the form of impressions left on those walls, which clearly demonstrates their method of casting walls in situ by means of wood framing. Rows of timber uprights, about 10 feet high, 6 inches wide, and 3 inches thick, were fixed along both faces of the intended wall. Boards about 10 inches wide and 1½ inches thick, in suitable lengths, were then nailed horizontally along the uprights, thus forming two parallel wooden walls, into which the concrete was laid and rammed until the space between the boards was filled to the top. When the concrete had set, the wood framing was removed, and refixed at the top of the concrete, the whole process being repeated until the wall was raised to the required height. This concrete was far more durable than brick or stone. The jerry-builders of the modern Rome had no difficulty in pulling down the stone wall of Servius, but the concrete walls required the use of dynamite to complete their destruction. After withstanding the wear and tear of many centuries, and the repeated onslaughts of the Goths and Vandals, it was left to the nineteenth-century speculative builder to destroy those interesting remains.

The use of concrete for floors and roofs is of great antiquity. It was employed for this purpose by the Romans in the time of Julius Caesar. Professor Middleton, in his first book, "Ancient Rome," states that the whole of the upper floor of the Antrium Vesta is formed of a great slab of concrete, 14 inches thick, and about 20 feet in span, merely supported by its edges on travertine corbels, and having no intermediate supports. In his second book, "The Remains of Ancient Rome," Professor Middleton mentions that the Romans used concrete for the construction of the Pantheon, which was erected about the time of Christ. A curious and apparently unaccountable feature as regards practical purposes is that the concrete is faced with bricks, which were faced again either with stucco or (in special cases) with marble veneer. The Professor gives a sketch showing the exterior facing and the section of a wall of this kind, the entire mass being composed of concrete, except a facing of thin bricks, triangular in plan, with the points inwards. As the author observes, these bricks could not possibly be intended as a matrix for concrete, as it would not have withstood the pressure of the latter while in a wet state. It must therefore have been necessary to retain the brick and the concrete with an external timber framing, as in the case of unfaced concrete. There could be no gain of strength or other benefit to compensate for the time expended setting the brick skin. The dome of the Pantheon is 142 feet in diameter and 143 feet high. This is also formed with brick-faced concrete. It has often been described and even drawn by various authors as essentially a brick dome. Professor Middleton remarks there must have been very elaborate construction of centring for this and other massive concrete vaults. He states they employed a method, which has become common of late, to avoid the necessity of building up the centring from the ground. They set back the springing of the arch from the face of the pier, so as to leave a ledge from which the centring was built, the line of the pier being afterwards carried up until it met the intrados of the arch, leaving it a segmental one. The Professor also found signs of timber framing for walls in the remains of the Golden House of Nero, under the Thermae of Titus, where, he says, "the channels formed by the upright posts are clearly visible. These upright grooves on the face of the wall are about 6 inches wide by 4 inches deep, and they are afterwards filled up by the insertion of little rectangular bricks, so as to make a smooth unbroken surface for the plastering." This method is difficult to understand. According to the present practice, the supports should be fixed outside the line of wall surface and leave no space to fill in afterwards. He also mentions a striking example of the tenacity of good concrete in the Thermae of Caracalla, at a part where a brick-faced concrete wall originally rested on a marble entablature supported by two granite columns. "In the sixteenth century," he says, "the columns and the marble architrave above them were removed for use in other buildings, and yet the wall above remains, hanging like a curtain from the concrete wall overhead." This proves that the Romans bestowed as much thought and care on the materials and their composition as they did on their construction. Professor Middleton notes that the larger pieces of aggregate in the concrete, which are not close together, are so evenly spaced apart as to lead to the conclusion that they must have been put in by hand, piece by piece.

Dr. Le Plongeon, during his explorations in Peru, found many remains of mud concrete walls. Although they were built many centuries ago, they have proved sufficiently durable to exist until to-day. The materials were placed between two rows of boards, and well beaten, and the exteriors were sometimes decorated with plaster work. Thus it appears that the Peruvian builders of the period of the Incas anticipated by centuries the method (but not the material) of our modern concrete buildings. Le Plongeon's researches conclusively establish the fact that these Indians were masters of concrete building and plastering. The walls of the fortress of Ciudad Rodrigo in Spain are built of concrete. There are over twelve miles of arches and tunnels constructed with concrete in the Varone Aqueduct, which supplies Paris with water. One of the arches over the Orleans Road, in the Forest of Fontainebleau, has a span of 125 feet without a joint, the arches and the water-pipe or tunnel being entirely composed of beton, made with Portland cement, hydraulic lime, and the sand found on the spot. Concrete blocks weighing over 20 tons were used in the construction of the Suez Canal, 3,000,000 tons of these blocks being required at Port Said alone. Besides the unquestionable durability of concrete, it also possesses fire-resisting and waterproof powers of the highest degree. Constructional works formed with concrete carefully made and applied may be considered absolutely fire-resisting and damp proof; in fact, in these respects concrete has long since passed the experimental period, inasmuch as numerous tests, under the most trying and adverse circumstances, attest the superiority of this material for sanitary and durable work.

The best concrete in France is that made under Coignet's system of "beton agglomere," and has been used with great success in the construction of various large and important works. In Paris many miles of the sewers have been formed of this material, and a church in the Gothic style, from the foundations to the top of the steeple (which is 136 feet high) is entirely formed of beton. The work was prosecuted without cessation for two years, and was exposed to rain and frost, but has not suffered in the slightest way from the extremes of temperature. The strength of this material for constructive work may be judged by the thickness, or rather want of thickness, in the construction of a house, six stories high, having a Mansard roof—cellar, 19 inches, first story, 15 inches; second story, 13 inches, and diminishing 1 inch every successive story, so that the sixth story was 9 inches. The cellars have a middle wall from back to front, from which spring flat arches having a rise of one-tenth of the span, the crown being 5 inches thick, and at the springing 9 inches, which formed strong damp-proof and fireproof cellars. There are many houses in Paris, and this country, constructed of this material. It has been used in London in the construction of sewers, &c. This concrete is composed of Portland cement, sand, and lime. Hydraulic lime is used for sewers and waterworks, and common lime for ordinary work. The lime is used in a powdered state. The whole of the materials are mixed in a dry state by hand, and afterwards gauged in a specially made pug-mill. The least possible amount of water is added by means of a fine jet while the pug-mill is in motion. The mixture is then spread in thin layers, and beaten by rammers formed of hardwood. The quantities for coarse work, where a fine face is not required, are: Portland cement, 1 part; common lime, ½ part; gravel, 13 parts; coarse and fine sand, 6 parts. And for sewers: Portland cement, 1-5 part; hydraulic lime, 1 part; sand, 6 parts. And for external work of good quality: Portland cement, 1 part; lime, ½ part; sand, 7 parts. The above proportions are all by measure. Specimens of Coignet beton at two years old have attained a crushing strength of 7,400 lbs. to the square inch.

Fine Concrete.—"No book on plastering," says Miller, "would be complete without a description of the methods for working 'fine concrete' (here termed 'fine concrete' to distinguish it from rough concrete as used for foundations, &c.), which is now coming into general use for paving purposes, staircases, and constructive and decorative works for buildings. Floors, roofs and similar works which are finished with fine concrete, being within the plasterer's province, also demand description. The proper manipulation of the plastic materials, which is imperative for sound concrete, is undoubtedly plasterer's work. The higher branches of concrete work, for architectural construction and decoration, embrace model-making, modelling, piece-molding and casting. Concrete construction is therefore essentially a part and parcel of the plasterer's art and craft. The construction of concrete staircases in situ affords a striking example of the necessity of employing plasterers. Only a plasterer can manipulate the materials correctly, make the nosing mitres sharp and true, and set the soffits of the stairs and landings, and form a true arris at the stringing, whereas the non-plasterer leaves the work uneven, rough and unsound. The non-plasterer can just manage to spread the stuff laid on the ground for him when laying paving, but he is entirely lost when the stuff has to be taken up on a hawk and laid with a trowel on an upright or overhead surface. He then gets upset, or rather he upsets the stuff. The non-plasterer possibly may have been an unfinished apprentice, or a dunce at his former trade, hence his trying another. These remarks are not caused by any hostility to other trades, but are inspired by the fact that many failures in the better class of concrete are due to the non-plasterer's incapacity in working, and his lack of knowledge of the materials. Portland cement concrete pavements were first used about sixty years ago. Its introduction, improvements, and subsequent rapid strides for paving, and in the construction of staircases, cast and made in situ, are due to the plasterers. Concrete is one of the best materials for paving the sidewalks of streets, abattoirs, stables, breweries, &c. It is jointless, impervious, non-slippery, and can be laid with a plain surface or grooved to any desired form. The only objection to paving laid in situ for streets is that when it is cut to repair or alter gas or water pipes it is difficult to make it good without the patches showing. This slight defect can easily be overcome by cutting out the whole bay where the patches are, or by forming a movable slab over the pipes.

There has been in recent years some controversy as to the department of the building trades to which laying concrete paving properly belongs. The claim is undoubtedly upheld in the strongest way for the plasterers. A further argument, if one is needed, to identify the operation as a plasterer's job, is that the tools, skill in which is necessary, are exclusively those of plasterers. The laying trowel and the hand-float are principally used, and none but plasterers exclusively employ them, no other workman in any branch of the building trades being habituated to their use. In every part of the world where concrete paving has been used it has been laid down by plasterers, so that it may be looked upon as their legitimate sphere of work.

Concrete is now extensively used in preference to earthenware for making sewer tubes. Experience has proved that the acids present in liquid sewage and the gases generated by the action of a faecal decomposition do not injure the concrete tubes, but on the contrary tend to harden them. Among the many unlikely purposes for which concrete has come into use may be mentioned statuary, vases, fountains, sinks, tanks, cisterns, cattle-troughs, silos, railway sleepers, platform copings, mantelpieces, chimney pots, tall chimneys, tombs, tombstones, and coffins. Concrete is slowly but surely coming to the front as one of the most useful, economical, constructive, and decorative materials for works requiring strength and endurance. It may now be said to be indispensable to the architect, engineer and builder. Concrete, when properly made with a Portland cement matrix, and slag or a similar aggregate, is undoubtedly the best fire-proof material used in any building construction. It can be made thoroughly waterproof and acid proof, and may be moulded or carved to any design and colored to any shade. After this brief historical review of concrete, the practical considerations of the modern working by plasterers claim attention. Before describing the methods of working the concrete, a description of the materials, with their characteristics and application, is given as a preliminary guide and reference.

Matrix.—Matrix is a word used to designate any material having a setting, binding, or cementing power, such as limes, plaster or cements. For concrete paving, stairs, floors, or cast work for external purposes, it may be truly said that there is only one matrix, namely, Portland cement.

Aggregate.—This is a term applied to those materials held or bound together by the matrix. Aggregates may be fibrous or non-fibrous, natural or artificial. The natural aggregates comprise granite, stone, shells, marble, slate, gravel, sand, metal filings, &c.; the artificial slag, brick, pottery, scharff, clinkers, coke-breeze, ashes, glass, &c.; and the fibrous slag, wool, coir, fibre, reeds, hair, cork, tow, chopped hay, straw, shavings, &c. The fibrous aggregates while being principally of a natural kind, are generally of a vegetable nature. They are commonly used with a plaster matrix for the interior works. The best aggregates for the upper coat of concrete paving are granite, slag, and some of the hard limestones. The best and cheapest for the first layer or rough coat are broken bricks, old gas retorts, clinkers, whin and other stones. Stone chippings from masons' yards and quarries are cheap and good. Shingles and gravel are also used, but owing to their round and smooth surfaces they afford little or no key for the matrix. When found in large quantities and at a cheap rate, they should be broken to render them more angular, so as to give a better key. Aggregates are broken by a crushing or stamping machine. In Paris, the stone aggregates used for casting figures, vases and similar ornamental works is generally broken by hand.

Aggregates should be clean, and their surfaces free from mud and dust. Coarse aggregates are easily cleaned by turning on a strong stream of water from the hose. The aggregates should be laid on an inclined plane to allow the water and dirt to run off. The importance of a clean aggregate is seen from the fact that briquettes made from washed particles resist a tensile strain from 15 to 20 per cent. higher than those made from unwashed particles, when tested under similar conditions.

Porous Aggregates.—All aggregates of a porous nature or having a great suction should be well wetted before being gauged, to prevent absorption of the water used for gauging the matrix. A porous aggregate requires more cement than one of closer texture, and is not as strong. Water has no power to harden or set an aggregate. It is used to render the mass plastic, and to set the cement. No more than is necessary for this purpose should be used. Sloppy cement will not attain the same degree of hardness as a firm or stiff gauged cement, consequently it stands to reason that if the water or a part of it be absorbed by a porous aggregate, it will render the matrix, or that part next to the aggregate, friable and worthless. This may be proved by gauging a part of neat cement and spreading it on a brick and another part on a slate. It will be found that the latter will set and become hard, whilst the former will either crumble before setting, or partly set, without getting hard. All aggregates are more or less absorbent, but while the porous kinds will absorb the water from the matrix, not only leaving the portions in immediate contact with the aggregate inert, but also weakening the whole body of the concrete, the non-porous have little or no absorption, water being retained in the matrix, or a portion may lie on the surface of each particle of aggregate, thus tending to harden the matrix and increase the general strength of the concrete. It may be thought that these defects are trivial, and can be overcome by thoroughly saturating the porous aggregate to prevent suction, but the fact still remains that after this or other excess water has dried out, the body of the concrete must still be porous, and this is one, if not the principal reason, why some concretes are not damp-proof. The quantity of matrix used for ordinary concrete being very much less than the quantity of aggregate, and the matrix not being of sufficient thickness to resist the force of atmospheric moisture, the damp finds a ready passage through the porous portions. A mass of porous aggregate will absorb external moisture, and this will gradually work through the body to the weakest or driest surface, or be retained for a time, according to the state of the atmosphere. The extra keying power claimed for a porous aggregate is infinitesimal. It may be said not only to be of no value, but unnecessary, bearing in mind that in well-made concrete every particle of aggregate is enveloped with matrix.

Another point to be considered is the great tenacity of Portland cement to most clean surfaces, however smooth. Many men will have noticed how it clings and adheres when set to iron, even to the smooth blades of trowels and shovels. The ultimate tenacity of neat Portland cement after being gauged twelve months is about 500 lbs. per square inch.

Compound Aggregates.—The proper selection and use of aggregates for a true concrete is not secondary, but of equal importance to the matrix. As inferior aggregates are in the majority, it is advisable to take their defects into consideration. For concrete floors, roofs, and stairs, where strength, durability, and fire resisting properites are imperative, gravel and coke-breeze as aggregates stand lowest in the scale. Owing to their abundance and cheapness, however, or for want of better materials, their use is often unavoidable. Their individual defects may be partly if not wholly corrected by a combination of two or more aggregates so as to balance their respective good and bad qualities. It is self-evident that the hard, non-porous, and incombustible nature of gravel will correct the soft, porous, and combustible nature of coke-breeze, and that the light, rough, angular, and elastic nature and variety of size of coke-breeze will counterbalance the disadvantages of the heavy, smooth, round, and rigid nature and uniformity of size of gravel. The strength, irregularity of size, and form of broken bricks and its incombustible nature, causes it to be a direct gain to either of the above. The mixing of various aggregates may seem of small importance, but if by their judicious amalgamation the strength is enhanced, or the weight or cost of the material decreased, or gained, if the practice enables any waste or by-product to be utilized, then the advantage becomes obvious. To argue by analogy, it is well known that it is by the judicious combination and manipulation of various materials that mortars and cements attain their strength and hardness, therefore the same course will give equally good results with concretes, while rendering economy with safety possible.

The compressive and tensile strength of concrete is influenced both by the matrix and the aggregate. Aggregates which are uniform in size (or if of various sizes which are not graduated in proportion to each other), or having their surfaces spherical, soft or dirty, will not bind with the matrix, or key or bend with each other, so well as those which are of various graduating proportional sizes, and have their surfaces hard, angular and clean.

Sand and Cement.—Sand is extensively used as an aggregate in Portland cement for cast work, mouldings, and wall plastering. Fine sand does not give so good results for strength as coarse sand, and a hard-grained sand is more durable than a soft one. Ground brickbats or pottery, sandstone and flints, fine gravel, smithy ashes, and coke-breeze are often used as substitutes for sand.

It has generally been assumed that sharp coarse sand is one of the best and strongest for gauging with cement, but, according to experiments made by Mr. Grant, clean sharp pit sand gives better results, as he found that whereas test briquettes having a sectional area of 2½ superficial inches, composed of equal proportions of coarse sand, broke at the end of twelve months with a tensile strain of 724 lbs., it required 815 lbs. to break briquettes composed of equal parts of cement and pit sand. With reference to various sands suitable for making mortar with cement, Mr. Grant's experiment is of a most surprising nature, as it indicates that sand made from ground clay ballast, or ground brick—which are identical—and Portland stone dust, were superior to pit or sea sand, or smiths' ashes.

The following shows the results of tests of various aggregates made by Lieutenant Innes. The briquettes are composed of Portland cement, sand, or other aggregates, in the proportions of 1 to 2, and were kept in water for seven days.

It will be seen that Portland stone dust gave the best results, and the others follow in this order—coarse sea sand, rough pit sand, smooth pit sand, drifted sea sand, and lastly smithy ashes. If the dust had been eliminated, the tests would be more valuable. The degree of coarseness has a considerable influence on the strength of the concrete and mortar. Fire sand makes weaker mortar than coarse. The following table gives the results of two series of tests carried out by Mr. Grant. The cement was sifted through a sieve with 2,580 meshes to the square inch, and was made into briquettes with 2

TESTS OF VARIOUS SANDS, &c., AND CEMENT.

NATURE OF SAND, &c.	Voids per cent.		Shrinkage per cent.	Grains above $\frac{1}{50}$ inch	Tensile Strength in lbs. per square inch.			
	Dry.	Wet.			Three Weeks.	Proportional Value of Sands.	Three Months	Proportional Value of Sands.
Neat cement	....	....	....	....	450	....	529	....
Sea sand, roughish and uneven grain, chiefly siliceous, clean	38	34	6	94	140	52.4	249	70.1
Sea sand (drifted), siliceous, clean	43	36	11	8	60	22.3	193	54.3
Pit sand containing small shells, &c., grains of unequal size, siliceous	32	19	16	15	108	40.1	248	69.8
Pit sand, grains smooth and uniform, siliceous, clean	41	34	11	76	94	34.9	175	49.8
Portland stone dust, grains rough and irregular, clean	46	34	18	56	165	61.3	254	71.5
Smithy ashes, containing much unburnt coaldust, grains rough and irregular	64	52	25	56	38	14.1	91	25.6

parts of sand by weight. All the briquettes are kept in water.

TENSILE TESTS OF PORTLAND CEMENT AND SAND (COARSE AND FINE).

No.		Sand tested by Sieves.	At 28 days.	60 days.	91 days.	182 days.	273 days.	364 days.
		Nos.	lbs.	lbs.	lbs.	lbs.	lbs.	lbs.
	First Series—							
1	1 cement to 3 sand.	20-30	78.5	113.9	116.9	142.3	178.	205.5
2	ditto.	10-20	137.1	239.5	223.	231.5	254.5	251.5
	Second Series—							
3	1 cement to 3 sand.	20-30	117.2	134.5	145.	156.	157.8	213.
4	ditto.	10-20	212.	236.5	206.	253.	267.5	273.5

In the above each figure is the average of ten tests, the result being given in pounds per square inch. The sand used in tests 1 and 3 passed a sieve with 400 meshes to the square inch, and the sand used in the tests 2 and 4, through a sieve with 100 meshes to the square inch.

Fireproof Aggregates.—The selection of the best known fire-resisting aggregate for fire-proof concrete construction is of vital importance. Granite, stone, and flints splinter and crack when subjected to great heat, or to the sudden reaction caused by cold water used for extinguishing fires. Coke-breeze concrete, when under the influence of intense heat, as for example in the midst of a building on fire (stated by Captain Shaw to be from 2000 degrees to 3000 degrees Fahr.), will gradually calcine and crack, and finally fall to dust.

Slag is one of the best fire-proof aggregates. It is a well-worn axiom that "what has passed through the fire will stand the fire." There is no other material that has passed the ordeal of fire like slag. Its great hardness, density, and angularity (when crushed) all tend to make it one of the best substances for fire-proof construction. Slag is cheap and abundant, but requires great care in selection, as some kinds contain a large amount of sulphur, which is very detrimental to Portland cement, causing the concrete to blow and expand. The presence of sulphur can often be detected by the smell alone. When sulphur is present in a heap that has lain for some time, or sufficiently long to allow the atmosphere to cleanse the outer surface, it is more difficult to detect. A hole should then be dug in the heap, and the presence of sulphur can be ascertained by smell, heat, and color. It will smell strong, and if new will be warm, and show yellow patches. The power of the sulphur is so great that washing the slag once will not entirely cleanse it. In some cases frequent washings and long exposures to the air are necessary. There are some slags that are free or nearly so from sulphur, and which can be had direct from the iron furnaces. The slag from coal and iron furnaces is largely employed for concrete paving. It is hard and practically free from sulphur. The best size is 3/8 inch screenings. This when sifted yields a fine kind for topping, and the residue is useful for the rough coat.

The next best fire-resisting aggregates are fine-bricks, pottery, scharff, hard clinkers, and pumice-stone. The last has the advantage of being extremely light, but it is too soft for the frictional wear. Coke-breeze may to a certain extent be deprived of its combustible nature and rendered more fire-resisting by washing and passing it through a 1/4 inch sieve, then adding 1 part flowers of sulphur and 10 parts fine broken bricks to 20 parts of Coke-breeze. The larger breeze rejected by the sieve can be broken small, or used for internal layers of concrete. The bricks should also be passed through a 1/4 inch sieve. The finer the breeze and brick, the better for receiving and retaining nails.

Voids in Aggregates.—The quantity of voids or interstices depends on the shape and size of the aggregates. The least quantity of voids will be found in those aggregates which are broken small, and contain pieces of various sizes. Gravel free from sand contains about 30 per cent. of voids, and broken stone of uniform size about 50 per cent. Sand is often mixed with gravel, stones, &c., to lessen the quantity, or fill the voids, so as to ensure the full strength of the concrete, without adding more cement than the proper ratio. The following method is used to ascertain the voids in aggregates:—Fill a box of known capacity with damp, broken aggregate; start shaking it during the operation; then fill the box to the brim with water; the quantity of water is the measure of the voids in the aggregate. Having now briefly reviewed the characteristics of the aggregates most used, the practical conclusions to be drawn are that they should be angular in form, hard in nature, graduated in size, and clean.

Crushing Strength of Concrete.—The crushing strength of concrete depends upon the ratio of cement, and the nature of the aggregate. Another important factor is compression, done by heating and ramming. Compression increases the weight of concrete about 4 per cent., and the strength about 25 per cent. The following table shows the crushing strength of concrete made with Portland cement and various kinds of aggregates as given by Mr. Grant. The tests were made with 6-inch cubes. One-half were compressed by heating the concrete into the mould with a mallet; the other half were not compressed. The whole were kept in the air for a year before being crushed.

The granite and slag might have been expected to have given the better results. It is probable that they were unwashed, and contained a considerable amount of dust. If the compression was done by hydraulic power, so as to obtain a uniform compression in all the cubes, the results would be more reliable.

CRUSHING STRENGTH (IN TONS PER SQUARE FOOT) OF PORTLAND CEMENT CONCRETES HAVING VARIOUS AGGREGATES.

Nature of Aggregate.	Six to One.		Eight to One.		Ten to One.	
	Compressed.	Not Compressed.	Compressed.	Not Compressed.	Compressed.	Not Compressed.
Ballast	81.6	72.8	54.	50.	42.	32.
Portland stone	162.4	120.	132.	98.	88.	76.
Granite	122.	98.	78.4	58.	62.	46.
Pottery	115.2	98.4	88.	72.	74.	56.
Slag	92.	80.	78.	56.	42.	34.
Flints	82.	62.	70.	56.	60.	51.2

Water for Concrete.—Water for concrete should be perfectly clean, and free from organic and inorganic impurities. As regards the quantity, it can only be said that for such purposes as the foundations for paving, casting blocks, &c., or where the material can be well rammed, so as to insure perfect consolidation, less is required than where the concrete can only be poured or laid in position. When mixed with sufficient water, the concrete occupies about one-eighth more space than when mixed with the full quantity, and percolation through the former gauge would be greater than through the latter. Yet by thorough ramming the former would occupy less space and offer greater resistance to moisture. An over-watered gauge is slow to set, difficult to work, liable to surface cracks, and often there is a loss of strength, caused by escape of a portion of liquid cement. The work will also be unequal in strength, owing to the liquid cement flowing to various or lower parts, leaving parts of the aggregate bare and weak.

It must not be inferred from the foregoing remarks that water is entirely unnecessary or of little value for concrete. On the contrary, it is of the utmost value. The evil is in the abuse, not in the use. Portland cement has a great affinity for moisture. For instance, if a sack of cement is left on or in a damp place, a part of the contents soon becomes set and extremely hard, which is a proof of its affinity, and that moisture alone will set cement without water, far less excess of water. Fresh cement requires more water than stale cement. Cement gauged with sea water sets more slowly than with fresh water. Sea water should not be used in concrete intended for paving stables, chemical tanks, or similar places where it will come in contact with ammonia. Sea water having a lower freezing-point than fresh water, is sometimes used in frosty weather to allow the work to be carried on. It ought not, however, to be used for external work, especially for plastering facade as it has the property of attracting moisture and causing an efflorescence on the surface. Sometimes in frosty weather hot water, also hot lime, is used for concrete; but although these hasten the setting and hardening of concrete, they also wash away some of the finest and best particles of the cement during the gauging. A part of the water also forms in little globules throughout the mass, and when the water-drops evaporate a series of small holes or bulbs are left, which deteriorate the strength of the concrete. Finally, it may be stated that the quantity of water required for gauging concrete is regulated by the class and condition of the aggregate, by the state of the atmosphere, and by the purpose for which the concrete is required. Another important point is the careful and thorough incorporation of all the materials when gauging. A mass of raw materials, if gauged carelessly, will require more water to attain the same plasticity than that which is carefully gauged. Approximate quantities of water are given for Portland cement plastering. For concrete the quantity is about 21 gallons of water to 1 cubic yard of dry materials, or about 1 part by volume to 8 parts. It is a good maxim to bear in mind when mixing water for concrete, that other things being equal, the minimum is better than the maximum. Water may be said to give birth to the strength of cement; to carry the simile further, the aggregate may be termed the bone, the matrix the skin and sinew, and the water the blood of concrete.

Gauging Concrete.—It is a common idea that concrete can be gauged and used anyhow, with any aggregate, or with any amount of water; and in consequence of a laxity in supervision in the selection of the materials, and their correct gauging and manipulation, unsatisfactory results are sometimes arrived at, the blame being attributed to the wrong cause. Gauging concrete requires considerable care to avoid waste of the materials and obtain the best possible work. Concrete can be gauged either by hand or by machinery. For small quantities, such as for stairs and similar work, the former is almost invariably used; and for large quantities, such as for foundations or buildings, &c., the latter, being more economical, is preferable. A careful and uniform method should be employed for hard gauging; nothing should be left to chance or rule of thumb. The gauge-board should be sufficiently large to allow the materials to be turned over without spilling, it should be placed as near the work as possible, and it should be cleaned after each gauge.

For fine concrete, no more than 1 cubic yard should be gauged at a time. This is as much as three men can properly gauge at once and in the proper time—that is, before the "initial set" begins. Portland cement concrete, unlike some mortars, does not improve by prolonged working. If larger quantities are desirable, then more men must be employed in the gauging. All materials should be measured for each gauge, to ensure uniform setting and strength, and also the best work. This, combined with the saving of time and materials, will repay a hundredfold the cost of the measures. It is a common yet a wrong way, when gauging for paving purposes, to measure the aggregate by so many barrowfuls to a sack of cement. Neither the aggregate nor the cement can be accurately measured in this haphazard way. No man fills a barrow twice alike, and the cement being turned out of the sacks direct onto the aggregate is apt to vary, as it may contain lumps caused by damp, and very often some of the finest cement is retained in the sack, as more often than not it is simply drawn up and then thrown on one side without shaking it, as would be, or at least should be done if the cement was emptied for air-shaking. The aggregate should be measured in a bottomless box or frame with handles at the ends, the cement in a box (with a bottom), and the water in a gallon metal measure or a pail made to contain 4 gallons. Five pailfuls of this size are about sufficient to gauge 1 cubic yard where the concrete can be well rammed or punned. For work that is simply laid, 1 gallon extra is required. The box frame is laid on the gauge-board and filled with aggregate (in a damp state). The frame is lifted off, and the aggregate spread over the board until about 6 or 7 inches thick. The cement is then distributed over the aggregate. The materials are then gauged by three men, two with shovels, and one with a rake or larry, the former facing the latter. The dry materials should be carefully but energetically turned over twice or even thrice, and then when being turned over the third time water must be gradually added by means of a rose fixed on a water-can. Water poured from a pail is apt to wash parts of the cement away; the water also cannot be regularly and gradually distributed over the dry materials as when a rose is used. The mass is again turned over twice or even thrice, until thoroughly incorporated. This turning over does not consist of merely turning the mass over in the centre or on one place of the board, but to be effectively done a shoveller should stand at each side of the board, and the raker at the end to which the mass is to be first turned; the shovellers lift the stuff and spread or rather scatter it on one end of the board with a jerking motion, and the raker further mixes the stuff by working each shovelful backwards and forwards. This is repeated, the stuff being turned to the other end of the board, after which it is turned to the center, the water being added as already described. The wet mass is then turned over twice in a similar manner, and finally finished in the centre of the board. The shovellers in the final mixing turn the stuff from the outside of the heap to the centre, while the raker gives the final touches. After being gauged, it should not be disturbed, but immediately shovelled into pails, and conveyed to the place of its use. The "initial set" begins nearly or as soon as gauged, and any after or unnecessary disturbance tends to destroy the setting properties of the cement. The practice of gauging, and afterwards regauging or knocking it up, is most objectionable, as it destroys its setting properties. No more should be gauged at one time than can be conveniently laid in one operation. The gauging of this valuable material should not be left entirely to unskilled labor, but ought to be carried out under careful supervision.

Ramming Concrete.—The ramming, beating, or punning of concrete is of great importance. It compresses the concrete, rendering it more dense and free from voids, and forces out all superfluous water. The resultant gain in strength, durability, and imperviousness is by no means to be despised. Without compression it is impossible to obtain impervious concrete. Prolonged ramming, however, is dangerous, as it may be continued until the cement is set, which would be a direct loss of strength. For this reason, the ramming of concrete made with quick-setting cement should immediately follow the deposition of the material, and be expeditiously done. The concrete should always be gauged rather stiff than soft. If in the latter form, the ramming will separate the more fluid portions, and produce strata of different densities. When the concrete is deposited in layers, the joints of each layer, if dry or exposed, should be well swept and watered before the next layer is deposited. It is often advisable, especially in very dry work, to brush the joints with liquid cement after they have been swept and wetted. For larger constructional work, the joints should also be keyed by aid of a pick, or by inserting stones at intervals into the concrete before it is set, leaving them projecting 3 or 4 inches above the level of the joint. Another method of forming a key is effected by forcing a batten on edge about 2 or 3 inches deep into the concrete, at the middle of the joint, and when the concrete is firm or nearly set the batten is extracted, thus leaving a groove which forms a key for the succeeding layer.

No layer that has to be left for some time, or until dry, should be less than 4 inches deep. Thin layers are always a source of weakness. If the successive layers can be laid before the previous one is firm or set, the thickness is not of so much consequence. For large work, when each layer has to stand until set, the thickness may vary from 9 to 12 or even 18 inches. Ramming may be done by using an iron punner, or one made of hardwood and bound with iron. Wooden mallets and punchers or iron hand-floats are most suitable for ramming stairs and cast work. The gain in strength is shown in the table of the crushing strength of Portland cement concrete.

Thickness of Concrete Paving.—The thickness of concrete paving laid in situ is regulated according to the purpose and the position of the work. The thickness also depends upon the nature and solidity of the foundations. It is obvious that a thicker paving is required for a foundation that is weak or soft than for one that is strong and hard. The best foundations are those composed of strong and well-laid rough concrete. Foundations composed of broken bricks or stone thoroughly consolidated by ramming are the next best. The thickness of foundations is also regulated by the nature of the soil and the subsequent traffic. Paving for the sidewalks of main streets, or where the traffic is heavy and continuous, should not be less than 2 inches. For a medium traffic, and on a strong foundation, a thickness of 1½ inches will be sufficient. For side streets, garden paths, passages in houses, or similar places where the traffic is light and limited, a thickness from 1 to 1½ inches will be ample if on a rough concrete foundation; but if on a dry "dry," that is, broken brick or stone one, the thickness should not be less than 1½ inches. The thickness for stable floors may vary from 3 to 4 inches, according to the class of horses. For instance, a thickness of 3 inches would be ample for race or carriage horses, but 4 inches is necessary for heavy cart horses. The same rule applies to yards, a thickness of 3 or 3½ inches being sufficient for carriages, while 4 inches is required for carts, wagons, &c. Factory floors are generally made 2 inches thick, but where there is machinery or wheel traffic a thickness from 2½ to 3 inches is employed. By computing the volume and nature of the traffic, and comparing the tests of concrete paving given herein, the requisite thickness will be readily obtained. It must of necessity greatly depend on the class of the materials and manipulation used for the paving. Like most other articles, a good material will go further and last longer than a bad one.

Concrete Paving.—Good pavements proclaim a city's progress. Isodorus states that the Carthaginians were the first people to pave streets. The subject of paving and floors will be best understood by dividing it into two parts—namely, paving, which is a floor surface laid and resting on solid ground; and floors, by which are meant floors over voids. The following items briefly embody the processes used for most concrete pavings now in use. Paving in situ is either laid in "one coat" or "two coats," the latter being in more general use than the former, yet each method has its individual merits. One-coat work is not so liable to rise or laminate as two-coat work. It takes slightly less labor, the whole thickness being laid in one operation. The aggregate is either granite or slag, or both in equal proportions, gauged with Portland cement in the proportion of 2 of the latter to 5 of the former. Two-coat is laid with two different aggregates and gauges. The first coat has a cheap aggregate, such as ballast, clinkers, bricks, or whinstone, broken so that they will pass through a 1 inch mesh riddle, and gauged in the ratio of 1 of Portland cement to 5 of the aggregate. It is laid till within 1 inch of the finished surface. The second coat is laid as soon as the first is set, and is composed of 1 part of Portland to 2 of the aggregate, the latter being either crushed granite, slag, limestone, or whinstone that will pass through a 3-16 sieve. In some districts fine shingle is used for the topping aggregate.

Quick-setting solutions are used to reduce the time required to allow the paving to harden before it is available for traffic. Many pavements are ruined by being used before having become sufficiently hard and set. Many of the so-called quick-setting materials have the desired effect of setting the concrete quickly, but the work in many cases is none the better for these solutions. On no account should these quick-setting materials be used, unless thoroughy tested and the concrete proved durable by use and time. In order to protect the surface and allow the paving to be used immediately, P. M. Bruner, an American engineer and concrete specialist, covers the surface of the pavement directly it is finished with a thin coat of plaster or Parian cement, which admits of walking upon in a few hours, and resists pedestrian traffic until the surface proper is sufficiently hard, after which it is shelled off with a trowel.

Eureka Paving.—This is the name for an improved concrete, which has been extensively used with good results for many purposes, such as pavements, floors and stairs. Eureka, if not exactly one-coat work, is nearer that than two-coat work, and may be said to be the happy medium, or a combination of both. Eureka is laid in two layers. The first is termed the "rough coat," and the second the "fine coat" or "topping." The topping is laid nearly as soon as the rough coat is laid, just as in rendering or dubbing-out plaster work. The materials and gauges are nearly alike for both layers. The gauged rough stuff is laid on the foundation, previously wetted to prevent suction, and spread and beaten with an iron hand-float. The laying, spreading and beating is continued until the rough surface is within ½ inch of the finished line. The surface of the rough coat is made fair, and a uniform thickness for the topping is obtained by passing a "gauge-rule" across the surface. A uniform thickness of topping gives an equal expansion, therefore the surface is not liable to crack. The suction is also more regular, which permits of the trowelling to be done with greater freedom, and without causing hard and soft places on the surface.

As many alternate bays are laid as will allow of all being topped and finished the same day. When the number of bays to be laid in on one day has been decided, and the last one roughened in, the first bay will be firm to receive the topping. The topping is laid and spread with a wooden hand-float, ruled and trowelled and brushed as afterwards described in the general process. This method of laying a part of the thickness of the paving, gauging stiff and beating the mass, forces it into the interstices of the broken dry foundation, and not only consolidates the foundation and the rough coat, but also forms a solid bed to receive the topping. The topping goes in sooner and more regularly on a stiff-gauged and well-beaten coat than on a soft-gauged one, or than if the whole thickness of the paving were laid in one coat.

Eureka Aggregate.—The method of preparing the aggregate for Eureka is of the utmost importance. The labor expended on its preparation is more than repaid, not only in the ease and rapidity when finishing, but also in the satisfaction of doing a strong and workmanlike job. Slag and granite is far more preferable to gravel or stone as an aggregate. Slag and granite in equal proportions have been used with good results. The size ordered from the furnace or quarry should be 3/8 inch screenings. It must be washed through a 1/8 inch sieve in a tub or iron tank. The coarse part rejected by the sieve to be laid aside for the rough coat. The fine aggregate is then washed again through a fine sieve to extract any mud or impalpable powder, as the presence of such impurities weakens the consolidating power of the cement, and decreases the ultimate strength of the concrete. This fine aggregate for the topping should be angular and of various graduating sizes, from that of fine sharp sand to the largest size that has passed through the 1/8 inch sieve. It has been proved by experience and the test of time that an artificial stone made with a fine aggregate has not only more resemblance to the grain or texture of natural stone, but is also denser, and wears better and with more uniformity, than one made with a large, round, or equal-sized aggregate. The use of small and angular aggregate of the graduating sizes ensures their fitting closer and interlocking together, thus forming a stronger bond, giving a regular key and freedom for each separate piece to be coated with cement, the whole forming a solid and homogeneous body with a hard surface. Concrete with large or round aggregate, and the various pieces disproportionate in size to each other, will fit loosely and unevenly, and only touch at their most prominent points, thus leaving voids, and consequently unsound work. The voids may perchance be wholly or partly filled with matrix, still this is an unnecessary waste of cement. Consequently, concrete paving having large or round aggregate wears unevenly, and leaves the large or round pieces uncoated and loose, or so exposed above the surface that they soon get dislodged, leaving a series of small holes, which sooner or later wear larger and larger. Another point of importance is that concrete with a fine hard aggregate is more plastic, works freer, and has a greater compressive strength than concrete with a large or soft aggregate. Eureka concrete, having a fine, clean, and regulated aggregate, should be used for the topping of paving, steps, landings, or for any class of work exposed to friction or wear. It is well to remember that a good matrix will not make a bad aggregate strong, although a bad aggregate will make a *good* matrix weak, or rather the resultant concrete weak.

Eureka Quantities.—The quantities for the rough coat are 1 part of Portland cement and 4 parts of the coarse portion of Eureka aggregate. These materials must be gauged stiff, only as much water being used as will allow the mass to be thoroughly mixed and plastic. The quantities for the topping are 2 parts of Portland cement to 5 of the fine aggregate, and gauged about the consistency of well-tempered "coarse stuff," as used for floating. Experiments prove that neat cement is inferior in wear-resisting qualities (such as frictional wear and pedestrian traffic) to mixture of cement with sand or other aggregate, being in fact equal to a mixture of about 1 part of cement to 3 parts of aggregate. The best wearing qualities are obtained by a mixture of 2 parts of cement to 3 of aggregate.

Levels and Falls.—Accurate levelling and adjustment of the requisite falls are important features for pavements and flooring. Levelling is the art by which the relative heights of any number of points are determined. Falls are used to allow rain and water used for cleansing purposes to run off into channels and drains. The levels and falls in good buildings are generally marked, on the drawings, but it is imperative that the worker should be conversant with the necessary amount of falls for paving purposes, as many unforeseen difficulties often arise in this class of work, especially in large surfaces. The most accurate and speedy way of setting out levels and falls is of special service to concrete paviors. The importance of these features will be readily appreciated, especially where these paving preliminaries are left to the care of the concrete layers. The amount of cross fall for street pavements varies according to the class and position of the work. The fall is also regulated by the gradient. For a level stretch of paving it is generally 1 to 60, therefore for a pavement 6 feet wide it would be 1 inch. The fall for rising ground is usually ¾ inch for every 2 feet in the width of the pavement. The falls for stables and yards are given under their respective headings. The points for levelling—also for falls—are formed by driving wooden pegs into the ground at the most suitable points. The heads of the pegs represent the finished face of the pavement. They are made level with each other by the aid of a parallel rule and a spirit-level. Intermediate pegs may also be levelled by means of boning rods.

Pavement Foundations—Good foundations for concrete paving are of primary importance, and unless the bottom is firm, and the foundation is sound, the best made and laid concrete will subside, crack, and be permanently spoilt. Pavements generally cover a large area, and the superstructure, however strong, must have a firm foundation. Foundations consist of two parts—the first is the bottom ground or natural foundation; the second is the made-up or artificial foundation; but for simplicity the first is termed the "bottom," and the latter the "foundation." The latter may be "dry" or "gauged." If the bottom is soft, it must be well rammed before laying the dry materials for the foundation, or a layer of common coarse concrete for gauged work. When excavating the ground to receive the foundation, the depth from the intended finished surface of the pavement should be about 5 inches for paving 2 inches thick, 6 inches deep for paving 2½ inches thick, and 7 inches deep for paving 3 inches thick. The above depths are for dry foundations, and where the traffic is light, such as side-walks, playgrounds, and passages. If the bottom is soft, or the paving intended for heavy traffic, the depths may be increased, and the bottom well rammed before the materials are laid. The materials for the dry foundations are broken bricks, stone rubble, or other hard core. They should be spread on the bottom, and broken in situ. The breaking in situ tends to consolidate the bottom and the foundation. When broken, no piece should be left that will not pass through a 2½ inch ring. If the paving is intended for heavy traffic (carts or the rolling of heavy casks) it is best to have a rough concrete foundation. The rough concrete should be from 4 to 7 inches deep, according to the firmness of the bottom and class of traffic. This concrete is composed of ballast or equal parts ballast and broken bricks, coke-breeze, or hard clinkers, gauged in the proportion of 1 of Portland cement to 5 or 6 of aggregate. It should be laid to the desired fall. If lime instead of Portland cement is used for the rough concrete, great care should be taken to thoroughly damp the surface, and allow a sufficient time for the lime to expand and any lumps of unslaked lime to slake, before the fine concrete is laid. No paving should be laid until the rough concrete is thoroughly set. Allowance must also be made for any settlement of the bottom, and for any subsidence, contraction, or expansion of the concrete foundation. The rough is not so liable to contraction or expansion as fine concrete, but it is more liable to subsidence. Expansion is due to the cement not to the aggregate; and as there is less cement in rough concrete than in fine, it has less power of expansion, and owing to the greater amount and weight of aggregate, there is the lesser power of contraction. The size of aggregate for rough concrete is also larger than for fine; consequently each piece offers a greater resistance to the cement. Subsidence is due to the settlement by gravitation of the aggregate to the bottom, which takes place after the excess water, or even the liquid cement, has percolated through voids or spaces of badly made or laid concrete. Unequal subsidence is caused by bad and unequal gauging; one gauge being firm, keeps in position; while if soft and sloppy, the excess water either settles in the deepest places, or escapes into the ground, thus allowing the body of the concrete at those parts to subside.

Screeds and Sections.—Screeds are used as guides and bearings for leveling and ruling off. They are generally formed with wood rules, planed on all sides, and in suitable sizes, and are termed "screed rules." Screeds are sometimes formed with the same kind of material as used for the pavement, and are termed "gauged screeds." Screed rules give the best results; they are speedily laid; can be used at once, and form a clean and square joint when laying work in sections. Screed rules are temporarily fixed on the foundation by laying them on narrow strips of gauged concrete, and then made straight, and to the proper falls, by laying the edge of a straight-edge on them, and tapping with a hammer till firm and true. When the bay is finished and set, the screeds are removed by gently tapping with a hammer, leaving a clean, straight, and square joint. Where there is only a small quantity of screeds required, or where time will not permit of waiting for the concrete bedding strips to set, the screed rules can be fixed on gauged plaster, which allows the screeds to be used at once. The plaster should be cleaned off at the side intended to be laid, to ensure a sound bed for the concrete, and a square joint. Gauged screeds may be also formed with gauged coarse plaster. They are best done as described for "pressed screeds.' In laying large surfaces it is best to arrange the screeds, so that the work can be laid in alternate sections or bays, which will afford greater facility to get at the work, and also to allow the isolated bays to expand. For instance, if laying a stretch of paving 50 feet long and 6 feet wide, this would be laid out in 5-feet bays, the screed rules, each 6 feet long, being laid so as to form the odd numbered bays to be laid and finished first. This allows the workmen more freedom by standing on the empty bays when finishing the laid bay. The screeds are then removed, and the intermediate bays laid, the sides of the finished bays serving as screed or bearing when ruling in. Boards or bags are laid on the finished bays to protect the surface, and give a footing for a workman to finish off the intermediate spaces. It must not be forgotten to fix the screed rules toward the curbs, also to keep the ends of the screed about ⅜ inch about the curb, to allow for any subsidence, and for the water to run off. This also provides for the greater amount of wear

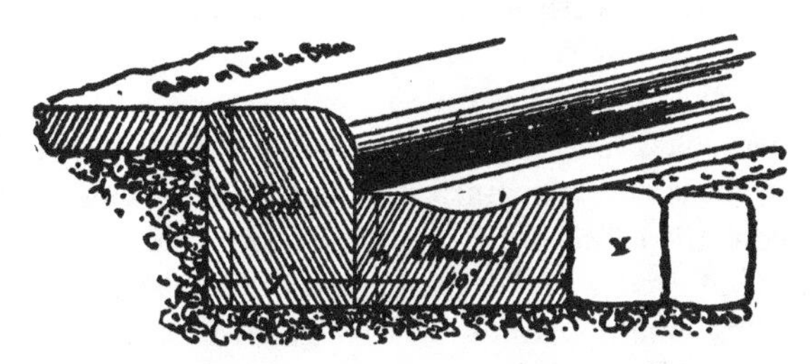

SECTIONS OF CONCRETE KERB, CHANNEL, AND PAVING.

NO. 1.

that takes place near to than actually on the curb. The foundations should be thoroughly saturated with water before the screeds are fixed. If this is not done, the brick or other dry material used will absorb the moisture or life from the concrete, and render it dry or dead. The drenching with water also frees the broken materials from the dust caused by breaking the large pieces in situ. In laying paving or a gauged foundation, the surface should be well swept with a hard broom and afterwards damped, so as to ensure the perfect cohesion and solidity of the foundation and the paving. The curbs and channels are sometimes made in situ, but more often they are cast and laid in the same manner as ordinary stone. Cast work is harder than laid work; it also allows the paving to be laid with greater freedom. Illustration No. 1 shows sections of the street curbing and channel which may be used in connection with slab paving, or pavements laid in situ.

Laying Concrete Pavements.—The foundations having been damped, and the rough stuff gauged, it is carried in pails and emptied at the top end of the bay. The plasterer spreads it with a layer float, and rams it well into the foundation. When he has laid a stretch the whole width of the bay, and as far as he can conveniently reach, he moves back and lays the remaining portions of the bay in the same way until complete. The rough stuff surface is then made fair, but not smooth, with the gauge rule. The remainder of the bays are dealt with in rotation. The fine aggregate is then gauged, and laid and spread until flush with the screeds. The stuff should be rather above than below the screeds, to allow for subsidence by subsequent ramming, ruling and patting. All concrete bodies over 2 inches thick should be deposited in layers. Each layer should be well rammed with an iron, or hardwood temp. bound with iron. Concrete gains strength by compression, and consequently its density, imperviousness, and durability are increased. Even for 2 inch pavement better results are obtained if the stuff is deposited in two layers, each layer well beaten with an iron hand-float. If only 1½ inches thick, it should be consolidated by being beaten with an iron float. The surface is next ruled with a floating rule.

The rule is worked square or edge, and the concrete cut and beaten in successive short and quick strokes. If the stuff is soft and laid too full, the rule is worked loosely on edge with a zigzag motion, so as to draw the excess stuff and water off the surface, and leave the body full and regular. If there are any hollow places, they are filled up with stuff, and the rule again applied. In all cases the surface should be finally straightened by beating with the rule. This process leaves the surface more uniform, straight, and solid than by dragging or working the rule.

Trowelling Concrete.—After being ruled, and when slightly firm, the surface is beaten with a wood hand-float, which lays any irregular parts or projecting pieces of aggregate. The beating or patting is continued until the "fat" appears on the surface. It is then trowelled, or rather ironed, the trowel being worked on the flat of the blade with a circular motion. The plasterer, when trowelling off, should have a hand-float in the other hand to lean on when reaching to a far off part. The float is also useful to pat any dry parts. The surface must be finished with a semi-dry stock-brush to obtain a uniform grain. A vast amount of care is required in trowelling off. Perfection can only be attained by practice, and a close observation of the materials, conditions, and the state of the atmosphere during the progress of the work. The best effects can only be attained by acquiring a knack of working the trowel on the flat, and by knowing when to begin and when to leave off. It is a waste of time, and the cause of an unequal surface, if the trowelling is begun before the stuff is firm; but time and labor will also be lost if the trowelling is left until the stuff is too stiff, or has nearly set, for then the surface will be rough and patchy. In either instance the surface is more or less spoilt, and the ultimate appearance and hardness seriously affected.

Grouting.—The use of neat cement for trowelling off should not be resorted to (this is termed "grouting"), and is used when the surface is left till set, or when it has not been properly patted and trowelled. The expansion of a strong and weak gauge being unequal, the result is that the surface peels, or should it adhere, it is patchy and discolored. Where grouting is unavoidable, the cement should be gauged with an equal part of fine aggregate, the aggregate being the same as used for the topping.

Dusting.—Another bad process is that of sprinkling dry neat cement over a soft surface (this is termed "dusting"), and is used to absorb the moisture caused by sloppy gauging. It has drawbacks similar to grouting. If unavoidable, the cement should be mixed with fine dry aggregate in the same proportion as the topping. If the stuff were trowelled at the correct time, there would be no necessity for grouting; and if properly gauged, no need for dusting. No concrete surface can be made so solid and hard as when it is finished in one body and at one time.

Temperature.—It is well known that extreme heat and cold effect the expansion and contraction of iron. These extremes have a similar effect on concrete, especially during the process of setting and hardening. Equality of temperature during setting is desirable. Cold and humid atmosphere retard setting; hot humidity accelerates it. Concrete laid in cold weather stands better than that laid during hot. Concrete laid in mild damp weather is better than in either extreme. During high temperatures, the surface, when sufficiently hard, should be covered with damp deal saw-dust, old sacks, mats, or sail-cloth, and saturated at intervals with water. If the sun's rays are hot, the surface of the work while in progress should be protected by extending tarpaulin or sail-cloths above the parts being laid. Concrete surfaces are further hardened by flooding with water, or where this is not practical, covering with wet saw-dust or sand as soon as set. Care must be taken that the saw-dust is clean and of a light color, as otherwise it will stain the work.

Non-Slippery Pavements.—Concrete pavements for special purposes are rendered non-slippery by mixing 1/8 inch lead cubes with the topping stuff. Lead cubes about 1/2 inch square laid by hand from 1 inch to 4 inches apart in the moist concrete surface, have been used for rendering concrete surfaces non-slippery. Iron and brass filings are also used for the same purpose, and also for increasing the wear-resisting of concrete surface. Roughened, indented, grooved, and matted surfaces are also used to obtain a better foot-hold on concrete surfaces.

Grooved and Roughened Surfaces.—Stables, yards, &c., are grooved and channeled on the surfaces to prevent animals from slipping, and also to carry off urine or other liquids to the traps or gulleys. Indented surfaces are useful on steep gradient to give a better foothold. Grooves are made with a special wood or iron tool, which is beaten into the surface as soon as the concrete is floated. The grooves for stables are generally made about 5 inches from centre to centre, and the depth about 3/4 inch. A line is first made at the one end of the work, and the groover is then laid on this line, and beaten down with a hammer to the desired depth. Before it is taken off, a parallel rule is laid on the surface and against the groover, which is then taken up and laid close to the other side of the parallel rule, and beaten in as before, and so on until the whole surface is done. The width of the parallel rule is equal to the desired width between the grooves, less the width of the groover. Grooves, however long, can be made by moving the tool along, and against a long parallel rule. After stretch of grooves have been sunk, the surface is trowelled, and the indentations made true. It may be necessary to apply the groover again, and beat or work it forward and backward and further regulate their depth and straightness. They are then made smooth with a gauging trowel and finished with a damp brush, the sides of the grooves being left smooth to give a free passage for liquids.

Grooves on a surface having a fall should radiate toward the deepest point. A level surface may be made to carry off the water by the indentation being formed wider and deeper towards the outlet. Street and other pavements are sometimes indented with metal rollers to give a better foot-hold. Platforms and other surfaces are sometimes made rough or indented by beating the moist concrete, with a "stamping-float." The sole has a series of squares projecting about 3/8 inch, each square about 1 inch, and a half inch apart. Concrete surfaces are also roughened or matted by dabbing the surface as soon as trowelled with a coarse stiff whale-bone brush. Illustration No. 2 shows three designs of grooved surfaces for carriage drives, conservatories, &c. A plain border, or one with a single width of the main design, is generally formed on the sides and ends of the floor. A rough matted surface may also be obtained by pressing or beating a wet coarse sack or matting over the moist concrete.

Stamped Concrete.—Various materials and methods are used for stamping or indenting concrete surfaces to obtain a better foot-hold, or to form any desired pattern. Iron stamps are generally used, but owing to their weight and rigid nature, are unsuitable for large sec-

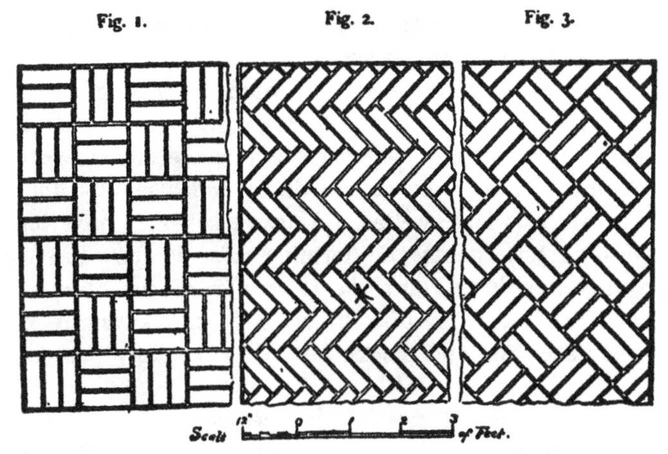

THREE EXAMPLES OF GROOVED SURFACES.

NO. 2.

tions. Plaster stamps are sometimes used for temporary purposes, or for small sections and quantities. Stamps for large concrete surfaces should be composed of a material that is easily made to the desired form durable and slightly flexible.

Expansion Joints.—Compressive or flexible joints are used to allow for any expansion or contraction that may take place in a large area of concrete exposed to atmospheric changes. There are various methods in use for the purpose. The first is to set out the area in small sections, and to lay them in alternate or isolated bays, thus giving time for their expansion before the intermediate bays are laid. This method, by dividing the area into small sections, is the best for preventing cracks, because small sections are stronger than large ones; and in the event of any subsidence in the foundation, the surface fissures are limited to the immediate joints of the section. Contraction and expansion is also less in small bodies than in larger ones.

Another method of forming joints is by cutting with a wide chisel or a cutting tool before the rough concrete is set, a corresponding joint being cut in the fine concrete topping. False joints are made by indenting the topping after it is trowelled. A metal roller is used for finishing true joints and forming false joints. Frame strong enough to resist the expansion of the concrete would not only increase the density and strength of concrete paving and blocks, but also effectually prevent its cracking.

Another method for forming sections in large surfaces of pavement of floors to prevent cracks is effected thus:—first set out the size of proposed sections on the rough or first coat, then with a straight-edge, a wide chisel, or a cutting tool and a hammer, cut through the rough coat, so as to divide it into sections as set out. This done, insert wood strips into the cutting, keeping their top edges about 1/8 inch below the screeds or rules which represent the finished surface. The strips are made from 3/4 to 1 3/4 inches wide, 3-16 inch thick, and in suitable lengths. The width is regulated according to the thickness of the paving. For instance, for two inch paving the widths should be 1 3/4 inches. This allows about $7/8$ inches in the rough coat (with $1/8$ inch play from the bottom), and about $7/8$ inch in the topping, and $1/8$ inch for the upper thickness of the topping to cover the top edges of the strips. After the strips are inserted the rough coat is beaten up or made good to the sides of the strips, and then the topping is laid and trowelled in the usual way. The surface joints are then made direct-

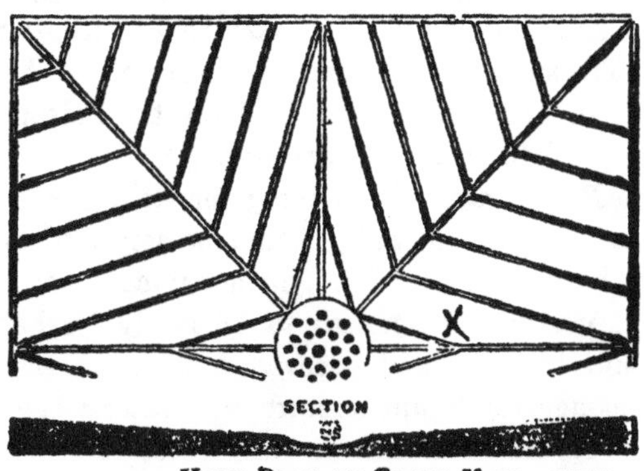

HALF PLAN OF COACH YARD, WITH SECTION THROUGH CENTRE.

NO. 3.

ly over the strips, with the aid of a straight edge, so as to form a clean and sharp joint. As already mentioned, these strips allow for any subsequent contraction or expansion, thus avoiding zigzag cracks; and in the event of repairs to underneath pipes, each section can be cut out and relaid separately without injury to the adjoining sections. This process of inserting strips in the rough coat, cutting nearly through the topping, gives the same results as if the strips were laid flush with the surface of the topping, with the advantages that the surface can be more readily trowelled, and is more pleasing to the eye, because the strips are not seen. A cutting tool is a blade of steel about 5 or 6 inches long and 4 inches wide, with a wood handle at one end. The section of the blade is well tapered, so as to obtain a sharp cutting edge, and form a wide top edge to offer a broad surface for the hammer while being beaten.

Washing Yards.—Eureka concrete being of a hard nature, and having a close and smooth surface, is well adapted as a flooring for all washing or cleaning purposes. The surface being smooth, it can in turn be readily cleaned. Illustration No. 3 shows the half plan of washing yard for washing carriages, &c.

Stable Pavements.—The paving for stables, and other places for keeping animals, should be jointless, non-absorbent, hard, and durable. Such paving must not be slippery, yet smooth enough to be easily washed, the whole laid to falls, and grooved to give an easy and ready passage for liquid manure and water when being washed. No material can so fully meet these requirements as a well-made and well-laid concrete. Granite sets are hard, but slippery. Bricks are too absorbent; the urine percolates between the joints and generates ammonia and other effluvia which are detrimental to the health of the animals. (See Nos. 4 and 5.)

Stables are generally laid with a fall toward the main channel. The amount of fall varies according to ideas of the horse owners. The fall adopted by the War office is 1 in 80 from the top of the manger to the main channel, and 1 to 36 from each side of the stall to the centre groove. The width of the main channels is usually set out with screed rules, which also act as screeds to work from. Channels are generally formed after the other surface is finished. Sometimes templates are fixed on the bed of the channels, and the space filled in and ruled off with a straight-edge while the whole surface is being formed. The thickness of stable paving varies from 2 to 3½ inches, according to the class of horse. The thickness of the stalls is often decreased toward the manger.

The most useful length is 2 feet 6 inches. They can be cut with a chisel as easy as cutting stone. Special slabs can be made for circular work, also with rebated sinking for metal plates, to cover coal-holes, drains, gas and water taps, &c. Concrete paving slabs are laid in precisely the same way as natural stone.

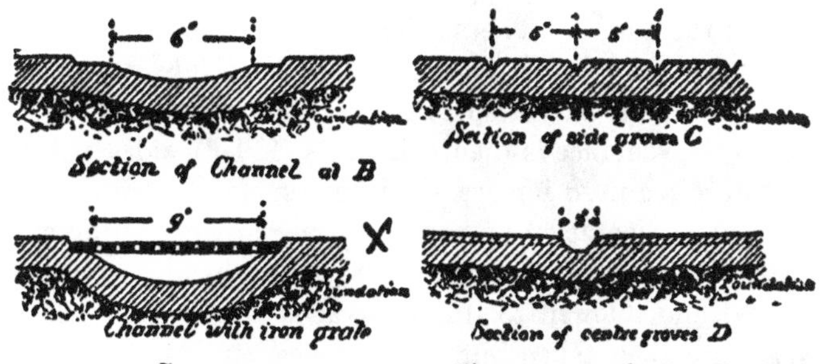

-SECTIONS OF THE VARIOUS PARTS OF THE STABLE FLOORS SHOWN ON ILLUSTRATION

NO. 4. NO. 5.

Concrete Slab Moulds.—Slab moulds are made with 1½ inch boards ledged together. On this ground, wood sides and ends (each being 2½ inches by 2 inches, or 3 inches by 3 inches, according to the desired thickness of slab) are fixed. One side and end is held in position with thumb screws, which fit into iron sockets, so that they can be unscrewed to relieve the slab when set. The bottom and the sides and ends are lined with strong iron or zinc plates.

Slab Making.—Slabs are mostly made by machinery. The materials are 1 part of Portland cement mixed dry with 2½ parts of crushed granite and slag in equal proportions that have been washed and passed through a ¼ inch sieve. They are thoroughly incorporated together in a horizontal cylinder worked by machinery, a minimum of water being added, and the mixing continued until the mass is well gauged. The mould, which has been previously oiled, is placed on a shaking machine known as a "trembler" or "dither," which gives a rapid vertical jolting motion to the mould and its contents. A small portion of "slip," that is, neat cement, is laid round the angles. The machine is then started, and the concrete laid on the mould by small shovelfuls at a time, a man with a trowel spreading it over the mould until full. The surface is then ruled off. If both sides of the slabs are required for use, the upper surface is trowelled. The whole operation of mixing, filling in, and ruling off takes about seven minutes. The filled moulds are removed and allowed to stand for about three days. The slabs are then taken out, and stacked on edge and air-dried for about five days. They are then immersed in a silicate bath for about seven days, and are afterwards taken out and stacked in the open air until it is required for use. They should not be used until three months old. Paving slabs are also made by hand, by ramming and beating the moist concrete into the mould with an iron hand-float. Powerful ramming, trituration, or violent agitation of the gauged material in the mould, tend to consolidate concrete, and it is possible to further increase homogeneity by the use of hydraulic pressure.

Induration Concrete Slabs.—The surface of concrete slabs or other work exposed to friction or wear may be hardened by soaking in a silicate solution. Silicate of soda has a great affinity for the materials of which concrete is composed, and by induration causes the surface to become hard, dense, and non-porous.

The silicate of soda and potash is known as soluble glass or dissolved flint. The soluble silicate is a clear viscous substance made from pure flint and caustic soda, which is digested by heat under pressure indigester. Its strength is technically known as 140 degrees, which shows 1,700 on a hygrometer. When used as a bath for concrete, it is diluted with water, the proportion varying from 6 to 10 parts of water to one of silicate. Concrete pavements, laid in situ, may also be hardened by washing with silicate solution. They should not be silicated until two days after being laid, to allow the moisture to evaporate and the silicate to penetrate.

Mosaic.—The art of making mosaic is at the present time scarcely within the province of plasterers, but in former times many kinds were made in situ or in slabs by plasterers. The subdivision of labor has to a great extent caused mosaic-making to be confined to specialists. Concrete is still made by plasterers. A brief description of this and other kinds may prove useful as well as interesting, especially to plasterers who are in the habit of fixing tiles and working in concrete. Mosaic is the art of producing geometrical, floral, or figured designs, by the joining together of hard stones, marbles, earthenware, glass, or artificial stone, either naturally or artificially colored. The term "mosaic" embraces a wide range of artistic processes and materials for the decoration of floors, walls, ceilings. The Egyptians were experts in mosaic. The Cairo worker as a rule had no drawings made beforehand, but the mosaic design was constructed by the artist as he arranged the pieces on the ground. The mosaic pavements of Cairo are of a slightly different character from those used for wall decoration, and are generally composed entirely of marble tesserae (and sometimes red earthenware) of larger size than the delicate pieces included in wall mosaics. They are arranged to form geometrical patterns within a space of about two feet square. Each square slab is made separately, and the pieces are set, not in plaster, but in a composition of lime and clay impervious to water. The clay must be unburnt, just as it comes from the pit. Saracenic mosaic in Egypt is a combination of the tesselated method with a large proportion of sectile mosaic. The Romans also were great workers in mosaic. The mosaics of Byzantium and Ravenna consisted of cubes of opaque and colored glass.

The general method used here for pavement mosaic is as follows: The repeated design is traced on stout paper and small pieces of marble, or more often tile, are gummed on the paper, following the design of form and color, one piece at a time (with the smooth face downwards) being laid until the design is completed. The mosaic slabs, which are thus temporarily kept in position, are sent to the building and laid where intended. A rough concrete foundation, which has previously been made level, is then floated with Portland or Keen's cement, and the slabs with paper are then damped and drawn off, and any openings or defects filled up with small pieces of the same form and color as the design. The slabs are made in various sizes according to the design. For instance, a border 12 inches wide may be made from 3 to 6 inches long. When laying the slabs, it is best to begin at the centre and work outwards, and any excess or deficiency taken off or made up in the plain part of the border at the walls. The tiles are made at pottery works in the required sizes and colors. The thickness is generally about 1/4 inch and the average surface size about 1/2 inch. Females are often employed fixing the pieces on the paper. The designs of coats of arms, monograms, dates, figures, flowers, and foliage are effectively produced by this simple and cheap process.

Concrete Mosaic.—All mosaics are more or less of a concretive nature, and the trade term of "concrete mosaic" is due to the fact that the matrix used is Portland or other cement gauged with the marble aggregate, and laid in most cases in a similar manner as ordinary concrete. Concrete mosaic is extensively used for paving halls, corridors, conservatories, terraces, &c. It is also used for constructing steps, landings, baths, pedestals, &c. Slabs and tiles made of this class of mosaic for paving purposes are slowly but surely proving a formidable rival to Italian mosaic encaustic tiles. It can be made in larger sections, thus facilitating rapidity of laying. It is more accurate in form, durable, non-slippery, and cheaper. The last reason alone is a favorable item in this keen age of competition. Where marble has been scarce, broken tiles, pottery, colored glass, flints, white spar, &c., have been used as aggregate. If the marble chips are obtainable as a waste, and near the place of manufacture, the primary cost is small. If the moulds are of metal, and made in sections so as to form a series of moulds in one case, and the casts are pressed by means of a hydraulic power, the cost of production is reduced to a minimum. If the casts are polished in large numbers by machinery on a revolving table, the total cost is further reduced. For local purposes they can be made by hand at a medium cost. Slabs are made in almost any size, but generally from 4 to 6 feet superficial. The thickness varies from 1 to 1½ inches. Tiles are usually made about 10 inches square and 1 inch thick. The tiles are generally made with a face of cement and white marble, or white and black marble chippings. They are backed up with a cheaper aggregate. Various tints of the face matrix are obtained by mixing the cement with metallic ovides. The tiles are made in wood or metal moulds, with metal strips to form the divisions of form and color in the design. If the design is fret pattern, the gauged material is put in between the strips that form the band of the fret. When the stuff is nearly set, the strips are taken out, and the other part filled in with another color. Sometimes the band or running designs are cast in a separate mould, and when set placed in position in a larger mould, and the ground filled in, covering and binding the whole in one tile. Another plan is to lay a thin coat of cement on the face of the mould, forming the design with small marble chips by hand, by pressing the marble into the cement as desired. When it is firm, it is backed up with the ordinary stuff, and when set, they are ground and polished.

Concrete Mosaic Laid "in Situ."—Pavements for halls, passages, shops, landings, &c., are also done in situ. A rough concrete foundation is first laid fair to falls and levels within ½ inch of the finished surface line. This ½ inch space is to receive the plastic marble mosaic. The main or centre part is generally done first and the border last. This allows a walking space or bearing for boards, laid from side to side to work on when laying the centre. A plank sufficiently strong to keep one or two crossboards from touching the work is laid along each side. On the side planks the crossboards are laid, and moved about when required. The width of the border is marked on the floor, and wood screed rules laid level to the marks to form a fair joint line for the border, also as a screed when floating the centre part. The screed rules are generally fixed with a gauge plaster, which is quicker than fixing on gauged cement. After the centre is laid, the plaster should be carefully swept off, and the concrete well wetted before the border is laid. The marble and cement is gauged in the proportion of 2 of marble to 1 of cement, and laid flush with screeds, laying and beating it in position with a long wood hand-float. The surface is ruled in from screed to screed with a straight-edge. The surface is then ironed with a laying trowel until it is smooth and fair. If the marble does not show, or is not regular, or is insufficient, the bare parts are filled in with marble by hand. When marble is scarce, the ½ inch of the top surface is laid in two coats, the first being composed of cement and a cheaper aggregate, such as broken stone, tiles, &c., and gauged in the same proportion as the upper or marble coat. It is laid about ¼ inch thick, and when it is firm, but not set, the marble coat is laid as before directed. The first coat saves the marble, and being firm, tends to keep the marble in the upper coat from sinking. The top coat is sometimes sprinkled over with fine marble chips by hand or through a fine sieve, then pressed into the surface and ironed with a laying trowel. Before ironing the surface, care should be taken that the chips are equally distributed, also that their flat surfaces are uppermost, and that the matrix and chips are perfectly solid and free from ridges and holes. After the centre is laid and the screeds removed, the border is laid in a similar way. If there are two or more colors or forms in the border, the divisions are formed with narrow screed rules, and arranged so that as many as practicable can be laid at the same time. This allows the various parts to set at one time, and saves waiting for each separate part to set. The screed rules for circular work or angles are formed with strong gauged plaster and then oiled.

The marble chips are either broken by hand or in a stone-breaking machine. The chips vary in size from 1-10 to ¼ inch. The best colors for borders are a black matrix with white marble or spar chips, or a white matrix with black marble chips. The white matrix is obtained by mixing the marble dust (produced when breaking the marble into chips) with a light colored Portland cement. The centres can be made in various tints, but the most general is a warm red, which is obtained by mixing the cement with red oxide. Cement colored with red oxide should be laid first, as it is liable to stain other parts of a lighter color. When the centre and border are laid, the floor is left until the whole is perfectly set and hard, and it is then fit to polish. This is done by means of a stone polisher, water and marble dust, or fine slag powder. The stone polisher is a piece of hard stone from 8 to 12 inches square, and about 3 inches thick, into which an iron ring is inserted and secured with lead. A wooden handle from 4 to 6 feet long, with an iron hook at one end, is inserted into the ring, so that the handle is firm on the stone, yet has sufficient play to be moved freely backwards and forwards. The polishing should not be attempted until the stuff is thoroughly set, because the polishing will destroy the face of the cement, and cause a vast amount of extra labor in grinding the surface down until free from holes. Small parts of the gauged stuff should be set aside as tests for determining when the stuff is set. Concrete mosaic, where economy is desirable, will make a strong, durable, and waterproof floor, and an excellent substitute for higher class mosaics.

A Bulletin (No. 235), prepared by P. S. Wormley for the U. S. government on cement, mortar, and concrete, from which I quote at length, contains some excellent information and instructions on the preparation and the use of the above materials. This bulletin is intended for free distribution and may be obtained by making application to the U. S. Department of Agriculture, Washington, D. C.

Storing Cement.—In storing cement care must be exercised to insure its being kept dry. When no house or shed is available for the purpose, a rough platform may be erected clear of the ground, on which the cement may be placed and so covered as to exclude water. When properly protected, it often improves with age. Cement is shipped in barrels or bags, the size and weight of which usually are given.

Cement Mortar.—Cement mortar is an intimate mixture of cement and sand mixed with sufficient water to produce a plastic mass. The amount of water will vary according to the proportion and condition of the sand, and had best be determined independently in each case. Sand is used both for the sake of economy and to avoid cracks due to shrinkage of cement in setting. Where great strength is required, there should be at least sufficient cement to fill the voids or air spaces in the sand, and a slight excess is preferable in order to compensate for any uneven distribution in mixing. Common proportions for Portland cement mortar are 3 parts sand to 1 of cement, and for natural cement mortar, 2 parts sand to 1 of cement. Unless otherwise stated, materials for mortar or concrete are considered to be proportioned by volume, the cement being slightly shaken in the measure used.

A "lean" mortar is one having only a small proportion of cement, while a "rich" mixture is one with a large proportion of cement. "Neat" cement is pure cement, or that with no admixture of sand. The term "aggregate" is used to designate the coarse materials entering into concrete—usually gravel or crushed rock. The proportion in which the three elements enter into the mixture is usually expressed by three figures separated by dashes—as, for instance, 1-2-5, meaning 1 part cement, 2 parts sand, and 5 parts aggregate. In the great majority of cases cement mortar is subjected only to compression, and for this reason it would seem natural that, in testing it, to determine its compressive strength. The tensile strength of cement mortar, however, is usually determined, and from this its resistance to compression may be assumed to be from 8 to 12 times greater. A direct determination of the compressive strength is a less simple operation, for which reason the tensile test is in most cases accepted as indicating the strength of the cement.

Mixing.—In mixing cement mortar it is best to use a platform of convenient size or a shallow box. First, deposit the requisite amount of sand in a uniform layer, and on top of this spread the cement. These should be mixed dry with shovels or hoes, until the whole mass exhibits a uniform color. Next, form a crater of the dry mixture, and into this pour nearly the entire quantity of water required for the batch. Work the dry material from the outside toward the centre, until all the water is taken up, then turn rapidly with shovels, adding water at the same time by sprinkling until the desired consistency is attained. It is frequently specified that the mortar shall be turned a certain number of times, but a better practice for securing a uniform mixture is to watch the operation and judge by the eye when the mixing has been carried far enough. In brick masonry the mistake is frequently made of mixing the mortar very wet and relying upon the bricks to absorb the excess of water. It is better, however, to wet the brick thoroughly and use a stiff mortar.

Grout.—The term "grout" is applied to mortar mixed with an excess of water, which gives about the consistency of cream. This material is often used to fill the voids in stone-masonry, and in brick work the inner portions of walls are frequently laid dry and grouted. The practice in either case is to be condemned, except where the conditions are unusual, as cement used in this way will never develop its full strength.

Lime and Cement Mortar.—L. C. Sabin finds that in Portland cement mortar containing three parts sand to 1 of cement, 10 per cent. of the cement may be replaced by lime in the form of paste without diminishing the strength of the mortar, and at the same time rendering it more plastic. In the case of natural cement mortar, lime may be added to the extent of 20 to 25 per cent. of the cement with good results. The increased plasticity due to the addition of lime much facilitates the operation of laying bricks, and has caused lime and cement mortar to be largely used.

Cement Mortar for Plastering.—In plastering with cement, a few precautions must be observed to insure good and permanent results. The surface to receive the plaster should be rough, perfectly clean, and well saturated with water. A mortar very rich in cement is rather a drawback than otherwise on account of shrinkage cracks, which frequently appear. The mortar, consisting of two or three parts sand to one of cement, should be mixed with as little water as possible and well worked to produce plasticity. It is essential that the plaster be kept moist until it has thoroughly hardened.

Materials for Making Concrete Sand.—In securing sand for mixing mortar or concrete, if it is possible to select from several varieties, that sand should be chosen which is composed of sharp, angular grains, varying in size from coarse to fine. Such sand is, however, not always obtainable, nor is it essential for good work. Any coarse-grained sand which is fairly clean will answer the purpose. If gravel, sticks, or leaves be present they should be removed by screening. The voids in sand vary from 30 to 40 per cent., according to the variation in size of grains. A sand with different-sized grains is to be preferred, because less cement is required to fill the voids. By mixing coarse and fine sand it is possible to reduce the voids considerably.

It is customary to use the terms "river sand," "sea sand," or "pit sand," according to the source of the supply. River sand as a rule has rounded grains, but unless it contains an excess of clay or other impurities, it is suitable for general purposes. When river sand is of a light color and fine-grained it answers well for plastering.

Sea sand may contain the salts found in the ocean. The tendency of these salts to attract moisture makes it advisable to wash sea sand before using it for plastering or other work which is to be kept perfectly dry.

Pit sand for the most part will be found to have sharp, angular grains, which make it excellent for mortar or concrete work. Where clay appears in pockets it is necessary either to remove it, or else see that it is thoroughly mixed with the sand. The presence of clay in excess frequently makes it necessary to wash pit sand before it is suitable for use.

The results of tests made in this laboratory would indicate that the presence of clay, even in considerable amounts, is a decided benefit to "lean" mortars, whereas it does not appreciably affect the strength of a rich mixture.

Gravel.—It is important that gravel for use in concrete should be clean, in order that the cement may properly adhere to it, and form a strong and compact mass. As with sand, it is well to have the pieces vary in size, thereby reducing the voids to be filled with mortar. The voids in general range from 35 to 40 per cent.

Crushed Stone.—The best stone for concrete work consists of angular pieces, varying in size and having a clean, rough surface. Some form of strong and durable rock is to be preferred, such as limestone, trap, or granite. The total output of the crusher should be used below a maximum size, depending upon the nature of the work in hand. All material under 1/8 inch will act as so much sand and should be considered as such in proportioning the mixture. Precautions must be taken to insure a uniform distribution of the smaller pieces of stone, otherwise the concrete will have an excess of fine material in some parts and a deficiency in others.

Less than 8 per cent. of clay will probably not seriously impair the strength of the concrete, provided the stones are not coated with it, and may even prove a benefit in the case of lean mixtures. The voids in crushed stone depend upon the shape and variation in size of pieces, rarely falling below 40 per cent., unless much fine material is present, and in some cases reaching 50 per cent. A mixture of stone and gravel in equal parts makes an excellent aggregate for concrete.

Stone Versus Gravel.—It would appear from tests that crushed stone makes a somewhat stronger concrete than gravel, but the latter is very extensively used with uniformly good results. This superiority of stone over gravel for concrete work is attributed to the fact that the angular pieces of stone interlock more thoroughly than do the rounded pebbles, and offer a rougher surface to the cement. A point in favor of gravel concrete is that it requires less tamping to produce a compact mass than in the case of crushed stone. Then, too, the proportion of voids in stone being usually greater than in gravel, means a slight increase in the cost of concrete.

Cinders.—Cinders concrete is frequently used in connection with expanded metal and other forms of reinforcement for floor construction, and for this purpose it is well adapted on account of its light weight. Its porosity makes it a poor conductor of heat and permits the driving of nails. Only hard and thoroughly burned cinders should be used, and the concrete must be mixed quite soft so as to require but little tamping and to avoid crushing the cinders. Cinder concrete is much weaker, both in tension and compression, than stone or gravel concrete, and for this reason admits only of light reinforcement.

Concrete.—General Discussion: Cement concrete is the product resulting from an intimate mixture of cement mortar with an aggregate of crushed stone, gravel, or similar material. The aggregate is crushed or screened to the proper size as determined from the character of the work. In foundation work, stone or gravel 3 inches in size may be used to advantage, whereas in the case of moulded articles of small sectional area, such as fence posts, hollow building blocks, &c., it is best to use only such material as will pass a ½ inch screen. An ideal concrete, from the standpoint of economy, would be that in which all voids in the aggregate were completely filled with sand, and all the voids in the sand completely filled with cement, without any excess. Under these conditions there would be a thoroughly compact mass and no waste of materials.

It is a simple matter to determine the voids in sand and also in the aggregate, but in mixing concrete the proportions vary a great deal, depending in each case upon the nature of the work and the strength desired. For example, in the construction of beams and floor panels, where maximum strength with minimum weight is desired, a rich concrete should be used, whereas in massive foundation work, in which bulk or weight is the controlling factor, economy would point to a lean mixture. When good stone or gravel is used, the strength of the concrete depends upon the strength of the mortar employed in the mixing and the proportion of mortar to aggregate. For a given mortar the concrete will be strongest when only enough mortar is used to fill the voids in the aggregate, less strength being obtained by using either greater or less proportion. In practice it is usual to add a slight excess of mortar over that required to fill the voids in the aggregate.

It is more accurate to measure cement by weight unless the unit employed be the barrel or sack, because when taken from the original package and measured in bulk there is a chance of error due to the amount of shaking the cement receives. As it is less convenient, however, to weigh the cement, it is more usual to measure it by volume, but for the reasons stated this should be done with care.

Proportioning Materials.—For an accurate determination of the best and most economical proportions where maximum strength is required, it is well to proceed in the following way: First, proportion the cement and sand so that the cement paste will be 100 per cent. in excess of the voids in sand; next, determine the voids in the aggregate and allow sufficient mortar to fill all voids, with an excess of 10 per cent.

To determine roughly the voids in gravel or crushed stone prepare a water-tight box of convenient size and fill with the material to be tested, shake well and smooth off even with the top. Into this pour water until it rises flush with the surface. The volume of water added, divided by the volume of the box, measured in the same units, represents the proportion of voids. The proportion of voids in sand may be more accurately determined by subtracting the weight of a cubic foot of packed sand from 165, the weight of a cubic foot of quartz, and dividing the difference by 165 degrees.

The following will serve as an example of proportion ing materials: Assume voids in packed sand to measure 38 per cent., and voids in packed stone to measure 48 per cent. Cement paste required per cubic foot of sand,

0.38 and 1-10 equals 0.42 cubic foot, approximately. By trial, 1 cubic foot of loose cement, lightly shaken, makes 0.85 cubic foot of cement paste, and requires $\frac{0.85}{0.42}$ or 2 cubic feet of sand, approximately, producing an amount of mortar equal to 0.85 and 2 (1-0.38) equals 2.09 cubic feet. Mortar required per cubic foot of stone equals 0.48, and 1-10x0.48 equals 0.528 cubic foot. Therefore 2.09 cubic feet mortar will require $\frac{2.09}{5.28}$ equals 4 cubic feet of stone, approximately. The proportions are therefore 1 part cement, 2 parts sand, 4 parts stone. Although such a determination is usually considered unnecessary in practical work, it may be of sufficient interest to justify giving it.

For general use the following mixtures are recommended: 1 cement, 2 sand, 4 aggregate, for very strong and impervious; 1 cement, 2½ sand, 5 aggregate, for ordinary work requiring moderate strength; 1 cement, 3 sand, 6 aggregate, for work where strength is of minor importance.

Aggregate Containing Fine Material.—In the case of gravel containing sand, or crushed stone from which the small articles have not been removed by screening, the amount of such fine sand or fine stone should be determined and due allowance made for it in proportioning the mortar.

When mixing an aggregate containing small particles with mortar, and in reality we have a mortar containing a larger proportion of sand than was present before the aggregate was incorporated. It is evident, then, that in such cases the quality of richness of the mortar should depend upon the proportion of fine material in the aggregate.

For example, suppose that 1 cubic foot of gravel contains 0.1 cubic foot of sand, and that the voids in gravel with sand screened out measure 40 per cent. For general purposes this would suggest a 1-2-5 mixture, but since each cubic foot contains 0.1 cubic foot sand, 5 cubic feet gravel will contain 0.5 cubic foot sand, and the proportions should be changed to 1 part cement, 1½ parts sand, 5 parts gravel.

Mechanical Mixers.—It has been demonstrated that concrete can be mixed by machinery as well, if not better, than by hand. Moreover, if large quantities of concrete are required, a mechanical mixer introduces marked economy in the cost of construction. None of the various forms of mechanical mixers will be described here, since concrete in small quantities, as would be used on the farm, is more economically mixed by hand.

Mixing by Hand.—In mixing by hand a platform is constructed as near the work as is practicable, the sand and aggregate being dumped in piles at the side. If the work is to be continuous, this platform should be of sufficient size to accommodate two batches, so that one batch can be mixed as the other is being deposited. The cement must be kept under cover and well protected from moisture. A convenient way of measuring the materials is by means of a bottomless box or frame made to hold the exact quantities needed for a batch.

A very common and satisfactory method of mixing concrete is as follows: First measure the sand and cement required for a batch and mix these into mortar as described on page 5. Spread out this mortar in a thin layer and on top of it spread the aggregate, which has been previously measured and well wetted. The mixing is done by turning with shovels three or more times, as may be found necessary to produce a thoroughly uniform mixture, water being added if necessary to give the proper consistency. The mixers, two or four in number, according to the size of the batch, face each other and shovel to right and left, forming two piles, after which the material is turned back into a pile at the centre. By giving the shovel a slight twist, the material is scattered in leaving it and the efficiency of the mixing is much increased.

Consistency of Concrete.—A dry mixture, from which water can be brought to the surface only by vigorous tamping, is probably the strongest, but for the sake of economy, and to insure a dense concrete well filling the moulds a moderately soft mixture is recommended for ordinary purposes. Where the pieces to be moulded are thin, and where small reinforcing metal rods are placed close together or near the surface, a rather wet mixture may be necessary to insure the moulds being well filled.

Use of Quick-Setting Cement.—In the manufacture of such articles as pipe, fence posts, and hollow blocks, a rather large proportion of quick-setting cement is sometimes used, the object being to reduce the weight and consequent freight charges by means of a strong mixture, as well as to make the concrete impervious to water. The use of a quick-setting cement permits the moulds to be removed sooner than would be possible with a slow-setting cement, thus reducing the number of moulds necessary for a given output. Quick-setting cements are not recommended for such purposes, however, as they are usually inferior to those which set slowly.

Coloring Cement Work.—In coloring cement work the best results are obtained by the use of mineral pigment. The coloring matter, in proportions depending upon the desired shade, should be thoroughly mixed with the dry cement before making the mortar. By preparing small specimens of the mortar and noting the color after drying, the proper proportions may be determined.

For gray or black, use lampblack.

For yellow or buff, use yellow ochre.

For brown, use umber.

For red, use venetian red.

For blue, use ultramarine.

Depositing Concrete.—Concrete should be deposited in layers of from 4 to 8 inches and thoroughly tamped before it begins to harden. The tamping required will depend upon the consistency of the mixture. If mixed very dry it must be vigorously rammed to produce a dense mass, but as the proportion of water increases less tamping will be found necessary. Concrete should not be dumped in place from a height of more than 4 feet, unless it is again mixed at the bottom. A wooden incline may be used for greater heights. Rammers for ordinary concrete work should weigh from 20 to 30 pounds and have a face not exceeding 6 inches square. A smaller face than this is often desirable, but a larger one will be less effective in consolidating the mass. In cramped situations special forms must be employed to suit the particular conditions. When a thickness of more than one layer is required, as in foundation work, two or more layers may be worked at the same time, each layer slightly in advance of the one next above it and all being allowed to set together. At the end of a day there is usually left a layer partially completed which must be finished the next day. This layer should not be beveled off, but the last batch of concrete should be tamped behind a vertical board forming a step.

To avoid introducing a plane of weakness where fresh concrete is deposited upon that which has already set, certain precautions have to be observed. The surface of the old work should be clean and wet before fresh material is put on, a thin coat of neat cement grout being sometimes employed to insure a good bond. The surface of the concrete to receive an additional layer must not be finished off smoothly, but should offer a rough surface to bond with the next layer. This may be done by roughing the surface while soft with pick and shovel, or the concrete may be so rammed as to present a rough and uneven surface. Wooden blocks or scantling are sometimes embedded several inches in the work and removed before the concrete hardens, thus forming holes or grooves to be filled by the next layer.

Retempering.—As stated before, it is important that concrete be tamped in place before it begins to harden, and for this reason it is proper to mix only so much at a time as is required for immediate use. The retempering of concrete which has begun to set is a point over which there is much controversy. From tests made in this laboratory it would appear that such concrete suffers but little loss of strength if thoroughly mixed with sufficient water to restore normal consistence.

The time required for concrete to set depends upon the character of the cement, upon the amount and temperature of the water used in mixing, and upon the temperature of the air. Concrete mixed dry sets more quickly than if mixed wet, and the time required for setting decreases as the temperature of the water rises. Warm air also hastens the setting.

Concrete Exposed to Sea-Water.—Portland cement concrete is well adapted for work exposed to sea-water, but when used for this purpose it should be mixed with fresh water. The concrete must be practically impervious, at least on the surfaces, and to accomplish this purpose the materials should be carefully proportioned and thoroughly mixed. It is also of great importance that the concrete be well compacted by tamping, particularly on exposed surfaces.

Concrete Work in Freezing Weather.—Although it is advisable under ordinary conditions to discontinue cement work in freezing weather, Portland cement may be used without serious difficulty by taking a few simple precautions. As little water as possible should be used in mixing, to hasten the setting of the concrete. To prevent freezing, hot water is frequently used in mixing mortar or concrete, and with the same object in view salt is added in amounts depending upon the degree of cold. A common practice is to add 1 pound of salt to 18 gallons of water, with the addition of 1 oz. of salt for each degree below 32° F. Either of the above methods will give good results, but it should be remembered that the addition of salt often produces efflorescence. It seems to be a fairly well-established fact that concrete deposited in freezing weather will ultimately develop full strength, showing no injury due to the low temperature.

Rubble Concrete.—In massive concrete work considerable economy may often be introduced by the use of large stones in the body of the work, but only in heavy foundations, retaining walls, and similar structures should this form of construction be permitted. In placing these large stones in the work the greatest care must be exercised to insure each being well bedded, and the concrete must be thoroughly tamped around them. Each stone should be at least 4 inches from its neighbor and an equal distance from the face of the work.

To Face Concrete.—A coating of mortar one-half inch in thickness is frequently placed next the form to prevent the stone or gravel from showing and to give a smooth and impervious surface. If in preparing this mortar finely crushed stone is used instead of sand, the

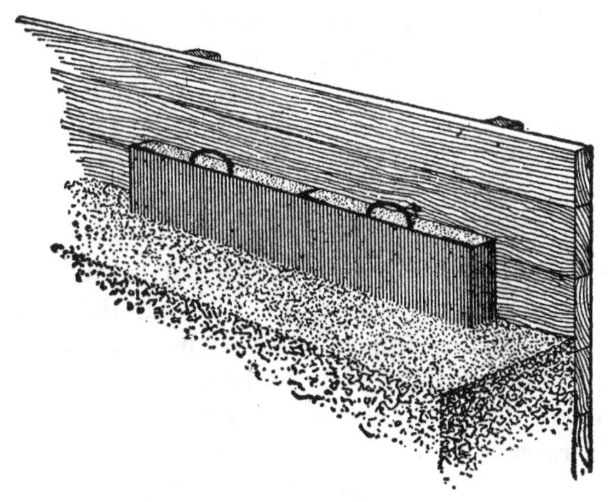

Sheet-metal plate used in facing concrete.

NO. 6.

work will more nearly resemble natural stone. A common method employed in facing concrete is to provide a piece of thin sheet metal of convenient length and about 8 to 10 inches wide. To this pieces of angle iron are riveted, so that when placed next to the mould a narrow space is formed in which the cement mortar is placed after the concrete has been deposited behind it. (No. 6.) The metal plate is then withdrawn and the concrete well tamped. The concrete and facing mortar must be put in at the same time so that they will set together. If the concrete is fairly rich, a smooth surface can usually be produced without a facing of mortar by working a spade up and down between the concrete and inner face of the mould, thus forcing the larger pieces of the aggregate back from the surface.

Wood for Forms.—Lumber used in making forms for concrete should be dressed on one side and both edges. The expansion and distortion of the wood due to the absorption of water from the concrete frequently make it difficult to produce an even surface on the work, and unless the forms are accurately fitted together more or less water will find its way out through the cracks, carrying some of the cement with it. A method sometimes adopted to minimize the effect of expansion is to bevel one edge of each board, allowing this edge to crush against the square edge of the adjacent board when expansion takes place. In the case of a wooden core or inside mold, expansion must always be taken into consideration, for if neglected it may cause cracks or complete rupture of the concrete. Sharp edges in concrete are easily chipped and should be avoided by placing triangular strips to the corners of moulds. To prevent cement from sticking to the forms they may be given a coating of soft soap or be lined with paper. This greatly facilitates their removal and enables them to be used again with but little scraping. A wire brush answers best for cleaning the forms.

Concrete Sidewalks.—A useful and comparatively simple application of concrete is in the construction of sidewalks, for which purpose it has been used with marked success for a number of years.

Excavation and Preparation of Subgrade.—The ground is excavated to subgrade and well consolidated by ramming to prepare it for the subfoundation of stone, gravel or cinders. The depth of excavation will depend upon the climate and nature of the ground, being deeper in localities where heavy frosts occur or where the ground is soft than in climates where there are no frosts. In the former case the excavation should be carried to a depth of 12 inches, whereas in the latter from 4 to 6 inches will be sufficient. No roots of trees should be left above the subgrade.

The Subfoundation.—The foundation consists of a layer of loose material, such as broken stone, gravel, or cinders, spread over the subgrade and well tamped to secure a firm base for the main foundation of concrete which is placed on top. It is most important that the subfoundation be well drained to prevent the accumulation of water, which, upon freezing, would lift and crack the walk. For this purpose it is well to provide drain tile at suitable points to carry off any water which may collect under the concrete. An average thickness for subfoundation is 4 to 6 inches, although in warm climates, if the ground is firm and well drained, the subfoundation may only be 2 to 3 inches thick or omitted altogether.

The Foundation.—The foundation consists of a layer of concrete deposited on the subfoundation and carrying a surface layer or wearing coat of cement mortar. If the ground is firm and the subfoundation well rammed in place and properly drained, great strength will not be required of the concrete, which may, in such cases, be mixed in about the proportions 1-3-6, and a depth of only 3 to 4 inches will be required. Portland cement should be used and stone or gravel under 1 inch in size, the concrete being mixed of medium consistency, so that moisture will show on the surface without excessive tamping.

The Top Dressing or Wearing Surface.—To give a neat appearance to the finished walk, a top dressing of cement mortar is spread over the concrete, well worked in, and brought to a perfectly smooth surface with straightedge and float. This mortar should be mixed in the proportion 1 part cement to 2 parts sand, sharp coarse sand or screenings below one-fourth inch of some hard, tough rock being used. The practice of making the concrete of natural cement and the wearing surface of Portland is not to be commended, owing to a tendency for the two to separate.

Details of Construction.—A cord stretched between stakes will serve as a guide in excavating, after which the bottom of the trench is well consolidated by ramming; any loose material below subgrade is then spread over the bottom of the trench to the desired thickness and thoroughly compacted. Next, stakes are driven along the sides of the walk; spaced 4 to 6 feet apart, and their tops made even with the finished surface of the walk, which should have a transverse slope of one-fourth inch to the foot for drainage. Wooden strips at least 1½ inches thick and of a suitable depth are nailed to these stakes to serve as a mould to concrete. By carefully adjusting these strips to the exact height of the stakes they may be used as guides for the straightedge in levelling off the concrete and wearing surface. The subfoundation is well sprinkled to receive the concrete, which is deposited in the usual manner, well tamped behind a board set vertically across the trench, and levelled off with a straightedge as shown in Fig. 7, leaving one-half to 1 inch for the wearing surface. Three-eighths inch sand joints are provided at intervals of 6 to 8 feet to prevent expansion cracks, or, in case of settlement, to confine the cracks to these joints. This is done either by depositing the concrete in sections, or by dividing it into such sections with a spade when soft and filling the joints with sand. The location of each joint is marked on a wooden frame for future reference.

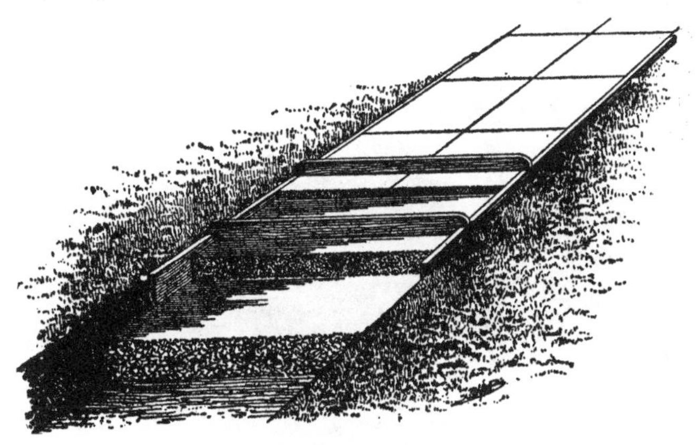

Details of concrete walk construction.

NO. 7.

Care must be exercised to prevent sand or any other material from being dropped on the concrete, and thus preventing a proper union with the wearing surface. No section should be left partially completed to be finished with the next batch or left until the next day. Any concrete left after the completion of a section should be mixed with the next batch.

It is of the utmost importance to follow up closely the concrete work with the top dressing in order that the two may set together. This top dressing should be worked well over the concrete with a trowel, and levelled with a straightedge (No. 7) to secure an even surface. Upon the thoroughness of this operation often depends the success or failure of the walk, since a good bond between the wearing surface and concrete base is absolutely essential. The mortar should be mixed rather stiff. As soon as the film of water begins to leave the surface, a wooden float is used, followed up by a plasterer's trowel, the operation being similar to that of plastering a wall. The floating, though necessary to give a smooth surface, will, if continued too long, bring a thin layer of neat cement to the surface and probably cause the walk to crack.

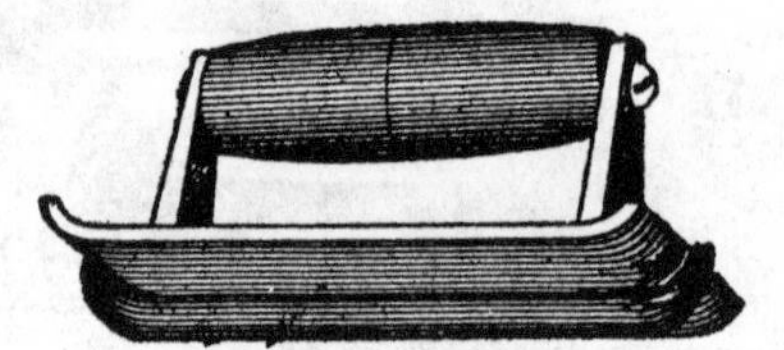

Jointer used in dividing walk into sections.

NO. 8.

The surface is now divided into sections by cutting entirely through, exactly over the joints in the concrete. This is done with a trowel guided by a straightedge, after which the edges are rounded off with a special tool called a jointer, having a thin shallow tongue (No. 8). These sections may be subdivided in any manner desired for the sake of appearance.

A special tool called an edger (No. 9) is run round the outside of the walk next to the mould, giving it a neat rounded edge. A toothed roller (No. 10) having small projections on its face is frequently used to produce slight indentations on the surface, adding somewhat to

Tool used in rounding edges.
NO. 9.

the appearance of the walk. The completed work must be protected from the sun and kept moist by sprinkling

Roller used in finishing surface
NO. 10.

for several days. In freezing weather the same precautions should be taken as in other classes of concrete work.

Concrete Basement Floors.—Basement floors in dwelling houses as a rule require only a moderate degree of strength, although in cases of very wet basements, where water pressure from beneath has to be resisted, greater strength is required than would otherwise be necessary. The subfoundation should be well drained, sometimes requiring the use of tile for carrying off the water. The rules given for constructing concrete sidewalks apply equally well to basement floors. The thickness of the concrete foundation is usually from 3 to 5 inches, according to the strength desired, and for average work a 1-3-6 mixture is sufficiently rich. Expansion joints are frequently omitted, since the temperature variation is less than in outside work, but since this omission frequently gives rise to unsightly cracks, their use is recommended in all cases. It will usually be sufficient to divide a room of moderate size into four equal sections, separated by ½ inch sand joints. The floor should be given a slight slope toward the center or one corner, with provision at the lowest point for carrying off any water that may accumulate.

Concrete Stable Floors and Driveways.—Concrete stable floors and driveways are constructed in the same general way as basement floors and sidewalks, but with a thicker foundation, on account of the greater strength required. The foundation may well be 6 inches thick, with a 10 inch wearing surface. An objection often sometimes raised against concrete driveways is that they become slippery when wet; but this fault is in a great measure overcome by dividing the wearing surface into small squares about 4 inches on the side, by means of triangular grooves ⅜ of an inch deep. This gives a very neat appearance and furnishes a good foothold for horses.

Concrete Steps.—Concrete may be advantageously used in the construction of steps, particularly in damp places, such as areaways and cellars of houses, and in the open, where the ground is terraced, concrete steps and walks can be made exceedingly attractive. Where the ground is firm it may be cut away as nearly as possible in the form of steps, with each step left two or three inches below its finished level. The steps are formed, beginning at the top, by depositing the con-

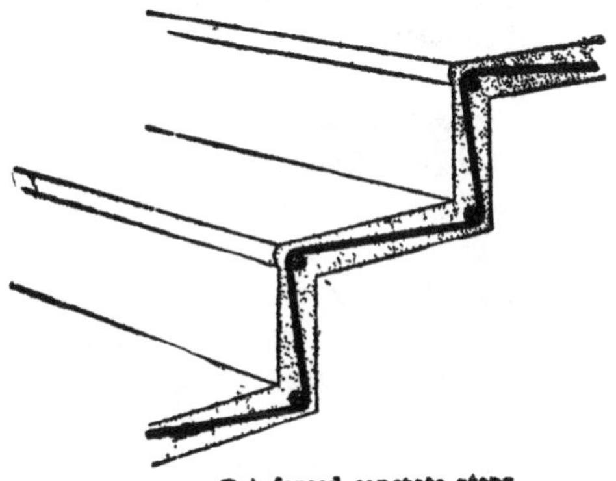

Reinforced concrete steps.
NO. 11.

crete behind vertical boards so placed as to give the necessary thickness to the risers and projecting high enough to serve as a guide in leveling off the tread. Such steps may be reinforced where greater strength is desired or where there is danger of cracking, due to the settlement of the ground.

Where the nature of the ground will not admit of its being cut away in the form of steps, the risers are molded between two vertical forms. The front one may be a smooth board, but the other should be a piece of thin sheet metal, which is more easily removed after the earth has been tamped in behind it. A simple method of reinforcing steps is to place a ½ inch steel rod in each corner, and thread these with ¼ inch rods bent to the shape of the steps, as shown in No. 11, the latter being placed about 2 feet apart. For this class of work a rich Portland cement concrete is recommended, with the use of stone or gravel under ½ inch in size. Steps may be given a ½ inch wearing surface of cement mortar mixed in the proportion of 1 part cement to 2 parts sand. This system, as well as many others, is well adapted for stairways in houses.

Reinforced Concrete Fence Posts.—Comparison of different Post Materials: There is a constantly increasing demand for some form of fence posts which is not subject to decay. The life of wooden posts is very limited, and the scarcity of suitable timber in many localities has made it imperative to find a substitute. A fence post, to prove thoroughly satisfactory, must fulfil three conditions: (1) It must be obtainable cost; (2) it must possess sufficient strength to meet the demands of general farm use; (3) it must not be subject to decay, and must be able to withstand successfully the effects of water, frost and fire. Although iron posts of various designs are frequently used for ornamental purposes, their adoption for general farm use is prohibited by their excessive cost. Then, too, iron posts exposed to the weather are subject to corrosion, to prevent which necessitates repainting from time to time, and this item will entail considerable expense in cases where a large number of posts are to be used.

At the present time the material which seems most nearly to meet these requirements is reinforced concrete. The idea of constructing fence posts of concrete reinforced with iron or steel is by no means a new one, but, on the contrary, such posts have been experimented with for years, and a great number of patents have been issued covering many of the possible forms of reinforcement. It is frequently stated that a reinforced concrete post can be made and put in the ground for the same price as a wooden post. Of course this will depend in any locality upon the relative value of wood and the various materials which go to make up the concrete post, but in the great majority of cases wood will prove the cheaper material in regard to first cost. On the other hand, a concrete post will last indefinitely, its strength increasing with age, whereas the wooden post must be replaced at short intervals, probably making it more expensive in the long run.

In regard to strength, it must be borne in mind that it is not practicable to make concrete fence posts as strong as wooden posts of the same size; but since wooden posts, as a rule, are many times stronger than is necessary, this difference in strength should not condemn the use of reinforced concrete for this purpose. Moreover, strength in many cases is of little importance, the fence being used only as a dividing line, and in such cases small concrete posts provide ample strength and present a very uniform and neat appearance. In any case, to enable concrete posts to withstand the loads they are called upon to carry, sufficient strength may be secured by means of reinforcement, and where great strength is required this may be obtained by using a larger post with a greater proportion of metal and well braced, as is usual in such cases. In point of durability, concrete is unsurpassed by any material of construction. It offers a perfect protection to the metal reinforcement and is not itself affected by exposure, so that a post constructed of concrete reinforced with steel will last indefinitely and require no attention in the way of repairs.

Reinforcement.—No form of wooden reinforcement, either on the surface or within the post, can be recommended. If on the surface, the wood will soon decay, and if a wooden core is used it will, in all probability, swell by the absorption of moisture and crack the post. The use of galvanized wire is sometimes advocated, but if the post is properly constructed and a good concrete used, this precaution against rust will be unnecessary, since it has been fully demonstrated by repeated tests that concrete protects steel perfectly from rust. If plain, smooth wire or rods are used for reinforcement they should be bent over at the ends or looped to prevent slipping in the concrete. Twisted fence wire may usually be obtained at a reasonable cost and is very well suited for this purpose. Barbed wire has been proposed and is sometimes used, although the barbs make it extremely difficult to handle. For the sake of economy the smallest amount of metal consistent with the desired strength must be used, and this requirement makes it necessary to place the reinforcement near the surface, where its strength is utilized to greatest advantage, with only enough concrete on the outside to form a protective covering. A reinforcing member in each corner of the post is probably the most efficient arrangement.

Concrete for Fence Posts.—The concrete should be mixed with Portland cement in about the proportions 1-2½-5, broken stone or gravel under ½ inch being used.

In cases where the aggregate contains pieces smaller than ¼ inch, less sand may be used, and in some cases it may be omitted altogether. A mixture of medium consistency is recommended on the ground that it fills the molds better and with less tamping than if mixed quite dry.

Molds for Fence Posts.—Economy points to the use of a tapering post, which, fortunately, offers no difficulties in the way of molding. All things considered,

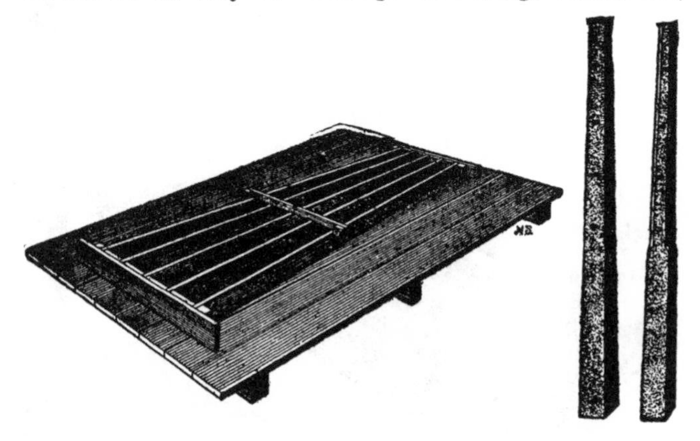

Wooden mold for making fence posts with four tapering sides.

NO. 12.

wooden molds will be found most suitable. They can easily and quickly be made in any desired form and size. Posts may be molded either in a vertical or horizontal position, the latter being the simpler and better method. If molded vertically a wet mixture is necessary, requiring a longer time to set, with the consequent delay in removing the molds. No. 12 shows a simple mold, which has been used with satisfactory results in this laboratory.

This mold has a capacity of four posts, but larger molds could easily be made on the same principle. It consists of two end pieces, (a) carrying lugs, (b) between which are inserted strips (c). The several parts are held together with hooks and eyes, as shown in No. 12. To prevent any bulging of the side strips they are braced, as illustrated. Dressed lumber at least 1 inch thick, and preferably 1½ inches, should be used. In No. 12 the

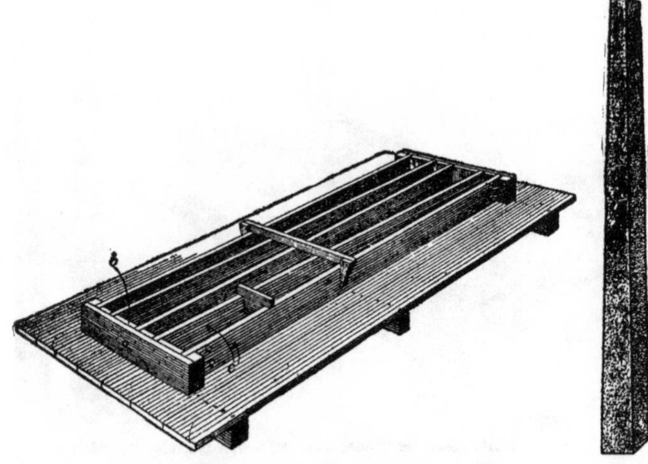

Wooden mold for making fence posts with two tapering sides.

NO. 13.

post measures 6 by 6 inches at the bottom, 6 by 3 at the top, and 7 feet in length, having two parallel sides. If it is desired to have the posts square at both ends the mold must be arranged as in No. 13. This latter form of post is not as strong as the former, but requires less concrete in its construction. Great care in tamping is necessary to insure the corners of the mold being well filled, and if this detail is not carefully watched, the metal, being exposed in places, will be subject to rust.

Attaching Fence Wires to Posts.—Various devices have been suggested for attaching fence wires to the posts, the object of each being to secure a simple and permanent fastener or one admitting of easy renewal at any time. Probably nothing will answer the purpose better than a long staple or bent wire well embedded in the concrete, being twisted or bent at the end to prevent extraction. Galvanized metal must be used for fasteners, since they

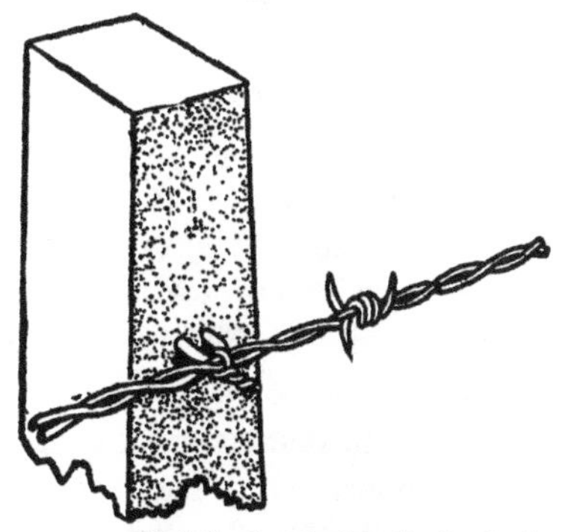

Detail showing method of attaching wire to post.

NO. 14.

are not protected by the concrete. A piece of small flexible wire, about two inches in length, threading the staple and twisted several times with a pair of pliers, holds the line wire in position. (No. 14.)

Molding and Curing Posts.—For the proper method of mixing concrete see previous pages. It is recommended that only so much concrete be mixed at one time as can be used before it begins to harden; but if an unavoidable delay prevents the posts being molded until after the concrete has begun to set, it is thought that a thorough regauging with sufficient water to restore normal consistency will prevent any appreciable loss of strength, though the concrete may have been standing one or two hours. In using a mold similar to those illustrated in Nos. 12 and 13 it is necessary to provide a perfectly smooth and even platform of a size depending upon the number of posts to be molded. A cement floor if accessible may be used to advantage. The molds when in place are given a thin coating of soft soap, the platform or cement floor, serving as bottom of mold, being treated in the same way. About 1½ inches is spread evenly over the bottom and carefully tamped, so as to reduce it to a thickness of about 1 inch. A piece of board cut as in No. 12 will be found useful in leveling off the concrete to the desired thickness before tamping. On top of this layer two reinforcing members are placed about 1 inch from the sides of the mold. The molds are then filled and tamped in thin layers to the level of the other two reinforcing members, the fasteners for fence wires being inserted during the operation. These reinforcing members are adjusted as were the first two, and the remaining 1 inch of concrete tamped and leveled off, thus completing the post so far as molding is concerned. To avoid sharp edges, which are easily chipped, triangular strips may be placed in the bottom of mold along the sides, and when the molds have been filled and tamped, similar strips may be inserted on top. The top edges may be beveled with a trowel or by running an edging tool having a triangular projection on its bottom along the edges. Such a tool is shown in No. 15, and can easily be made of wood or metal. It is not necessary to carry the bevel below the ground line.

The ends and sides of the mold may be removed after twenty-four hours, but the posts should not be handled for at least one week, during which time they must be well sprinkled several times daily and protected from sun and wind. The intermediate strips may be carefully withdrawn at the end of two or three days, but it is better to leave them in place until the posts are removed. Although a post may be hard and apparently strong when one week old, it will not attain its full strength in that length of time, and must be handled with the utmost care to prevent injury. Carelessness in handling green posts frequently results in the formation of fine cracks, which though unnoticed at the time, give evidence of their presence later in the failure of the posts.

Tool used for beveling edges of posts.

NO. 15.

Posts should be allowed to cure for at least sixty days before being placed in the ground, and for this purpose it is recommended that when moved from the molding platform they be placed upon a smooth bed of moist sand and protected from the sun until thoroughly cured. During this period they should receive a thorough drenching at least once a day.

The life of the molds will depend upon the care with which they are handled. A coating of mineral oil or shellac may be used instead of soap to prevent the cement from sticking to the forms. As soon as the molds are removed they should be cleaned with a wire brush before being used again.

The cost of reinforced concrete fence posts depends in each case upon the cost of labor and materials, and must necessarily vary in different localities. An estimate in any particular case can be made as follows: One cubic yard of concrete will make twenty posts measuring 6 inches by 6 inches at the bottom, 6 inches by 3 inches at the top, and 7 feet long, and if mixed in the proportions 1-2½-5, requires approximately:

1.16 barrels of cement, at $2	$2.32
0.44 cubic yard of sand, at 75 cts	.33
0.88 cubic yard of gravel, at 75 cts	.66
Materials for 1 cubic yard cement	$3.21
Concrete for one post	.17
28 feet of 0.16 inch steel wire, at 3 cts a pound	.06
Total cost of concrete and metal for 1 post	.23

To this must be added the cost of mixing concrete, molding and handling posts, and the costs of molds, an addition which should not in any case exceed 7 cents, making a total of 30 cents per post.

Concrete Building Blocks.—Concrete building blocks, or cement blocks, as they are frequently called, are more extensively used now than ever before. These blocks are molded hollow primarily to reduce their cost, but this hollow construction serves other useful purposes at the same time. The fundamental principles governing ordinary concrete work, so far as proportioning and mixing materials is concerned, apply equally well to the manufacture of building blocks, and it should be borne in mind that strength and durability can not be obtained by the use of any machine unless the cement, sand, and aggregate are of good quality, properly proportioned and well mixed. The aggregate for blocks of ordinary size should be crushed stone or gravel not larger than ½ inch. One of the chief causes of complaint against the concrete building block is its porosity, but this defect is in a great measure due to the fact that in an endeavor to economize too little cement is frequently used. It is not unusual to give the blocks a facing of cement mortar consisting of about 2 parts sand to 1 of cement, while the body of the block is composed of a concrete of sufficient strength, though not impervious. This outside layer of mortar adds practically nothing to the strength of the block, and is used simply to give a uniform surface and to render the face of the wall more clearly impervious to water.

It would not be practicable as a rule to attempt the manufacture of concrete blocks without one of the many forms of molding machines designed for the purpose, nor would it be economical to purchase such a machine unless a sufficient number of blocks were required to justify such an outlay. Blocks in almost any desired shape and size, with either plain or ornamental faces, may be obtained on the market, and in the great majority of cases it is best to buy them from some reliable firm. Among the advantages claimed for hollow concrete block construction may be mentioned the following:

(1) Hollow block construction introduces a saving of material over brick or stone masonry.

(2) The cost of laying concrete blocks is less than for brick work. This is due to the fact that the blocks, being larger, require a much smaller number of joints and less mortar, and, being hollow, are of less weight than solid brick work.

(3) A wall constructed of good concrete blocks is as strong or stronger than a brick wall of equal thickness.

(4) Concrete blocks, being easily molded to any desired form, will prove to be a far more economical building material than stone, which has to be dressed to shape.

(5) Experience has proved concrete to be a most excellent fire resisting material.

(6) Concrete blocks, being hollow, tend to prevent sudden changes of temperature within a house, making it cool in summer and easily heated in winter.

(7) The hollow spaces provide an easy means for running pipes and electric wires. These spaces may also be used wholly or in part for heating and ventilating flues.

Tests of Concrete Fence Posts.—In the summer of 1904 a number of reinforced concrete fence posts were made for experimental purposes, with a view to determining their adaptability for general use. These posts were made both with and without reinforcement, and tested at the age of 90 days. The reinforcement, ranging from 0.27 per cent. to 1.13 per cent., consisted of four round steel rods, one in each corner of post about 1 inch from surface, the posts having a uniform cross-section of 6 by 6 inches. The posts were molded in a horizontal position, as this was found by trial to be more satisfactory than molding them vertically.

The concrete was mixed moderately soft, crushed stone between 1 inch and ¼ inch and gravel under ¾ inch being used as aggregate. River sand, fairly clean and sharp, was employed with Portland cement. The posts were tested as beams, supported at both ends and loaded at the centre, with spans varying from 4 feet to 5 feet 6 inches. An attempt was made to prevent slipping by providing the reinforcing rods with collars and set screws at the ends, but in every case, with but two exceptions, the rods slipped under a comparatively light load, thus showing the necessity for some form of mechanical bond. As would be expected, those posts which were not reinforced possessed very little strength.

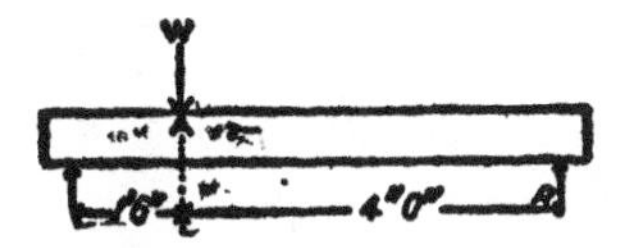

Method of testing posts under static loads.

A series of tests was made with sheet-iron reinforcement, in the form of round and square pipes, embedded in the posts, but these posts, though developing considerable strength, proved less economical than those reinforced with plain rods, and at the same time were less simple in construction. The results of these tests, as recorded in Table I., do not properly represent the strength of similar posts in which some form of mechanical bond is provided to develop the full strength of the reinforcement.

TABLE 1.—SHOWING RESULTS OF PRELIMINARY TESTS OF REINFORCED CONCRETE FENCE POSTS.

No.	Kind of Reinforcement.	Per Cent of Reinforcement.	Mixture.	Material.	Span.	Load at First Crack.	Maximum Load.	Equivalent Load on 4-foot Cantilever at First Crack	Equivalent Maximum Load on 4-foot Cantilever.
					Ft. In.	Pounds.	Pounds.	Pounds.	Pounds
1	No Reinforcement	....	1-3-5	Stone	4 0	1,435	1,435	359	359
2	do	....	1-3-5	do	4 0	670	670	168	168
20	do	....	1-3-7	Gravel	4 6	700	700	196	196
25	do	....	1-3-5	do	4 6	320	320	90	90
26	do	....	1-2-5	do	4 0	1,100	1,100	275	275
30	do	....	1-2-5	do	4 0	1,000	1,000	250	250
4	Plain Steel Rods	0.27	1-3-5	Stone	4 0	1,580	1,850	395	463
17	do	.27	1-3-5	do	4 0	1,135	1,945	284	486
21	do	.27	1-3-5	do	4 6	920	1,690	258	473
24	do	.27	1-3-5	do	4 6	940	1,660	263	465
28	do	.27	1-3-5	do	4 6	800	1,720	224	482
35	do	.27	1-2-5	Gravel	4 0	1,100	1,550	275	388
36	do	.27	1-2-5	do	4 6	900	1,460	252	409
39	do	.27	1-2-5	do	4 0	1,340	1,640	335	410
40	do	.27	1-2-5	do	5 6	760	1,120	258	381
42	do	.27	1-2-5	do	4 6	1,100	1,290	308	361
44	do	.27	1-2-5	do	5 6	......	1,080	....	367
3	do	.52	1-3-5	Stone	4 0	1,800	2,530	450	633
7	do	.52	1-3-5	do	4 6	1,600	2,155	448	603
13	do	.52	1-3-5	do	4 0	1,640	2,500	410	625
15	do	.52	1-3-5	do	4 0	1,960	2,400	490	600
27	do	.52	1-3-5	do	4 0	1,680	2,220	420	555
45	do	.52	1-2-5	Gravel	5 6	920	1,800	313	612
46	do	.52	1-2-5	do	4 0	900	2,740	225	685
47	do	.52	1-2-5	do	4 6	1,000	2,450	280	686
50	do	.52	1-2-5	do	4 0	1,200	3,125	300	781
5	do	.81	1-3-5	Stone	4 0	2,640	4,800	660	1,200
10	do	.81	1-3-5	do	4 0	1,480	4,100	370	1,025
12	do	.81	1-3-5	do	4 6	1,860	4,100	521	1,148
14	do	.81	1-3-5	do	4 6	1,800	3,915	504	1,096
19	do	.81	1-3-5	do	4 0	1,800	4,160	450	1,040
22	do	.81	1-3-5	do	4 6	1,900	2,900	532	812
34	do	.81	1-2-5	Gravel	4 6	1,750	4,100	490	1,148

TABLE 1.—SHOWING RESULTS OF PRELIMINARY TESTS OF REINFORCED CONCRETE FENCE POSTS.
(CONTINUED.)

No.	Kind of Reinforcement.	Per Cent of Reinforcement.	Mixture.	Material.	Span.	Load at First Crack.	Maximum Load.	Equivalent Load on 4-foot Cantilever at First Crack	Equivalent Maximum Load on 4-foot Cantilever.
					Ft. In.	*Pounds.*	*Pounds.*	*Pounds.*	*Pounds.*
37	Plain Steel Rods	.81	1-2-5	Gravel	4 0	1,500	3,545	375	886
43	do	.81	1-2-5	do	4 0	1,700	4,200	425	1,050
48	do	.81	1-2-5	do	4 6	1,240	3,575	347	1,001
6	do	.95	1-3-5	Stone	4 0	1,980	5,150	495	1,288
11	do	.95	1-3-5	do	4 6	2,380	4,300	666	1,204
18	do	.95	1-3-5	do	4 6	1,800	4,240	504	1,187
49	do	.95	1-2-5	Gravel	5 6	900	2,600	306	884
51	do	.95	1-2-5	do	4 6	1,380	3,160	386	885
52	do	.95	1-2-5	do	4 6	1,200	3,345	336	937
53	do	.95	1-2-5	do	4 0	1,340	3,840	335	960
54	do	.95	1-2-5	do	5 6	980	2,600	333	884
8	do	1.13	1-3-5	Stone	4 6	2,220	3,820	622	1,070
9	do	1.13	1-3-5	do	4 0	2,560	5,080	640	1,270
16	do	1.13	1-3-5	do	4 6	2,000	3,100	560	868
23	do	1.13	1-3-5	do	4 0	1,800	4,900	450	1,225
29	do	1.13	1-3-5	do	4 0	2,400	4,460	600	1,115
32	do	1.13	1-2-5	Gravel	4 6	1,500	2,900	420	812
33	do	1.13	1-2-5	do	4 0	1,400	2,320	350	580
38	do	1.13	1-2-5	do	4 6	1,500	3,270	420	916
41	do	1.13	1-2-5	do	4 6	1,250	4,300	350	1,204
55	Pipe 5 inches diameter, 1-40 inch thick	1.10	1-2-5	do	4 6	1,800	4,000	504	1,120
56	do	1.10	1-2-5	do	4 6	1,720	4,000	482	1,120
57	do	1.10	1-2-5	do	4 6	......	4,660	....	1,305
58	□ 5 by 5 inches, 1-40 inch thick	1.39	1-2-5	do	4 6	2,400	6,320	672	1,770
59	do	1 39	1-2-5	do	4 6	2,100	5,880	588	1,646
60	do	1.39	1-2-5	do	4 6	2,200	6,040	616	1,691
61	X 5 by 5 inches, 1-40 inch thick	.98	1-2-5	Stone	4 6	1,100	2,450	308	686
62	do	.98	1-3-5	do	4 6	860	2,660	241	745
63	do	.98	1-3-5	do	4 6	1,800	2,400	504	672

In order to obtain more data on the subject, this investigation has been supplemented by a second series of tests, the results of which form the subject matter for the sections on concrete fence posts and are expressed numerically in Table II.

In these tests it was decided to make the posts tapering in order to economize material and reduce their weight. For the concrete, Portland cement, river sand, and gravel were used in the proportion 1-2½-5, measured by volume, the gravel being screened below ½ inch. Sufficient water was used in mixing to produce a plastic mass, requiring only a moderate degree of tamping to bring water to the surface. The posts were molded and kept under wet burlap for four weeks, and tested at the end of sixty days. The reinforcing members were placed in the corners of the posts about 1 inch from the surface, being looped and bent, as indicated in Table II. These posts were not designed with a view to developing the ultimate compressive strength of the concrete, but where greater strength is necessary it may be obtained at small expense by increasing the percentage of reinforcement. It is important that fairly rich concrete should be used in all cases to enable the posts to stand exposure and to prevent chipping.

All of these posts measured 6 by 6 inches at the bottom and 6 by 3 inches at the top, except Nos. 29, 30, 31, 32, 33, and 34, which were 6 by 6 at the bottom and 3 by 3 at the top. It will be noticed that the saving in concrete introduced in the construction of these posts is accompanied by a marked decrease in strength as compared with the other posts similarly reinforced. It would also appear that the twisted wire has a slight

TABLE II. SHOWING THE STRENGTH OF REINFORCED CONCRETE FENCE POSTS.

No.	Kind of reinforcement.	Total sectional area of reinforcement. In square inches.	Load at first crack. In Pounds.	Maximum load. In Pounds.	Equivalent load on 4-foot cantilever at first crack. In Pounds.	Equivalent maximum load on 4-foot cantilever. In Pounds.	Form of reinforcement.
1	Drawn steel rods	0.08	800	1120	218	306	
2	......do.........	.08	820	1145	224	313	
3	......do.........	.08	640	1080	175	295	
4	......do.........	.08	795	1040	217	284	
37	......do.........	.08	940	1170	257	319	
38	......do.........	.08	740	1075	202	298	
9	......do.........	.19	1140	1280	311	349	
10	......do.........	.19	1170	1885	319	515	
11	......do.........	.19	1020	1950	278	532	
39	......do.........	.19	760	1945	207	531	
40	......do.........	.19	820	1925	224	526	
13	Twisted fence wire	.06	825	935	225	255	
15	......do.........	.06	755	905	206	247	
16	......do.........	.06	800	940	218	257	
17	......do.........	.06	815	935	222	255	
18	......do.........	.06	770	980	210	268	
19	......do.........	.06	780	975	213	266	
21	......do.........	.13	1550	1920	423	524	
22	......do.........	.13	1275	1670	348	456	
23	......do.........	.13	1200	1830	328	500	
24	......do.........	.13	1500	1955	410	534	
25	Barbed wire	.06	980	980	268	268	
26	......do.........	.06	820	820	224	224	
27	......do.........	.06	590	740	161	202	
28	......do.........	.06	745	745	203	203	
29	......do.........	.06	590	590	161	161	
30	......do.........	.06	550	640	150	175	
31	......do.........	.06	560	635	153	173	
32	......do.........	.06	480	530	131	145	
33	......do.........	.13	680	1040	186	284	
34	......do.........	.13	840	1010	229	276	
35	......do.........	.13	1280	1515	349	414	
36	......do.........	.13	800	1375	218	375	
6	Drawn steel rods	.08	Tested by impact.....				
7	......do.........	.19	......do...............				
8	......do.........	.19	......do...............				
14	Twisted fence wire	.06	......do...............				
20	......do.........	.06	......do...............				

advantage over the barbed wire as a reinforcing material, particularly when two wires are used in each corner of the post.

As stated before, it is impracticable to make a reinforced concrete fence post as strong as a wooden post of the same size, and this is more especially true if the post

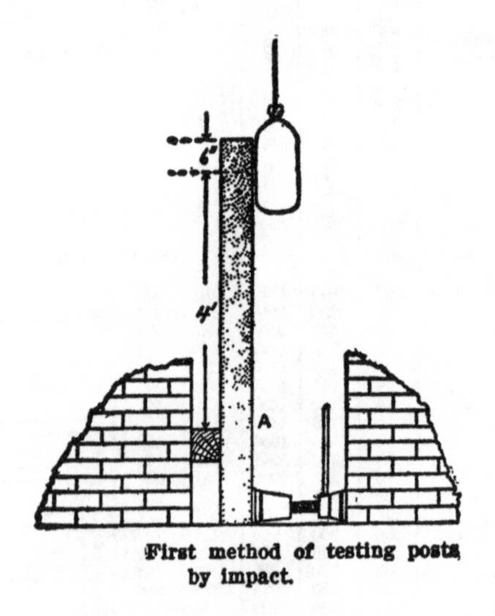

First method of testing posts by impact.

NO. 17.

has to withstand the force of a sudden blow or impact. In order to study the behavior of these posts under impact, a number of them were braced, as illustrated in No. 17, and subjected to the blow of a 50-pound bag of gravel, suspended from above by a 9-foot rope. The first blow was delivered by deflecting the bag so as to give it a vertical drop of 1 foot, and for each successive blow the drop was increased 1 foot. None of the posts showed any signs of failure under the first blow. Posts Nos. 14 and 20 cracked under the second blow, and failed under the third. Post No. 6 cracked under the second blow, which cracked open under the third blow, causing a momentary deflection of 5 inches. Posts Nos. 7 and 8 each developed a crack under the second blow, but showed no further signs of weakness after the fifth blow,

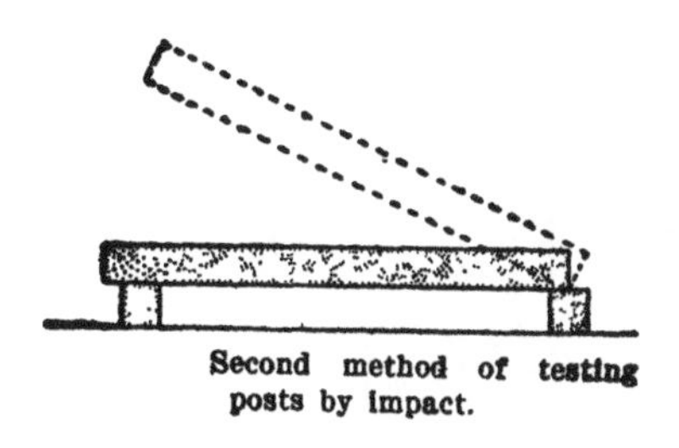

Second method of testing posts by impact.

NO. 18.

other than a slight opening of the initial crack. In each case the only crack developed was at point A. Posts 6, 7, and 8, which cracked but did not fail under the impact test, were further tested, as indicated in No. 18, by raising the small end and allowing them to drop from successive heights at 1, 2, 3 and 4 feet. Under this test a number of cracks developed, but in no case did the reinforcement fail.

Although it might appear from these results that posts as here described have hardly enough strength to recommend them for general use, it should be remembered that in many cases fence posts are not subjected to impact, and it may prove more economical to replace from time to time those which fail in this way than to use wooden posts, which, being subject to decay, must all be replaced sooner or later.

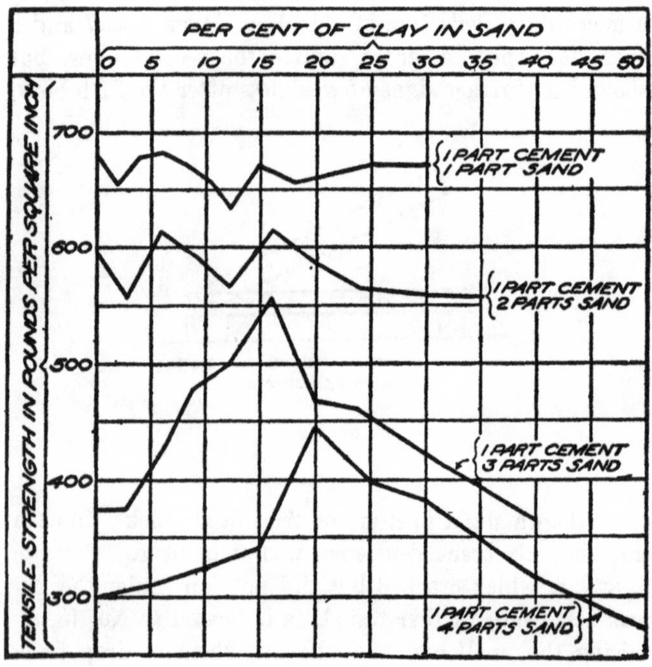

Diagram showing the effect of clay on cement mortars.

NO. 19.

Retempering.—Table III. illustrates the effect of retempering Portland cement mortar. The mortars used consisted of Portland cement and crushed quartzite between 1 and 2 millimeters in size, mixed in different proportions. In each case, after the initial or final set had taken place, sufficient water was added in retempering to

TABLE III.—EFFECT OF RETEMPERING ON CEMENT MORTARS.

Treatment of Mortar.	Tensile Strength, in Pounds Per Square Inch.			
	Neat Cement. *a*	1 Part Cement, 1 Part Sand *b*	1 Part Cement, 2 Parts Sand. *c*	1 Part Cement, 3 Parts Sand. *d*
Mortar made up into briquettes immediately after mixing......	651	624	527	417
	650	701	493	385
	673	624	529	421
	634	581	480	403
	679	610	492	409
Average	657	628	504	407
Mortar allowed to take initial set, then broken up and made into briquettes............................	671	692	589	326
	593	670	554	349
	644	654	559	330
	633	676	534	358
	724	700	532	267
Average	653	678	554	326
Mortar allowed to take final set, then broken up and made into briquettes	455	527	492	364
	522	569	491	380
	525	587	497	361
	558	566	486	315
	642	568	531	345
Average	540	563	499	353

a Initial set, 1 hour 42 minutes; final set, 7 hours 15 minutes.
b Initial set, 1 hour 30 minutes· final set, 7 hours 15 minutes.
c Initial set, 2 hours; final set, 7 hours.
d Initial set, 2 hours 20 minutes; final set, 7 hours.

restore normal consistency. The briquettes were tested at the age of four months.

Some Practical Notes.—Spencer B. Newbury, who is an authority on the subject, says "that the making of good cement concrete is a comparatively simple matter, and yet, like most simple operations in engineering, there is a right way and a wrong way of doing it. Probably nine-tenths of the concrete work done falls far short of the strength it might develop, owing to the incorrect proportions, use of too much water, and imperfect mixing. All authorities are agreed upon the importance of thorough mixing and the use of the minimum quantity of water in all classes of concrete work. The matter of correct proportions of cement, sand, broken stones, etc., is one which requires some thought and calculation, and by proportioning these ingredients correctly an immense saving in cost and increase in strength can easily be secured.

The chief object in compounding concrete is to produce a compact mass, as free as possible from pores or open spaces; in short, to imitate solid rock as closely as possible. Cement is the "essence of rock" in portable form, and by its judicious use granular or fragmentary materials may be bound together into solid blocks of any desired size and shape, which in strength and wearing qualities are at least equal to the best stone that comes from the quarries. Cement is, however, very costly in comparison with the other ingredients of concrete, and must not be used wastefully. A little cement, judiciously used, is better than a large quantity thrown in recklessly, as a little study of the principles involved will plainly show.

To produce a compact mass from fragmentary materials, the voids must be filled. Imagine a box holding 1 cubic foot. If this were filled with spheres of uniform size, the voids or open spaces would be one-third the total volume, or 33 1-3 per cent., with spheres of various sizes, as, for example, from large marble down to fine shot, the voids would be much less, and it would theoretically be possible, by the use of spheres of graded sizes, from the largest down to dust of infinite fineness, to fill the box completely, so that there would be no voids whatever. In practice it is well known that the use of materials of varying fineness gives the best concrete, since the voids are much less than in materials composed of pieces of uniform size. Hence the common practice of making concrete with cement, sand and broken stone, instead of with cement and sand, or cement and stone only. The sand fills the voids, and if the proportions are correct, a practically solid mass results. As an example of this, the writer found the briquettes of cement with three parts of sand and four parts gravel showed higher tensile strength at 28 days than those made with three parts sand only.

The following table gives the relative weights of a given volume of different materials, and also the percentage of voids, as determined by the writer. The materials were shaken down in a liter measure by giving one hundred taps on the table, and weighed. In the case of the broken stone a larger measure was used. The voids were calculated from the specific gravity.

Comparison of the three different grades of Sandusky Bay sand shows how greatly the percentage of voids varies with the proportion of fine and coarse grains present. The first is the natural sand, not screened, as pumped up by the sand sucker from the bottom of the bay, and contains a large amount of fine gravel. The second is the same, passed through a 20-mesh screen to

remove the coarse particles. It will be seen that thi
operation increases the proportion of voids from 32 t
38 per cent. The third is the same sand passing a 20
mesh and retained on a 30-mesh screen, thus brought t
the fineness of the "standard sand" used in cement test
ing. This shows 40.7 per cent. of voids, owing to the uni
form size of the grains. The same relation is seen in th

WEIGHT OF UNIT MEASURE AND PERCENTAGE OF VOIDS I
VARIOUS MATERIALS.

	Weight of 1 Liter.	Per Cent of Voids.
Portland cement	1720 g	....
Louisville cement	....	....
Sandusky Bay sand, not screened	1780 g	32.3
Sandusky Bay sand, through 20-mesh screen	1630 g	38.5
Sandusky Bay sand, 20–30 mesh (standard sand)	1570 g	40.7
Gravel, ¼ to ⅜ inch	1510 g	42.4
Gravel, ¼ to $\frac{1}{10}$ inch	1680 g	35.9
Marblehead broken stone (chiefly about egg size)	1380 g	47.0

two grades of gravel given in the table, that containing finer grains showing much the lower percentage of voids. These figures illustrate the imprudence of screening any of the materials used in making concrete. The presence of clay in sand is, however, objectionable, not because of its fine state of subdivision, but because the clay coats the sand particles and prevents the adhesion of the cement. Such sand might be improved by washing, but probably not by screening. It has been found that cement which has been ground to dust with an equal amount of sand goes much further when used for concrete than the same quantity of cement when used in the ordinary way. This is doubtless owing to the fact that the sand dust aids in filling the voids. It is also well known that slaked lime, when added to cement mortar, greatly increases the strength of mixtures poor in cement.

From the figures given in the above table the composition of a theoretically perfect concrete may readily be calculated. The existence of voids in the cement may be disregarded, since in the process of hardening the cement sends out crystals in all directions, completely encrusting the sand particles and practically filling all the voids which the cement itself contains. Examination of a well-hardened briquette of cement with 3 parts sand, after breaking, with the aid of a lens, will show this clearly

Suppose, for example, we wish to make the best possible concrete from Portland cement with the sand and gravel given in the above table. We should, of course, choose the unscreened sand and gravel as containing the least proportion of voids. One hundred measures of gravel would require 35.9 measures of sand. As the sand contains 32.3 per cent. of voids, we require 32.3 per cent. of 35.9, or 11.6 measures of cement. The proportions would, therefore, be: Cement, 11; sand, 3, and gravel, 9. It is customary, however, to increase the proportion of mortar (cement and sand) by about 15 or 20 per cent., in order that the coarser materials may be completely coated with the finer mixture. Making this addition, we find the concrete proportions to be: Cement, 1; sand, 2.8; gravel, 7. Allowance must also be made in practice for imperfect mixing, since the materials can never be distributed in a perfectly uniform manner. Practically, with these materials, a concrete of cement 1, sand 2½, and gravel 6, would probably give the best result, and little or no improvement would result from increasing the proportion of cement.

A similar calculation shows that the correct proportions for a concrete made of the sand and broken stone given in the table would be 1 to 3 to 6½. Increasing the amount of cement and sand by 20 per cent., we have 1 to 3 to 5½. Probably 1 to 2½ to 5 would be found to give the best results in practice. The determination of the voids in the sand, gravel and broken stone used is of the greatest value in adjusting the proportions of concrete.

The simplest method of determining this in the case of gravel and broken stone is to have a metal box made of 1 cubic foot capacity; this is filled with the material to be tested, well shaken down and struck off level. The box and contents are then weighed. Water is now poured in until it rises even with the surface, and the total weight again taken. The difference in the weights is the weight of the water filling the voids of the material. Now 1 cubic foot of water weighs 64 4-10 lbs., and from the weight of the water found the percentage of voids can be simply calculated. For example, in one experiment the box and broken stone weighed 88 lbs. After filling the spaces in the stone with water the weight was 117½ lbs., a difference of 29½ lbs. The percentage of voids is, therefore, 29½x100 divided by 62.4 equals 47 per cent.

In the case of sand this method will not answer, as it is difficult to completely fill the voids of the sand by adding the water. The voids can, however, be readily calculated from the weight of a cubic foot and the specific gravity. The specific gravity of quartz sand is about 2.65. A cubic foot of sand, free from voids, would therefore weigh 2.65x62.4 equaling 165.4 lbs. The weight of a cubic foot of sand, well shaken down, was, however, found to be only 112 lbs., a difference of 53.4 lbs. The proportion of voids was, therefore, 53.4x100 divided by 165.4 equals 32.3 per cent. The percentage in voids in clean natural sand does not vary greatly, and may be taken as 33 to 35 per cent. for coarse and 35 to 38 per cent. for fine sand.

We have already seen that with the materials above described, concrete composed of

Cement 1, sand 2½, gravel 6, or

Cement 1, sand 2½, broken stone 5

by measure, will be practically compact and non-porous, and that there is no object in increasing the proportion of cement. Such concrete, if made from Portland cement, will, however, be rather expensive, requiring about one barrel of cement (equals 3½ cubic feet) for every cubic yard. This is unnecessarily good for ordinary work, and will only be required for foundations of engines and other heavy machinery, in which the best possible result must be secured regardless of cost. In cheaper concretes the relative proportions of sand and broken stone should be the same, as determined by the voids in the coarser materials, while the proportion of cement may be varied according to the required conditions of quality and cost. Most excellent concrete may be made by using:

Portland cement 1, sand 7, stone or gravel 14.

Here are specimens of these two concretes, taken from trial blocks laid Oct. 1, 1894, to determine the best proportion for the foundation of brick pavement. The richer of the two, 1-5-10, is certainly good enough for any purpose, even for engine foundations. A cubic yard of such concrete requires about ½ barrel of cement; the total cost of the cement, sand and stone is about two dollars per cubic yard. This is no more expensive than concrete made from Louisville cement with 2 of sand and 4 of broken stone, and is immensely superior to the latter in strength.

The following table shows the results obtained in Germany by R. Dykerhoff in determining the crushing strength of various concretes. The blocks used were 2½ inches square, and were tested after one day in air and 27 days in water.

Proportions by Measure.			Strength under Compression. Pounds per Square Inch.
Portland Cement.	Sand.	Gravel.	
1	2	..	2125
1	2	3	2747
1	2	5	2387
1	..	5	978
1	3	..	1383
1	3	5	1632
1	3	6½	1515
1	4	..	1053
1	4	5	1273
1	4	8½	1204

These figures prove the statement already made, that mixtures of cement and sand are strengthened, rather than weakened, by the addition of a suitable quantity of gravel. It will be noticed that the mixture—cement 1, sand 2, gravel 5—is actually stronger than cement 1, sand 2, without gravel. The same is shown in the mixtures 1 to 3 and 1 to 4.

In estimating the amount of material required to produce a given volume of concrete, it may be stated that when very strongly rammed into place the volume of concrete obtained from correct proportions of the materials will be about 10 per cent. more the volume 1 cubic foot cement, 2½ cubic feet sand, and 5 cubic feet stone, and will therefore yield about 5½ cubic feet concrete.

Another Concrete Stairway and Steps.—A good staircase is one of the essential features in a building. The safety and convenience of persons using a staircase are not only affected by the due proportions and arrangements of the steps, but by the strength and fire-resisting properties of the materials employed, and the manner of construction. The wells are in many cases too small, out of proportion to the structure, which necessitates dangerous winders, tiring high risers, narrow treads, or insufficient headway. Some architects when designing a staircase pay little attention to the practicability of construction. What may seem easy in theory or on paper is often found impracticable or unnecessarily difficult when reduced to actual practice. The errors of omission and commission are left for the workmen to contend with and overcome as best they may at the employer's expense. Happily such cases are few, the majority of architects supplying figured drawings, which are not only a help and guide to the workmen, but also ensure a practical staircase in due proportion and without unnecessary expense. Staircases should be spacious, light, and easy of ascent. It is generally admitted that a 12 inch tread and a 6 inch rise is the most convenient. and that no tread should be less than 8 inches or more than 16 inches, and no rise less than 4½ inches and more than 7 inches. According to Blondel, the rise should be reduced ½ inch for every inch added to the tread, or the tread reduced by 1 inch to every ½ inch added to the riser, taking a 12 inch tread and a 6 inch rise as the standard. Treads may be increased by means of a nosing, which usually projects from 1 inch to 1½ inches. Nosing not only gives more available space for the tread, but also affords some advantage to persons going down stairs, as the heel cannot strike against the rising. In setting out a flight of stairs, the tread of the steps are measured from riser to riser. Where practicable, the number of steps from landing to landing should be odd, because when a person begins to ascend with the right foot first (as most people do) he should end with the same foot. Rectangular steps are called fliers. Winders, being narrowed at one end, are always more inconvenient and dangerous than straight steps, and should not be used for public buildings or other places where there is a crowded traffic. Winders are also more expensive to construct. They are, however, unavoidable in circular staircases, also in some instances in angles, where a quarter or half space landing would not give the desired rise. Winders should be so made that the tread 6 inches from the end of the narrow point should be wide enough to step upon without danger of slipping. No stairs should be less than three feet from the wall to the hand-rail. A width of 3 feet 6 inches will allow two persons to walk arm in arm up or down stairs. A width of 4 feet 6 inches is generally used; this gives plenty of space for two persons to pass each other. No hard and fast rules can be laid down for the size of treads and risers, as they are regulated more or less by the size of the well and the height from floor to floor. Too few steps in a flight are as bad as too many. There should not be less than three. Long straight flights of steps are tiring and dangerous. The straight line of length should be broken by landings, so that there may not be more than eleven continuous steps. Landings give ease in ascending and safety when descending. No landing should be less in length than the width of the staircase. The staircases in the pre-Elizabethan style were usually plain, dark and in long narrow flights; but with the Elizabethan architecture came in a more commodious, light and decorative style. Wood stairs are often enriched with plaster work, the soffits being panelled with plaster, and the strings adorned with composition or plaster enrichments. Stone stairs are also frequently enriched with plaster mouldings in the angles of the soffits and walls. External steps and landings are usually made with a fall of 1/4 inch to the foot to allow rain to fall off.

Cast Concrete Stairs.—Concrete is now fast superseding stone, wood and iron for staircase construction, where strength, durability and economy and fire-resisting properties are required. Cast concrete stairs were first introduced nearly sixty years ago. The stairs were cast in single steps, or in treads or risers, and fixed in the same way as natural stone. Square and spandrel steps, risers and treads are cast in wood moulds; circular steps and curtails in plaster moulds. Spandrel steps should have the wall or "tail" end formed square, and about 4 1/2 inches deep, to give a better bed and bond in the wall. A good mixture is 3 parts of granite or slag chippings and 1 of Portland cement, gauged stiff, and well rammed into the moulds. When set they are removed from the moulds, air dried, and placed in water or a silicate bath, and treaded in a similar way to that described for slabs. For long steps pieces of T iron, or iron pipes, are sometimes inserted in the centre of the concrete while being cast. The iron is not actually required to strengthen concrete properly made, but is used to give a temporary strength to the cast while it is green, so as to allow more freedom and security in handling the cast when it is being taken from the mould and moved about till permanently fixed. Landings are cast in a similar way, but unless very small, they are best done in situ. I have made landings up to 40 feet superficial, but owing to the cost of transit, hoisting and fixing they were not profitable.

Tests of Steps.—The following examples show the strength of concrete steps: In Germany, when constructing a concrete stair, with square steps 3 feet 4 inches long, and 6-inch tread, and 6½-inch rise, and one end set 8 inches into the walls, four steps were submitted for trial, and 5,940 lbs. weight of iron were gradually piled on them. The steps showed no signs of fracture, but no more weight could be put on because the masonry began to yield. The load was left on three days, and the steps remained unaffected. Although numerous tests have been made of concrete floors and blocks, few have been made for concrete steps. The following may be given as a reliable one: The steps were about 6 feet long, 11-inch tread and 6-inch rise. Every step was tested in the presence of the foreman concreter and author. The steps were supported at both ends, and weighed with a distributive load. The majority, which were matured by age, passed the specification standard.

Concrete Stairs Formed "in Situ."—Concrete stairs are an outcome of stairs built with cast concrete steps. Stairs formed in situ were introduced in 1867. The idea was suggested by the use of reverse moulds for fibrous plaster work, and in the formation of concrete dormer windows made in situ on some mansions. The step landings and the wall bond, being a monolith structure, were to a certain degree self-supporting. They tend to strengthen instead of to weaken the walls. Architects generally supply drawings of the intended staircase, but as there is often a difference in the size of the details of the actual work and the drawings, it is necessary that the workman should have a practical knowledge of setting out the "height" and "go" for the pitch board, to suit the landings and the well of the staircase, and ensure the necessary headroom.

Setting Out Stairs.—A correct method of setting out the framing for concrete stairs is of primary importance. The height of a stair is the length of a perpendicular line drawn from the upper of a floor to that of the one immediately above it. The "go" is the length of a horizontal line drawn along the centre line of the flight of steps or stair space. The exact height and widths should be taken on a rod, which should afterwards be used for setting out the work. Never work without this rod, as it is quicker and more accurate than measuring with a 2-foot rule. There are various ways of getting the dimensions of treads and rises. The following is a simple one and answers for most purposes. The height and go are taken and suitably divided. For example, if the height from floor line to floor line is 9 feet 3 inches, and it is proposed to make each rise 6 inches high, reduce the weight to inches, which would be 111; divide by the proposed height of each step—6 inches—the quotient will be 18, giving the same quotient 6 and 3-18. If there are intermediate landings, or half spaces, their dimensions must be allowed for. The size of the tread is obtained by dividing the "go" by the number of steps. The quotient will be the width of the tread. Great care should be taken in setting out the rods and pitch boards. It is better to measure thrice than to cut twice. When the string line is marked on the wall, a chase about 4½ inches deep is cut into the wall. It is not necessary to cut the chase straight at the soffit line, as it is apt to cut into a half, or rather a whole brick, and leave the ends loose. The irregular line of chase below the soffit line can be made solid during the process of filling in the steps. The chase should be cut as the work proceeds. Not more than one flight at a time should be cut, to avoid weakening the wall. In some instances a brick course in sand is left by the bricklayers. The bricks are then taken out as the work proceeds.

Nosings and Risers.—Nosing mouldings should be strong and bold. A simple but well-defined moulding not only gives greater strength, but is more in keeping with its purpose than one with numerous or small members. Nosing and riser moulds are best formed in two parts, the nosing moulds being one part and the riser board the other. To cut them out of the solid would not only be expensive, but also cumbrous to fix. They can be run at most saw and moulding mills.

They should be run in lengths and then cut and mitred on the job. Illustration No. 20 shows various forms of nosing. Fig. 1 is a simple nosing for common work. Fig. 2 may be used for school stairs, etc. Figs. 3 and 4 are well adapted for a good class of work. It will be seen that the lower edges of the riser boards are splayed. This is to admit the shoe of the running mould; also a trowel to work close up to face of the

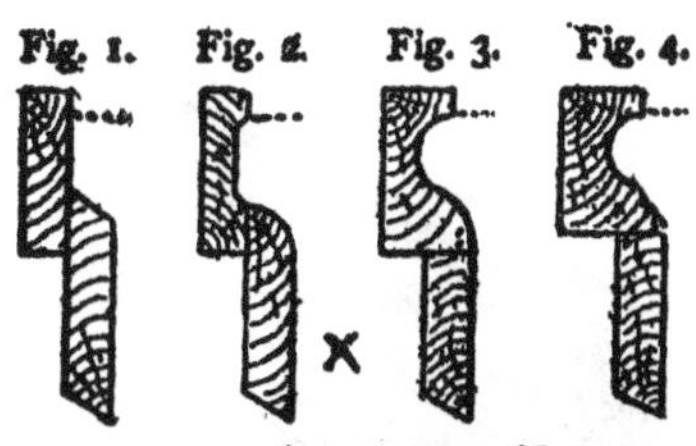

SECTIONS OF NOSING MOULDS WITH RISER BOARDS.
NO. 20.

concrete riser when running and trowelling off the treads. The dotted lines indicate the line of tread. Nosing moulds are cut in the centre of the section, and afterwards the two parts are held in position with screws while the steps are being filled in. This allows the upper part to be unscrewed and taken off when the stuff is nearly set, thus allowing more freedom to trowel the surface of the tread; also to make a better joint while the stuff is green, and at the part that is cast and the part to be trowelled. The joint in the nosing mould leaves a thin seam which is easily cleaned off, whereas the joint of the tread and nosing is not only seen more, but is also more difficult to make good.

Illustration No. 21 shows the mould and joint and screws for fixing same.

Framing Staircases.—The wood framing for concrete stairs differs from and is partly the reverse to that used for wood stairs. The nosings are formed the reverse of the moulding, and the whole framing is so constructed that it forms a mould to cast all the steps and landings, from floor, in monolithic form, or one piece. When the positions of half spaces or other

JOINTED NOSING MOULD
WITH RISER BOARD.
NO. 21.

landings are set out on the walls, strong planks are fixed on edges so as to give fixing joints for the carriage and outer strings. The strings are then fixed to act as guides for fixing the centring, risers and nosing moulds. Where practicable, the outer string should be so arranged in the fixing that it can be taken off after the concrete is firm without disturbing the centring. This allows the returned ends of the steps to be cleared off while the work is green. The carriage boards are fixed from landing to landing. Illustration No. 22 shows the forms and positions of the vari-

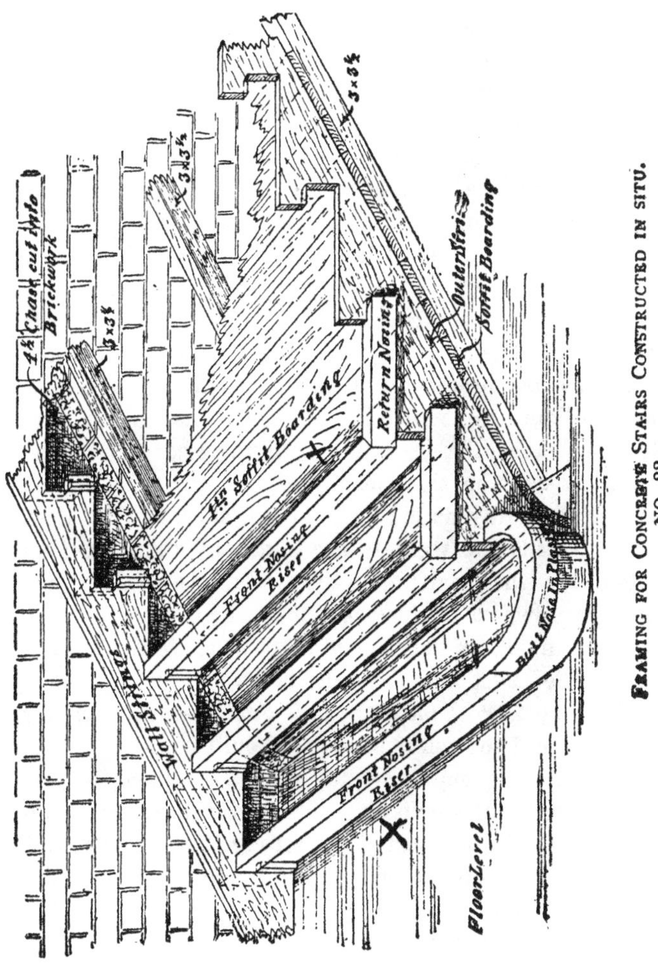

FRAMING FOR CONCRETE STAIRS CONSTRUCTED IN SITU.
NO. 22.

ous parts, with their names. Bullnoses or curtails and circular parts of nosings are formed in plaster moulds, which are run with several reverse running moulds.

Staircases between walls are more simple than open staircases; therefore they are more easy to frame up. The string boards are cut to the reverse of that used for wood stairs. A string is cut for each wall. The riser boards are then fixed to the wall strings. The centring for the soffits is fixed independently, the boards being laid on fillets which are nailed on each wall. For short flights of steps or common stairs, such as for cellars, etc., string boards may be dispensed with. The positions and sizes of the risers, treads, soffits and landings are first set out and marked on the walls. Riser fillets are then nailed on the walls, taking care to keep each fillet in a line with the riser mark, and to allow for the thickness of the riser boards which are subsequently nailed on the inner sides of the fillets. Riser boards for winders are generally hung on long fillets and then nailed on the walls. Long fillets extending upwards enable the work to be easier and more strongly fixed, as they cover more brick joints than if cut to the exact height of the riser.

Centring for Landings and Soffits.—Centring for landings and the soffits of stairs should be made strong and true. The timber should be well seasoned, to prevent warping or shrinkage. The outer angles of landings should be supported by strong wood props, not only to carry another prop for the landing above. All centrings should be made perfectly rigid, to stand the weight of the concrete and the ramming. Great care should be taken that the timber framing is securely supported, as any deflection will not only throw the work out of level, but will also tend to crack the concrete. The principal props should be cut about ½ inch shorter than the exact height. They are placed on a solid bed, the ½-inch space at top being made up with two wedges, the thin ends being inserted in opposite directions and gently driven home from each side until the exact height is obtained. If it is difficult to get the top of the prop, the wedges can be inserted at the bottom. The use of the wedges will be seen when the centring is struck. If there are winders in the stairs, the centring for the soffit will be more or less circle on circle. This form of centring is done by lathing, with 1-inch boards, cut to a taper, the surface being made fair with a gauged lime and hair. Rough 1½-inch boards are used for the centring. This should be close-jointed. Open joints or sappy timber act as a sieve, and allow liquid cement to drip through, thus robbing the concrete of its strength.

Waterproof Centring.—The following is a method that has been used with marked success for the soffits of stairs, landings and the ceilings of floors. The initial cost of preparing is small, and is repaid with interest by the decreased cost of setting and the increased strength and solidity. For ordinary work, such as warehouses, etc., it is very suitable, as a finished surface is formed, and no setting required. It seems strange that, when casting concrete work out of a wood or a plaster mould, the mould is seasoned, and every precaution taken, not only to stop suction, but also to prevent the escape of liquid cement; but when casting a large surface in situ (where every precaution should be taken to obtain the maximum of strength), any kind of centring (which is a mould) is thought good enough, if only sufficiently strong to carry the concrete till set. I am aware that many workers in concrete think that an open or porous centring is a benefit instead of a defect, simply because it affords an escape for excess of water. But why have excess of water at all? There is no gain in time or strength, but a direct loss in both points. The excess water descends through the concrete by force of direct gravitation, and always carries a certain amount of liquid cement with it to the centring, leaving the aggregate more or less bare, and the body of the concrete weak. A part of the liquid cement also oozes through the joints and crevices, which leaves the skin of the concrete bare and broken. There is no reason or excuse for excess water, and it is simply the result of ignorant or careless gauging, which is not only a waste of time, water and cement, but a loss in the ultimate strength, and the cause of cracks. Porous centring is also a dirty process. The overhead drip, drip, is neither good for the workmen nor the material underneath.

The process of forming the rough centring boards watertight is simple and expeditious, being done by laying the rough board surface with a thin coat of gauged plaster; and when the centring has been struck the plaster will come with the boards, leaving the concrete with a fair face. The ramming forces a certain amount of water to the lower surface or centring, and this is so close and fine that it takes an exact impress of it; consequently the truer and smoother the centring the truer and smoother the concrete surface. The film of water indurates the skin of the concrete and prevents surface or water cracks. It will be noticed when filling in dry or porous plaster moulds that the concrete cast produced has a surface either friable when newly cast, or when dry the surface is full of small water lines, like a map, or a broken spider's web. This is owing to the suction caused by the porous nature of the mould and the water escaping through the weak or open parts leaving corresponding lines on the concrete surface. These defects are obviated by using waterproof centring.

Where fineness of finish is not required, such as warehouse floors, the surface can be made sufficiently fair and smooth when filling in the concrete without subsequent setting. The plaster is laid on the centring, and made fair and smooth, and then the surface is saturated with water to correct the suction; or the surface, if dry, may be brushed over with a thin soap solution to prevent adhesion. On this surface a coat of neat cement about 1/8 inch is laid, and on this the concrete is placed. The two unite in one body, and when set, and the centring struck, the plaster sheet comes with the boards, leaving a smooth surface. This surface can be made in color by lime washing, which will also give more light, or a finished white surface can be obtained by substituting parian or other white cement for the neat Portland cement. The concrete must not be laid until the white cement is firm, not set, otherwise the concrete will force its way in thin or soft parts and disfigure the surface. I have successfully used this method for obtaining a finished surface when encasing iron girders with concrete for fireproof purposes.

Staircase Materials.—With regard to the materials for a concrete staircase, no one who intends to construct them substantially, fireproof and economically, can afford to use common substances, when by judicious selection and for a trifling additional first cost a combination of materials can be obtained, which, if not (strictly speaking) fireproof, is at least the most incombustible constructive compound known. This is a quality of the most vital importance in modern house construction. Portland cement and slag cement are the best known matrices. The finer Portland cement is ground, the greater its heat-resisting powers. Slag cement is lighter than Portland cement, and its fire-resisting properties exceed those of both gypsum and Portland cement. But as its manufacture is as yet somewhat limited, and its strength not uniform, exceptional care must be exercised in testing its general qualities before using it for staircases. Broken slag, firebricks, clinkers and pottery ware are the best aggregates, being practically fireproof. All should be clean, and in various graduating sizes, from that of a pin's head to that of a walnut, for roughing out with. The topping should be the same as that described for Eureka paving.

Filling in Stairs.—Before gauging the materials, sweep out all dust in the interior of the framing and the wall chase and then wet the latter, and oil the woodwork. If the wood of the nosing moulds and risers is sappy or open grained, the long lengths, before being cut and fixed, should be made smooth and indurated by coating with a solution of hot paraffin wax. The smoother and less absorbent the surface of the wood, the more readily and cleaner will the mould leave the cast work. Paraffin also renders the wood damp-proof, thus preventing swelling or warping. For ordinary purposes one or two coats of paraffin oil will be found sufficient. This should be done two or three hours before the steps are filled in, so as to allow the oil to partly dry in and stop the pores of the wood. If the wood absorbs all the oil, and has a dry surface, brush the surface again with paraffin, using a semi-dry brush. This should be done as the work proceeds. If the surface is over wet, the oil mixes with the cement, thus causing a more or less rough surface. Soap solution may be safely used for rough concrete, or where a rough surface is left to be subsequently set. In the latter case the surface must be well wetted with water and scrubbed before the final coat is applied. Soap solution may also be used for rough framing, such as soffit boards, but soap should not be used for fine concrete or a finished surface, as it leaves a film of grease which has a tendency to prevent the cement adhering when clearing up or making good the finished surface. As the work of filling proceeds, the surface should be brushed over with a slip, that is, neat cement, to fill up all angles, and obtain a surface free from "bulbs" and ragged arrises.

The coarse concrete for roughing out the stairs is composed of 1 part of Portland cement and 3 parts of coarse fireproof aggregate. These materials must be gauged stiff and laid in small portions of about a pailful at a time, taking care to thoroughly consolidate by ramming and beating with a wooden mallet, using a wooden punner or punch to get into the angles and deep parts. When the first layer, which may be about 3 inches thick, is rammed, another layer is deposited and rammed, and so on until the rough stuff is within

½ inch of the line of tread. It must not be omitted to brush the strings, treads and nosing moulds with slip as the work proceeds. This is most effectually done by the aid of a tool-brush. Care must be exercised when ramming stairs with mallets or punches that the mallet or other implement used is not too large or too heavy, for it would most likely cause the framing to bulge out, and the form of the work would be irretrievably spoilt. During the operation of ramming some of the water and a part of the constituent of the cement is forced upwards, and leaves a thin, smooth, clayey film on the surface, which prevents the adhesion of the next layer. For this reason the successive layers should be deposited before the previous one is set, and the topping should be laid while the coarse concrete is yet green. Too much stress cannot be laid upon the importance of topping the rough coat while it is green. This is one of the secrets of success of solid and strong work, so no more rough stuff should be laid than can be topped before the rough is set.

The fine stuff for the topping is the same as for Eureka paving, viz., 1 part of cement to 2 parts of fine aggregate, gauged firm and plastic. The tread is made level and fair by means of a running mould so formed that it bears on the nosing moulds above and below the tread. The mould has a metal plate or "shoe" fixed so as to run and form the tread. The shoe projects so that it will work under the riser board close up to the concrete riser. Illustration No. 23 shows a section of steps with the mould in position; also a section of the nosing mould and soffit boards and carriage. The end of the slipper next to the wall is cut short to allow the mould to run close up to the wall. A section of a T iron is shown as sometimes used as an internal support. Iron is used for long steps, or where stairs are intended for heavy traffic. Iron helps to sup-

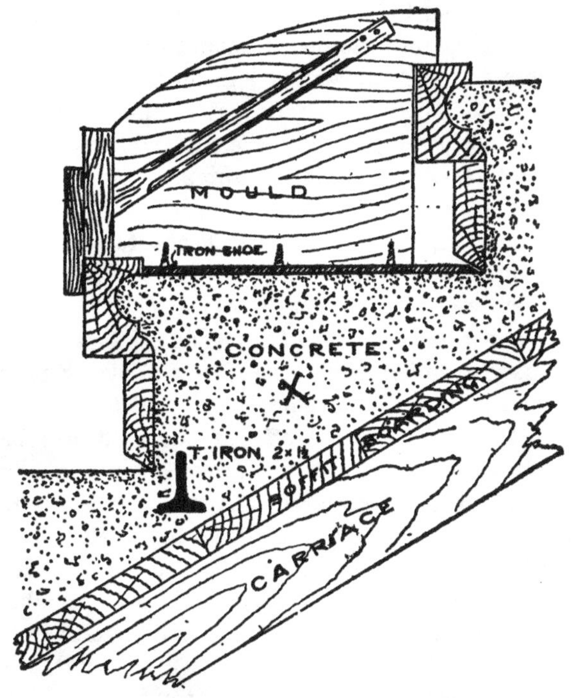

—SECTIONS OF FRAMING OF SOFFIT OF STAIR, RISER AND NOSER MOULD, WITH CONCRETE AND TREAD RUNNING MOULD IN POSITION.

NO. 28.

port the concrete until set; it is placed in alternate steps, or in every third or fourth step, according to the length of step. Ordinary sized steps require no iron, unless as a support for the concrete while green, and during the process of making.

Finishing Stairs.—When the treads are firm after being run, the upper part of the nosing moulds are removed, the surface and joists trowelled off. The advantages of having the nosing mould in two parts will thus be seen, as it allows the joint at this most noticeable part to be neatly cleaned off while the work is green. The lower part of the mould will support the concrete nosing during the finishing of the tread and until the concrete is set. If the work is done with a nosing mould in one piece, which necessitates its being left on until the concrete is set, the joint has then to be filed down and stopped, and however well done, has a patchy appearance. When the treads are finished, and the work set, but not dry, the riser and string boards are taken off, the joints made good, and the returned end of the steps cleaned off. If the stuff has been properly gauged and rammed, there should be little or no making good required, but it is important that if necessary it should be done while the work is green. A thin layer of neat cement will not adhere on a dense and dry body of concrete. The only way to obtain perfect cohesion is to cut the damaged surface out to a depth of not less than 1/4 inch, then thoroughly wet it, brush the surface with liquid cement, and fill it in with gauged cement. No traffic should be allowed on the treads during the process of setting and hardening. The work is further protected and hardened by covering with sacks kept wet for several days by frequent watering. Where there are several flights of stairs to construct, there should not be less than three sets of strings and riser boards, which will enable the carpenter to fix one set while the plasterers are filling in and cleaning off the others.

Non-Slippery Steps.—Incessant traffic tends to make the treads of steps more or less slippery. In order to obviate this, the surface is indented with a concrete roller, similar to that used for some kinds of paving. Another way is to form three or four V-shaped grooves from 1 inch to 2 inches apart on the treads while the concrete is moist. Another way is to insert leaden cubes about 1 inch square from 2 to 3 inches apart in the surface of the treads. Well-seasoned, hard wooden blocks, about the same size as the lead and fixed in a similar way, keeping the end grain vertical, are also used for this purpose. India rubber and cork cubes may also be used.

Striking Centrings.—This should not be attempted until all the other work, with the exception of finishing the soffits, is done. It will be understood that the framing can be arranged so that the string and riser boards can be taken off without disturbing the soffit centring, which is kept up as long as possible. The time for striking centring greatly depends upon the class of cement used, the manner of gauging and laying the concrete, and the temperature; but generally speaking, centring should not be struck for at least ten days. A stair between the walls can be struck much sooner than one having only one bearing by which its own weight is carried. I have seen a stair, with steps projecting 3 feet 6 inches from the wall, cleared of all supports in five days from the time of filling in; but this was with good cement, gauged 1 part to 2 of aggregate, and in warm weather, and the stair was strengthened with T iron.

The centring and framing for a flight of stairs should, where practicable, be independent of other stairs above or below, so that they can be struck in due rotation. The wedges of the main props should be gradually withdrawn. This tends to avoid the sudden jar which otherwise often happens when the centring is too suddenly struck. The sudden removal of centring and the inflexible nature of concrete are the cause of body cracks. The damage caused by the sudden jar may not be seen at the time, but it will be eventually developed by the force of expansion, which always finds out the weak spots.

Concrete and Iron.—Iron pipes, bars and T pieces are sometimes used with concrete stairs where the steps are long, or where landings have little support from walls. They help to carry the dead weight until the mass is thoroughly set, and also prevent sudden deflection if the centring is struck too soon. When iron pipes are used for steps they should go right into the wall chase. Iron T pieces are used for long landings. Care must be taken that, if the iron is used, no part should be left exposed. It must be embedded in the concrete to protect it from oxidization and the effects of fire. When iron girders, etc., are partly exposed, they should be painted. Iron bars or pipes are occasionally used to strengthen the outer strings of spandrel stairs. The iron is laid in the moist concrete near and along the string, having the ends projecting into the walls or landings. Angle irons are often used for unsupported concrete angles. Iron pipes, bars or joists are used as integral supports for landings and floors having unsupported ends.

The tensile strength of bar iron is materially increased by twisting. A bar ½ inch square with three twists per foot will gain about 50 per cent. in tensile strength when embedded in concrete, and give a corresponding strength to the concrete. A combination of iron and concrete is of special service where space is limited. For instance, if a beam or landing requires a certain thickness to carry a given weight, and it is inconvenient or difficult to obtain that thickness, the requisite degree of strength with a reduced thickness may be obtained by the combination of both materials. This gives the combined iron and concrete a useful advantage over stone. It is important to secure the full strength of the iron, and that none be lost or neutralized. In order to obtain the full strength the iron should be judiciously placed. Thus, a piece of iron surrounded by twenty times its sectional area of concrete would increase the weight-sustaining power of the iron in the centre and would have its strength increased about twice. If the same quantity of iron was placed in several pieces, so as to throw as much tensile strain on the iron as possible, the strength would be increased nearly four times. In order that none of the strength be lost or neutralized, the iron should be placed near the lower surface; if fixed higher, they are nearer the axis of neutral stress, and are correspondingly less effective. The use of iron in concrete is invaluable for many constructive purposes, but for general work, unless as a temporary aid and in a few exceptional cases, it is unnecessary. For all other things being equal, the huge board of reserve strength in good concrete is alone sufficient to sustain as great if not a greater weight than that sustained by natural stone. No other artificial compound exceeds the strength of the natural substance, as does artificial stone composed of Portland cement concrete.

Setting Concrete Soffits.—The soffits of stairs and landings, if neat cement has been used on a waterproof centring, as already described, only require a little stopping and coloring, but for work done on rough centring a setting coat has to be laid. This is usually done with neat Portland cement, though it is frequently gauged with lime putty to make it work more freely. The surface should be well roughened and wetted, to give a key and obtain perfect cohesion. It requires great care and time to make a good and true surface with Portland cement on a body of concrete, especially if the concrete is dry, which is generally the case where there are several flights of steps in a staircase, and the setting of the soffits and landings are left to the last part of the work. I have obtained equally good results by using Parian or other white cements for setting the soffits of staircases. When using white cements for this purpose it is better to brush the concrete surface with liquid cement before laying the gauged cement. The laying trowel should follow the brush, or at least before the liquid cement dries in. This not only secures better cohesion, but tends to prevent the setting coat peeling when trowelling it off. Soffits are sometimes set with gauged putty. This is like putting a beggar on horseback, and the work is never satisfactory.

Fibrous Concrete.—As already mentioned, canvas and other fibrous materials may be advantageously used with Portland cement for several purposes. Canvas forms a good ground for a setting coat on concrete surfaces. It gives a uniform and strong key, prevents surface cracks, and the final coat from peeling. Coarse canvas cut to convenient sizes is used. It is laid on the centring, and held in position with tacks, or with the same kind of cement as intended for the final coat. The canvas is then brushed with liquid cement, and then the concrete is laid while the canvas is moist, so that the whole will form one compact body. When the centring is struck, the fibrous concrete surface is roughened with a sharp and fine drag, so as to raise the fibre of the canvas, thus giving a fine, regular and strong key. This surface requires less material for the final coat than the ordinary concrete surface. If tacks are used they must be extracted before the final coat is laid, to avoid discoloration. The rough concrete and the white surface coat may also be done in one operation. The centring is made fair and smooth, and then oiled with chalk oil. The white cement is gauged stiff and laid on the centring. Coarse canvas is then laid on and well brushed with liquid cement. When this is firm (but not set) the surface is again brushed, and then the concrete is laid. The concrete is deposited in two or more layers. The first must not be too thick, taking care that it is well rammed or pressed on the moist canvas surface without disturbing the white cement. After the centring is struck any defects on the surface are made good. The surface may be then left white, or painted, or polished as required.

Polished Soffits.—Soffits, landings and strings of concrete stairs that are finished in white cement may be polished. The material may be tinted, or left in its natural white or creamy color. Polished cement work is always bright, and has a lustre like marble. Being durable and easily cleaned, it is more sanitary and cheaper than paint. The polishing is done the same way as described for "white work."

Concrete Staircases and Fibrous Plaster.—Fibrous plaster is well adapted for concrete surfaces when an enriched finish is desirable. I have introduced this material for decorating the soffits of steps and landings; also the strings of concrete stairs. By this method the soffits may also be enriched, and strings can be panelled, or enriched with medallions or foliage, as required. The soffits may also be enriched with modelled work done in situ, with some of the white cements, or with plaster and tow. The strings may be decorated with hand-wrought gesso. In order to obtain a fixing or keying substance that will receive nails or screws to sustain the fibrous plaster, a rough plan of the design, or rather the fixing points, is set out on the inside of the centring before the concrete is laid. On these plans wood plugs, fillets or concrete fixing blocks are laid, and held in position with nails, plaster or cement until the concrete is laid and set. Care must be exercised when fixing the plugs or fillets that the centring will leave freely without disturbing the plugs, etc.

Dowel Holes.—Cutting dowel holes in concrete to receive iron or wood balusters is a slow and tedious process. They are best formed by means of wooden plugs, which are fixed before treads; the plugs are driven into the rough concrete before it is set, leaving them flush with the line of tread, so that when the topping is laid they will not be in the way. Plugs are best fixed by the aid of a wooden gauge. The gauge is made the same thickness as the topping, the length being equal to the distance between the nosing mould and the riser board, and as wide as will admit of plug holes and the plugs to be driven through. The plugs are made a little larger than the baluster ends to allow for the lead. The gauge is laid on the rough concrete, using the returned nosing as a guide, and then driving the plugs flush with the top of the gauge. The gauge is then lifted up and laid on the next step, and so on until the finish. This method is accurate and saves measuring and marking the position of each hole on every step. When balusters are fixed on the ends of the steps, the plugs are fixed on the inside of the outer string. The plugs are generally left in until the balusters are ready for fixing. A ready method for forming "lewis" holes or other undercut sinkings in concrete is performed by casting wedge-shaped blocks of plaster of the required form and size, and then laying them in the desired positions while the concrete is soft. When the concrete is set, the plaster blocks can then be easily cut out, leaving the undercut sinking as desired.

Summary of Staircases Constructed "in Situ."—It will be seen from the foregoing that the operations employed in the construction of concrete staircases formed in situ are: (1) setting out the stairs and landing; (2) fixing the wood framing; (3) gauging the materials and filling in; (4) removing the framing; (5) cleaning up the treads, risers and strings; (6) striking the soffit centring and finishing the soffits; (7) protecting and wetting the work until set and hard.

Cast Steps.—Staircases are also constructed with steps cast separately, and then built in, in the same way as stone. Illustration No. 24 shows various sections of steps. Fig. 1 is a spandrel step, which may be used for model dwellings, factories, etc. The tread is grooved to afford a good footing and prevent dipping. The dotted line indicates a square seating or tail-end of the step, which is embedded in the wall. Fig. 2 is a square step. Fig. 3 is a step with a moulded and returned

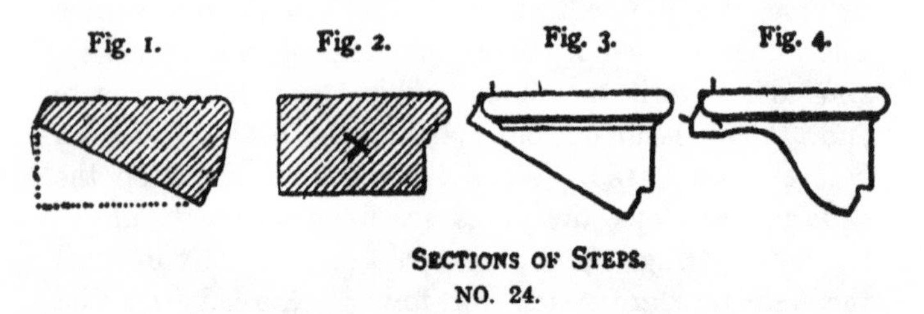

SECTIONS OF STEPS.
NO. 24.

nosing. Fig. 4 is a similar step, but having a moulded soffit. For cast work these steps must have a square seating or tail-end, as indicated by the dotted lines on Fig. 1, so as to bond into the wall.

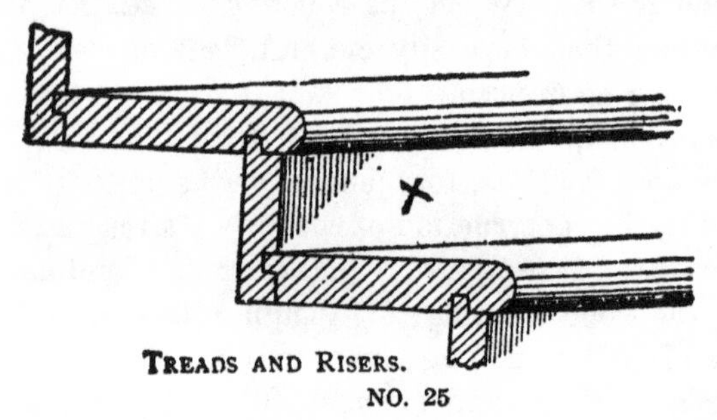

TREADS AND RISERS.
NO. 25

Treads and Risers.—Stairs between walls are sometimes formed with treads and risers. The treads and risers are cast and built in as the construction of the work proceeds. Sometimes they are let into chases and pinned after the walls are built. Illustration No. 25 shows a section of treads and risers.

Closed Outer Strings.—Staircases are sometimes finished with a close outer string, which prevents dirt or wet falling into the well. Illustration No. 26 shows the section, Fig. 1, and the elevation, Fig. 2, of a moulding outer string. The dotted line at A indicates a dowel hole for the balusters. Outer strings, whether plain or moulded, are much stronger when formed in

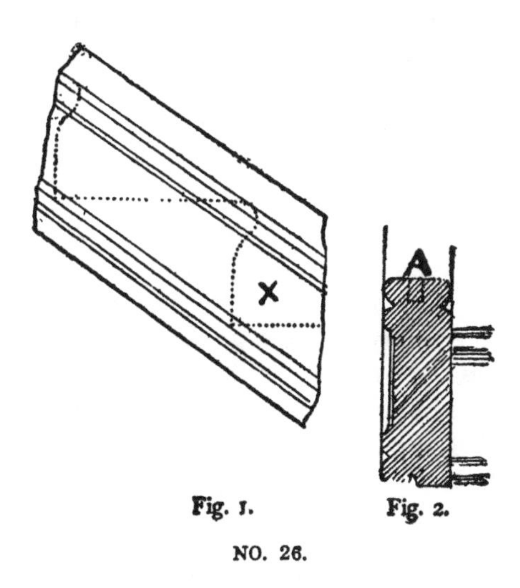

Fig. 1. Fig. 2.

NO. 26.

situ. This is best effected by fixing a reverse mould at each side, then filling in the space from the top. The top is finished by hand and the aid of a template. The dowel holes are formed as already described.

Concrete Floors.—It has been mentioned that the Romans, in the time of Julius Caesar, were in the habit of constructing their floors and roofs, as well as their walls, of concrete. According to an article in Archaeologia, the cementitious agent was pozzolana. The lime was obtained by burning "traverstine." The aggregate usually consisted of broken tufa for walls, of broken lava for foundations where great strength was required, and of broken pumice where lightness was essential. The floors were generally constructed of large slabs of concrete, supported on sleeper brick walls. The upper surface was finished with a layer of finer concrete and mosaic. The roofs were made flat, resting on brick pillars. The first known English patent fireproof construction was obtained by one Dekins Bull, in 1633; but as at that period patentees were not compelled to disclose what their patents covered, no description of the materials and methods can be given. Up to the middle of the eighteenth century fireproof their great weight and cost, were seldom used. But towards the close of that century cast-iron girders and segmental brick arches were gradually coming into use where strength was essential. Up to a century ago plaster was largely employed as a floor material. In floors usually consisted of brick arches, but owing to 1778 Earl Stanhope invented pugging for rendering wooden floors fireproof. By this process fillets were paled to the joists at about one-third of the height. Laths were laid on the fillets and plastered above and below with a coat of lime and chopped hay. The under sides of the joists were then lathed and plastered in the usual way to form the ceiling. About the early part of the last century wrought iron joists were substituted for cast iron girders. Fox & Barret's floor, designed about 1830, was the first in which an attempt was made to protect the exposed faces of the iron joists with a fire-resisting material. Hornblower's floor is one of the earliest for resisting the effects of fire. Iron, bricks and plaster are chiefly used in the French and American systems. For the sake of simplicity and reference, concrete floors may be divided into three kinds: (1) "Joist floors," in which the concrete is laid slid between the joists; (2) "Tabular floors," formed with fireclay tubes or hollow lintels placed between the joists and covered with concrete; (3) "Slab floors," formed in one piece or slab. Portland cement concrete laid in situ on and between iron joists is extensively used for fire-resisting structures. Cast concrete is used for some parts of tabular floors. Cast concrete blocks are used for the ceiling surface, and as a support for the rough concrete floor surface. The blocks are hollow, and have male and female dovetails on the sides. The ceiling surface of the floors and the outer surfaces of the partitions are finished with a thin setting coat of gauged putty or Parian. The chief objects of fireproof floors are to render each floor capable of resisting the effects of fire, so that fire cannot be communicated from one floor to another, and by making the roof fireproof, to prevent the fire from spreading from one compartment to another; to gain additional strength, so as to avoid as far as possible lateral thrust on the walls, and to secure the building from attacks and effects of both dry rot and damp. There have been about a hundred patents for fireproof floors during the past generation, of which about five or six survive.

Plaster Floors.—Plaster concrete, that is, plaster and broken bricks, or similar aggregates, also neat plaster, were at one time used largely for the formation of floors. The use of plaster floors was common in some districts, and up to a century ago the rough plaster, known as "floor plaster," was in general use where gypsum was found in abundance. Plaster floors were rarely used on the ground level, because they could not resist moisture, which caused them to become soft and retain the damp. They were principally used for upper floors. The gauged plaster was laid upon reeds. These reeds were spread upon the tops of joists, and over them was laid straw to keep the soft plaster from percolating through the reeds. The floors were about 3 inches thick, floated fair, and finished the following day. Wood strips were placed around the walls, and drawn out when the plaster began to set, to allow for the expansion of the plaster. The materials being so light, the timbers were less in size and number than those now in use. The joists were in some instances 3½ inches by 2½ inches, fixed wide apart, and supported by small beams about 4½ inches by 3½ inches. The undersides between the joists were made fair by plastering the reeds, but in the better class of work the joists were covered with reeds, and held in position with oak laths, and plastered. Bullock's blood was used to harden the floors after they were dry. In some instances they were coated with linseed oil to increase their hardness. Their use is now practically superseded by Portland cement concrete.

Joist Concrete Floors.—For this form of floor the concrete is laid between, over and under the iron joists. Beyond the supervision of the fixing of the centring and the gauging of the materials, little skilled labor is required. The rough concrete is laid between and partly under the iron joists, which are fixed from 3 feet to 5 feet apart, according to the span and strength of the joists. The centring is supported, or rather hung, by the aid of timber laid across the joists and secured by bolts. The materials are generally Portland cement and gravel, coke-breeze, clinkers and broken bricks, gauged in the proportion of 1 part of matrix to 5 of aggregate. Sand equal to one-third of the bulk should be added. Coke-breeze is weak, light and elastic, but combustible and porous. A mixture of gravel and breeze in equal proportions is better than either alone. The proportion of cement varies according to the span and class of aggregate. All other things being equal, the strength of concrete is influenced by the strength of the aggregate, so that it would take a greater proportion of cement to make coke-breeze concrete equal in strength to a concrete made with hard aggregate, such as granite, slag or brick. The upper surface of this class of floor may be finished with wood, tiles or fine concrete, as required. Joist concrete floors have been largely used. This is principally owing to their supposed cheapness, but it is more than probable that, in the event of fire, they would be dear in the end, because the lower part of the flanges are barely protected from the effects of fire, as the concrete, being thin at these parts, and also on a comparatively smooth surface, would soon crack or scale off, and leave the flanges of the joists exposed to the ravages of fire. They are also more or less conductors of sound. Caminus concrete cement is an excellent material for the construction of fireproof ceilings and partitions.

Caminus Concrete Cement.—This material is specially designed to produce a hard and practically indestructible concrete for the construction of fireproof floors and walls. It is manufactured from a waste product, and all inflammable material, such as coke-breeze, being entirely dispensed with, the concrete is thoroughly fire-resisting. It is lighter and much cheaper than Portland cement concrete, and is perfectly free from expansion and contraction whilst setting. It can be manufactured to set in a few hours, so that the centres can be struck the day after the floor is laid. It can be supplied in a ready aggregated condition, so that the bags may be hoisted direct to the floor where the concrete is being laid, and gauged on the floor, thus saving a great amount of waste, and also labor in handling, mixing and laying.

Concrete Floors and Coffered Ceilings.—A method was patented by E. Ransom for decreasing quantity of material and yet obtaining equal strength in floors. The floor is divided by a series of beams at right angles to each other, so as to form a series of coffers in the ceiling. For instance, for a floor 12 inches thick, the floor proper would be about 4 inches thick, and beams about 3 inches thick and 8 inches deep—a rod of twisted iron being placed in the centre of the thickness, and near the lower surface of the beams. The beams are generally about 2 feet 6 inches from centre to centre. The method of construction is as follows: First, form a platform or centring; on this a series of core boxes 2 feet 3 inches is placed, 3 inches apart, so as to form a 3-inch beam. The core boxes must be tapered and their upper edges rounded, so that they will draw when the centring is struck. The size of the core boxes may be altered to suit the size and requirements of the floor. With regard to the iron bars, the inventor says: "It is of vital importance for the strength of the structure that the iron bars be placed no higher in the beam than calculated for; that the longitudinal centre of these bars should be at the lowest point; and it is advisable that the bars curve upwards slightly and uniformly each way from the centre to the ends, so that the ends are from 1 to 3 inches higher than the centres. By preparing the concrete bed on a corresponding curve, the natural sag of the bar, as it is being handled to its place, gives all the requisite facility to accomplish this purpose. No crooked or irregular twisted iron must be used; otherwise, when the strain comes upon it, it will perforce straighten and lengthen out, and weaken the structure in so doing. After placing the iron, the rest of the concrete is tamped in place, and the whole made to form a monolithic block. It is of vital importance that no stop be made in the placing of concrete from the time the beam is begun until the thickness of the beam is in place and a 'through joint' is made. The web and the thickness must be one solid piece of homogeneous concrete."

Combined Concrete Floors and Panelled Ceilings.—A combined floor and panelled ceiling may also be formed in concrete. This is executed as follows: First, form a level platform or centring, and on this fix the reverse plaster mould, run and mitred, according to the design of the ceiling. The intervening panels are then made up with framing, and the concrete filled in the usual way, and when set the centring and reverse mould are removed, and the ceiling cleared off. If desired, a finely finished and smooth white surface may be obtained by coating the surface of the moulds and panels with firmly gauged Parian, or other white cement, until about 3/8 inch thick, and when this is firm (but not set), the rough concrete is deposited in layers and tamped to consolidate the concrete, and unite it with the white cement. The surface may also be finished with fibrous concrete. The method of doing this, also for carrying out the above white cement process, is described in "Fibrous Concrete."

Concrete and Wood.—Concrete floors finished with flooring boards require special care to prevent damp or dry rot. There are various methods in use for fixing and keeping the flooring boards from contact with the rough concrete, one way being to fix wood fillets to the joists by means of wedges or clamps. Another way is to embed wood fillets or fixing blocks in the rough concrete, leaving them projecting above the level of the iron joists, to give a bearing and fixing points to the flooring boards; or fine coke-breeze, concrete or plaster screeds, may be laid at intervals on the rough concrete, onto which the boards are nailed. Fixing blocks, concrete or plaster screeds, are preferable to wood fillets, as they do not shrink or rot, and will better resist fire. All these methods leave intervening spaces between the concrete and the boards, and unless thoroughly ventilated, they harbor vermin, dirt and stagnant air. Unless the wood is thoroughly seasoned, and the boards grooved and tongued, dust and effluvia will find egress through the joints. A portion of dust and water when sweeping and washing the floors also finds egress through the joists; and as the concrete will not absorb the water, or allow the dust to escape, they accumulate and become unseen dangers. These sanitary evils may be obviated, or at least reduced to a minimum, by laying the boards direct on the concrete. This not only forms a solid floor with no interspaces, but admits of thin boards being used with as much if not greater advantage than a thick board.

There is no uneven springing between the joists, which causes friction and opening of the joints, and the whole thickness is available for wear. There is also less total depth of floor, consequently less height of building and general cost. Another important advantage of a solid floor is that it will resist fire better than one with hollow spaces. It is here that the sponginess and elasticity of coke-breeze concrete as a top layer is of special service, and where it may be utilized with advantage. Owing to its being able to receive and retain nails, the boards can be nailed at any desired place. Wood blocks for parquet floors can also be bedded or screwed on the concrete surface. Flooring boards will lie even and solid on this surface, and if a thin layer of felt or slag-wool be spread on the concrete before the boards are laid, a firm and noiseless floor is obtained. Slag-wool is an imperishable non-conductor of heat, cold and sound, and it will not harbor vermin. If the work is in humid climate, the coke-breeze surface when dry should be coated with a solution of tar and pitch, to prevent atmospheric moisture being absorbed by the porous coke-breeze.

Concrete Drying.—To prevent dry rot it is of the utmost importance that the concrete should be thoroughly free from moisture before the flooring boards are laid and fixed. The drying of concrete is a question of time, which depends upon the amount of water used for gauging, the thickness and the temperature. It may take from three days to three weeks or even three months. The drying can be accelerated by directing currents of hot air on the lower surface, or by laying some absorbent material, such as dry sawdust or brick dust, on the upper surface. As soon as the surface moisture is absorbed, or the dry material has no further absorbent power, it should be removed to allow the mass to be air dried. Another way is to lay the floor in two coats, and to allow one coat to dry before the other is laid. For instance, if the floor is to be 6 inches thick, the first coat is laid with rough, but strong concrete, the aggregate being the best available; but taking gravel and coke-breeze to be the most plentiful, it will be best to assimilate and combine the good qualities of each to equalize their defects by mixing them in equal proportions. If brick is plentiful, and broken to properly graduated sizes, it will give better results than gravel or breeze. The mixed aggregate is gauged 5 parts to 1 of cement, and laid 4½ inches thick, and gently but firmly beaten in situ, the surface being left rough to give a key for the second coat. The second coat is not laid until the first is dry, and consists of one part cement to 5 of sifted and damped coke-breeze, gauged stiff, and laid 1½ inches thick, beaten in situ, ruled level, and any ridges being laid fair with a long hand-float. The moisture of the second coat, by reason of the density of the first coat, will only be absorbed to a small degree, while the greater portion will be taken up by the atmosphere, and enable the combined coats to dry sooner than if laid in one. The first coat should be laid as soon as the roof is on, so as to give all possible time for it to dry, and the second coat to be laid and dried before the flooring is laid. When coke-breeze is not available for the second coat, use soft brick, broken to pass through a 3-16-inch sieve. The method of laying floors in two coats is only given as an alternative plan, and as an example of a process used in some parts. Greater strength, as a whole, and more perfect cohesion between the two coats, is obtained by laying the second coat as soon as the first is laid, or at least while it is green.

Concrete Slab Floors.—The term, slab floor, is applied to a concrete floor formed in situ, and in one piece or slab. It must not be confounded with slab pavements, which are constructed with a number of small cast slabs. Slab floors are usually made without exterior iron supports, but in a few instances iron T pieces or bars have been used as internal supports. Bearing in mind the lasting properties of the old Roman slab floors, and the enormous strength of the modern examples at home, which are unsupported by iron, and are practically indestructible, it seems strange that they are not in more general use, and that for some inexplicable reason preference is given to shrinking, rotting and combustible floors, composed of poor iron and timber instead of the best work and material, which, if a little dearer at first, is infinitely superior and vastly cheaper in the long run. The great sanitary advantages and fire and damp resisting powers of concrete slab floors are the highest known. The construction of slab floors is simple, and similar in many respects to that already described for stair landings and ordinary concrete and joist floors. There are several methods of supporting the floors, the first and most common being to leave a sand course or to cut a horizontal chase in the walls to receive the ends of the floors. The second is to lay the floors when the walls are floor high, and build the higher walls on it when set. This method, while making sound work, is not always practicable or convenient, owing to the delay in building while waiting for the floors to set. The third method is to build corbelled ledges in the walls, so as to carry the floors. The centring for slab floors should be perfectly rigid, water-tight and slightly cambered towards the ceiling centre. This camber gives more strength to the floor, and lessens liability to crack when removing the centring. If joists are not used, the centring is supported on wall boards and centre struts. Another way which gives great additional strength is to form the centring level, but having all the edges at the wall rounded off, so as to form the floor like an inverted sink or tray. The horizontal chases in this case should be made wider than the thickness of the floor to allow for a thickness of rim. The extra width of chase, which may be one or two bricks thick, according to the width of span, is made below the centring or line of ceiling, the angles being coved by rounding the edges of centring. The coved rim gives greater strength with a less thickness of floor. The cove may be left plain or used for a cove for a plaster cornice, or roughened and used as a bracket for the same purpose. The expansion of concrete floors having large areas, or where hot cement has been used, has been known to disturb the walls, causing cracks and displacement of brick and stone work. This may be prevented by isolating the floor ends from the walls. This is done by forming expansion partitions or linings in the chases, the linings being composed of slag, felt or wood shavings, straw, reeds or other compressible material. The chase should be sufficiently deep to allow for a compressible lining about 1½ inches thick, and a fair bed for the slab floor. Care must be taken to leave a few half bricks solid at intervals, say from 3 to 4 feet apart, to support the upper walls until the floor is set. Compressible linings may be used for floors supported on corbelled ledges; and when the expansion, and in many cases subsequent contraction, has finally finished, the linings can be taken out, and the vacant space filled up with fine concrete, or utilized as a ground key for cement skirtings. If girder or iron posts are isolated from the walls by means of compressible linings, the effects of expansion and sound are limited. In some instances a judicious use of iron may be made. For instance, large areas may be divided with three or four rolled iron joists, so as to form shorter spans or smaller bays. Joists tend to bind the walls together, and to serve as scaffold bearings for building the upper parts of walls. They may also be used for hanging the centring on instead of strutting, or as aids to the strutting. Joists may also be used as integral supports at unsupported ends of concrete floors. They should be so fixed that the lower flanges are not less than 1 inch above the lower surface of the concrete. The whole strength of iron is brought more fully into use by fixing it near the lower surface. If fixed near the centre, or at the axis of neutral stress, a corresponding part of the strength is comparatively of little value.

Construction of Slab Floors.—Portland cement as a matrix is indispensable. The unequal nature of gravel and coke-breeze renders them unfit and unsafe aggregates for this class of work. Broken brick being cheap, and obtainable in most districts, affords a ready aggregate, and may be used with safety and success. In ordinary cases of concrete construction, the whole thickness is usually made with one rate of gauge; but for slab floors covering large areas, and unsupported by iron or other supports, exceptional strength is required. Stronger results are obtained by making up the whole thickness with different rates of gauge. Taking the usual gauge for floors as from 4 to 5 parts of aggregate to one of cement, and used for the whole thickness, it gives an unequal strength, a part of which is comparatively of little use, especially at the neutral axis; but if the cement is divided so as to form an ordinary coat in the centre, and stronger coats at the upper and lower surfaces at the points of greatest strain, the upper being compressive and the lower tensive, a better and more accurate arrangement of strength and allowance for disposition of strains is obtained. The additional strength at the proper places is obtained not only by the use of additional cement, but by the method of construction, which enables the same quantity of cement as gauged for the usual rate for forming the whole thickness in one coat to be used more profitably. Take the section of an iron joist as an example; this gives divided yet united strength, which sounds paradoxical, but is true. The flanges sustain the greatest strains, and the web comparatively little. With concrete, the strong coats at the upper and lower surfaces represent the flanges, and the ordinary coat the web. As already stated, the increased and profitable distribution of strength is obtained by the method of construction. For instance, take a slab floor 20 feet by 14 feet and 12 inches thick, without iron joists or other supports, and intended to carry a safe load of 2½ cwt. per superficial foot, in addition to its own weight of say 1 cwt. per square foot. This floor is laid in three coats, the first composed of 1 part cement and 2 of fine broken bricks gauged stiff, and laid 2 inches thick; the second composed of 1 part cement and 6 of coarse broken bricks gauged stiff and laid and rammed 8 inches thick; and the third composed of 1 part cement and 2 of fine broken bricks gauged stiff and laid 2 inches thick. If the upper surface is intended for hard frictional wear a slight difference is made in the gauge and materials. The first coat is composed of 2 parts of cement and 5 of fine broken bricks gauged stiff and laid 2 inches thick; the second of 1 part cement and 6 of coarse broken bricks gauged stiff and laid and rammed till 8 inches thick; and the third coat composed of 1 part cement and 2 of fine crushed slag or granite. It will be seen that this constructive method gives the desired positions of strength, and the total quantity of cement in the united gauges is 1 part to 4, and up to 5 parts of aggregate. The fine broken bricks should be passed through a ½-inch sieve, and the coarse through a 2-inch screen, taking care that the latter contains a greater quantity of the smaller pieces than of the larger. It must be clearly understood that the second coat must be laid before the first is set; also that the third is laid before the second is set, so as to ensure perfect cohesion between each coat, and the absolute homogeneity of the whole mass.

Hollow Floors.—Greater lightness in concrete floors is obtained by the use of concrete tubes. If the tubes are placed apart and in the centre of the floor thickness, a hollow homogeneous concrete slab is formed. The vertical divisions between the tubes connect the upper and lower coats, as with a web of a joist connecting the upper and lower flanges. The method of construction is simple and expeditious. For example, for a slab floor 10 inches thick, first lay a coat 2 inches thick of the stronger and finer concrete, as described for the 12-inch slab floor, and when this is firm lay 5 or 6-inch tubes from wall to wall. Bed the sides with rough concrete, and lay another row of tubes parallel with the first row and about 2 inches apart, and so on until the floor area is covered; then make up interspaces with rough concrete till level with the upper surfaces of the tubes, and then cover this with a coat of fine concrete 2 inches thick. Concrete tubes or common earthenware drain pipes may be used. Half-circle pipes, laid on their side edges, may be used to save concrete and weight in joist floors, etc.

Concrete Roofs.—Concrete roofs require special care to render them watertight. Subsidence in the brick work of new buildings is often the cause of cracks on concrete roofs. The roof should have a good camber, to give greater strength and allow for the fall of water to the outer edges. The rough coat should be laid and well consolidated by ramming or beating, and then left for seven days (the longer the better) before the topping is added. The upper coat should be strongly gauged with fine aggregate, as in "Eureka." If possible, the topping should be laid in one piece. If the area is too large to be laid and finished in one piece, the joints of the bays should overlap. This is done by rebating the screed rules, so as to allow one-half of topping thickness to go under a part of the rule and form an underlap or ledge about ½ inch wide, and when the adjoining bay is laid an overlapped but level joint is the result. Roofs exposed to the sun's heat should be kept damp for several days after being laid, as joints are affected by the heat as well as by deflection of centring or subsidence of walls. Compressible linings or wood strips should be used round the walls to counteract any expansion. All concrete roofs should have a cement skirting 6 inches high and 1 inch thick well keyed into the walls. If linings are not used when the topping is laid, the topping should be turned up on the walls, so as to form a rim, to prevent water getting between the roof and the walls. Greater heat and damp-resisting powers are obtained by laying the upper surface with ½-inch thick coat of special concrete, composed of 1 part of Portland cement, ½ part of slaked lime and 1 part of firebrick dust. This should be consolidated with a hand-float, and finished fine and close with a trowel.

Notes on Concrete.—When calculating the strength of floors, stairs, etc., the following facts should be borne in mind: Portland cement, when new, is too hot; sets more rapidly and expands more than old cement. The finest ground cement is the best and strongest. The time in setting, and in which the maximum strength is attained, varies according to the age of the cement, the quantity of water used, and the mode of gauging and the mean atmospheric temperature. The maximum strength of a briquette of mature cement is maintained, while one of new cement "goes back." A briquette of matured cement will stand a tension strain of 550 pounds per square inch, and a crushing weight of 6,000 pounds per square inch. A briquette of neat cement is more brittle than one of concrete. Briquettes mature more rapidly than thick slab floors. The adhesive strength of Portland cement is about 85 pounds per square inch. The adhesive strength increases more rapidly than the cohesive. A mass with a surface large in proportion to its volume sets more rapidly than a mass with a small area in proportion to its volume. Masses subject to pressure set more rapidly and attain greater hardness than masses not so pressed. The average compressive strength of concrete is about eight times its tension strength. The proportion of compressional and tensional strength varies according to the quality and quantity of the aggregate. The strength of concrete depends greatly on the proportion of the matrix and aggregate; also on the strength of the latter. As regards bricks, it must be remembered that there is a wide difference between the tensile strength of hard, well-burnt bricks and soft stocks. No bricks are so strong as cement, the best kinds being about one-fourth the strength of neat cement. Taking the gauge as one part of cement to 4 of broken brick, the strength of the concrete will be about two-fifths of neat cement, but for safe and practical calculations it will be best to take the strength as one-fourth of neat cement. Square slabs are stronger than rectangular slabs. Slab floors being homogeneous throughout, the whole weight is a dead weight, and consequently there is no thrust on the walls. With regard to the live load or weight which floors should be constructed to carry, some difference of opinion exists. Hurst says that for dwellings 1¼ cwt., public buildings ½ cwt. and warehouses and factories 2½ cwt. are safe calculations. Others assert that for domestic buildings 1 cwt. per foot would be ample for all contingencies. An American authority states 40 lbs. is sufficient for ordinary purposes. The following table shows the results of tests of slab floors made without iron. The slabs were supported all round, and uniformly loaded with bricks.

TEST OF SLAB FLOORS.

No.	Length between Supports, feet.	Breadth between Supports, feet.	Thickness, feet.	Age in Days.	Breaking Weight, in cwt. per sq. ft.	Weight of Slab, in cwt. per sq. ft.	Total Breaking Weight, in cwt. per sq. ft.
1	14.5	6.75	.5	7	3.	.54	3.54
2	"	"	"	14	2.76	"	3.30
3	"	"	"	21	8.88	"	9.42
4	"	13.5	"	7	1.07	"	1.61
5	"	6.75	"	14	2.51	"	3.05
6	"	"	"	21	2.84	"	3.38

Cast Concrete.—Innumerable patents have been obtained for a combination of materials, also moulds for the construction of artificial stone. Among the many that may be mentioned is Mr. Ranger's system. He obtained a patent in 1832 for artificial stone formed with a lime concrete. The aggregate consisted of shingle, broken flints, mason's chippings, &c. The inventor stated that the best results were obtained by using 30 lbs. of an aggregate of a siliceous or other hard nature, 3 lbs. powdered lime, and 18 ozs. boiling water. No more of the materials were gauged at the time than were sufficient to fill one mould, as the boiling water caused the concrete to set very rapidly. This material, after fifty years' exposure is still sound and shows no sign of decay. No artificial stone equals, far less excels, the strength and durability, sharpness, and evenness of Portland cement concrete. This form of artificial stone is now extensively used as a substitute for natural stone, for window heads, string courses, sills, columns, copings, keystones, and many other architectural, constructive, and decorative features. Figures, animals, bas-reliefs, capitals, panels, can be made in fine concrete with all the relief, undercut, and fine detail which distinguishes high-class from inferior work. Cast work has the advantage over in situ work that any defect can be detected previous to fixing. The methods of moulding and casting various works are given in the following pages.

Concrete Dressings.—Architectural works, especially large or plain parts, are generally cast in wood moulds. If there are ornamental parts in the blocks, a combination of wood and plaster, and sometimes gelatine, is used for the moulds; wood for the main or plain parts, plaster for circular or moulded parts, and gelatine for undercut parts. The plaster or gelatine, as the case may be, is screwed on or let into rebated parts of the wood. Ornamental parts are sometimes cast separately. and then fixed on the main cast. They may also be cast separately and laid into the main mould (face inwards), and the whole is cast together in a somewhat similar way to that described for ''bedded enrichments'' in fibrous plaster cornices.

Considerable skill and ingenuity has been displayed in the construction of wood moulds for casting concrete blocks for architectural purposes. Many methods have been employed for fixing the sides and ends together, and also to the bottom of the mould, leaving one or more parts unfixed to facilitate the release of the cast. The primitive method is to fix the various parts of the mould with screws. This is a slow and unreliable process, as the continual screwing and unscrewing for each cast soon wears the screw-holes, and the sides become loose and out of square, causing the casts to get out of their true form. Hinges, also hooks and eyes, have been used for the same purpose, but they are liable to the same defects as the screws when subject to long use.

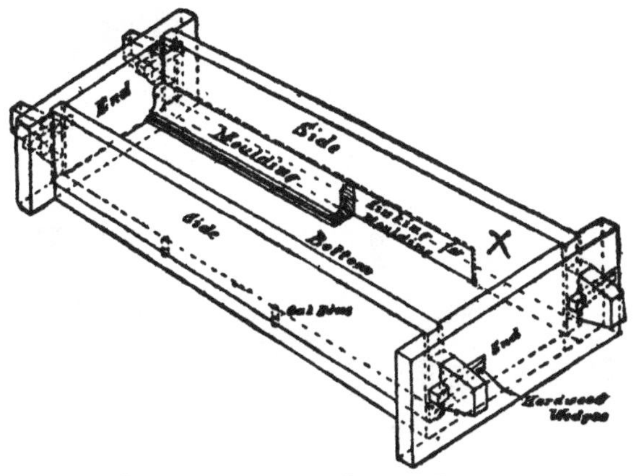

—WEDGE MOULD FOR CASTING BLOCKS, MOULDED LINTELS, &c.

NO. 27.

Thumbscrews to fit into iron sockets are also used, but they are too expensive for ordinary work, and are unsuitable for small moulds. One of the most simple and reliable methods is the "wedge mould," invented by an architect. It is easily made, and expeditious in working. Even after long and constant use, the casts are always accurate in form and size. The wedges and the rebated ends allow the various parts to be correctly fixed and held in position. Illustration No. 27 shows the method of construction. The various parts are named, and the sketch is self-explanatory. When the moulds are extra deep, it is necessary to make two or more sets of tenons and wedges at each angle. When there are a large number of casts required the mould ends are strengthened by binding the projecting ends with hoop iron. This method has been adopted for casting a lot of blocks. Illustration No. 28 shows two useful kinds of moulds. Fig. 1 is a simple form of mould adapted for plain blocks, caps, lintels, &c. A, A, are the sides, which are grooved into the ends B, B, and

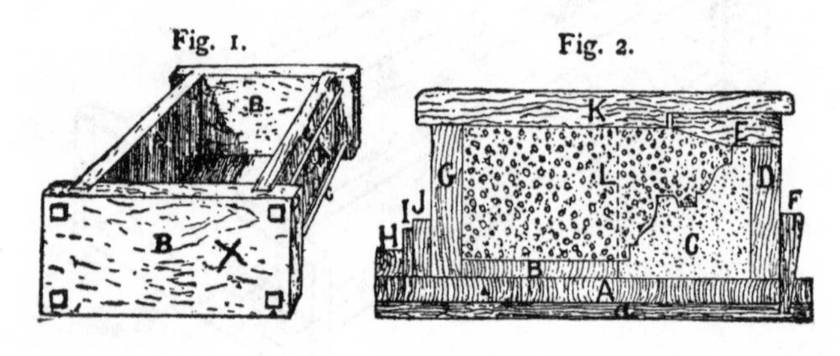

NO. 28.

held together by the bolts and nuts, C, C, two on each side. The bolts may be about 3/8 inch diameter, with a good-sized square-head at one end, and a washer and nut at the other. This, having no bottom, is termed a bolted frame mould. It should be laid on a bench or moulding board before the cast is filled in. Fig. 2 is a section of a combined wood and plaster mould on the wedge principle, adapted for casting a strong course moulding. A is a moulding board, 1½ inches thick, formed with two or more boards; a is one of two or more cross ledges, 1 inch thick, on which A, the ground, is nailed. B is a width board, 1 inch thick, which is nailed on to A. This gives a point of resistance to the plaster piece C and the side board G. D is a side board on which E is screwed. E forms the sloping part of the weathering. F is one of two or more vertical wedges which hold D E in position. The sockets for the wedges F are made between the cross ledges, so that the wedge will project below the ground A. This allows the wedges to be more easily driven out when the cast is set. G is the back or plain side board. H is a fillet, 1½ inches square, screwed on to the ground A. I and J are two folding wedges, or, in other words, wedges driven in opposite directions. These hold G in position. Two or more of these folding wedges are required, according to the length of the mould. The same remarks apply to the vertical wedges F. The latter form of wedge is only given as an alternative. The end pieces are held in position by dropping them into grooves in a similar way as shown in the previous figure, with the exception that the grooves are cut in the sides instead of the ends. K is a gauge rule which is used for ruling the upper surface of the cast fair. This may also be done by working a straight-edge longitudinally. The dotted line at L, the concrete, indicates the wall line. The level part of the weathering up to this line, or if splayed from the outer member of this line, must be finished smooth to allow the water to run freely off. When the cast is set, the wedges are withdrawn, and the sides and ends released. The cast is then turned over on its back end or top side on a board, and then the plaster piece and the wood ground is taken off. If the cast is green, it should be turned over on old sacks or wet sawdust, so as to protect the arrises, and avoid fractures.

Illustration No. 29 shows a method commonly adopted for constructing moulds for sills and copings. Fig. 1 is the section of a mould for a window sill. A is the moulding board, made with two or more pieces, each 1¼ inches thick; a is one of two or more cross ledges, made with 1 inch stuff, on which A is nailed. B is the width board, made of ¾ inch stuff, nailed on to A. C is a block, 1¼ inches thick, which is nailed on to B. These blocks are placed about a foot apart, or so that they will carry the lining D, 1 inch thick. A

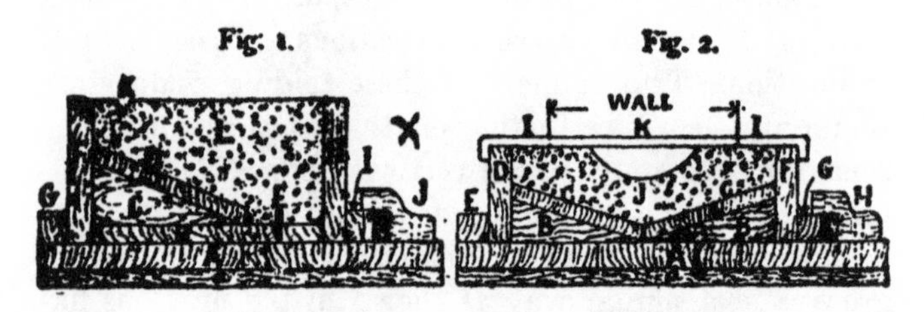

FIG. 1.—SECTION OF MOULD FOR CASTING SILLS.
FIG. 2.—SECTION OF MOULD FOR CASTING COPING.
NO. 29.

groove or an iron tongue E is made in B, and a piece of thick hoop iron or iron bar is placed loosely in the groove before the cast is filled in. F is a fixed side, 1¼ inches thick. G is a fillet, 1½ inches square, nailed on to F, and screwed on to moulding board A. H is a loose side, 1¼ inches thick, on which the fillet I is nailed. J is one of two or more clips, which turn on a screw, and are used to hold the loose side H in position. These clips are made and used in the same way as described for fibrous slabs. As compared with wedges, clips are always in position ready for use, are not liable to be mislaid, and when the fillets are fixed on to the side pieces, the clips keep the sides from rising as well as expanding. K is a throating or water groove, which is formed in the concrete L, with a rule having a rounded edge. Two blocks, dished at the inner ends, must be fixed one at each end of the mould, so as to form a stool or bed for the superstructure. The position and form of the groove is obtained from sinkings cut in the end pieces of the mould. The end pieces are held in position by grooves cut in the side pieces in a similar way, as already described, with the exception that the grooves are cut in the side pieces, instead of the end pieces. When setting out the mould, an extra length must be allowed for the side pieces for the grooves. A part of the upper surface of the cast (being the part which projects beyond the line of wall) must be finished fair by hand at the same time as forming the water groove. This must be done while the cast is green. When the cast is released from the mould, the iron tongue will be found firmly embedded in the concrete. Fig. 2 is a section of a wood mould adapted for casting wall copings. A is the ground of a moulding board, which may be made of 1¼-inch stuff, and in 2 or more widths; a is one of two or more cross ledges, 1 inch thick, on which A is fixed. B, B, are blocks about 1¼ inches thick, placed about 1 foot apart. C, C, are linings, 1 inch thick, nailed to B, B. D is a fixed side, 1¼ inches thick. E is a fillet, 1½ inches square, fixed to D, and then screwed on to A. F is a loose side, 1¼ inches thick, on which is nailed the fillet G, 1½ inches square. This strengthens the sides and affords the fixing point for the clip H. The water grooves I, I, and the hollowed part in the middle of the concrete J (made to save materials in weight) are worked from the end pieces of the mould, which are let into the grooves, as described in the previous diagram. If the moulds are deep, wood or iron clamps may be fixed across the sides to keep them in position, as shown by K. The moulding boards in this and the previous figures, if strongly made, can be used for a variety of similar purposes. When introducing cast instead of run moulded work, I used iron and zinc plates to strengthen and make more durable plain surfaces on wood moulds; but owing to the expense and trouble in fixing the plates to the woodwork, they were abandoned, and by using a better class of wood, and indurating the surface of the mould with hot paraffin wax, sharp and clean casts were more cheaply produced. Cast-iron moulds may be used where there is a large number of casts required. They may also be advantageously used for stock designs, such as plain moulded balusters. Wood moulds are rendered more durable and impervious to wet by brushing them with hot paraffin wax, and then forcing it into the wood by ironing with a hot iron. The use of paraffin wax and oil has already been described.

Mouldings Cast "In Situ."—Casting cornices, copings, &c., in situ is now frequently employed for concrete. The advantages of this system over shop cast work, are, that the work is readily done, and the cartage or moving from the workshops to the building, and the fixing, are dispensed with.

Illustration No. 30 shows the method of constructing and fixing various kinds of casting moulds for in situ work.

Fig. 1 shows the section of a cornice, casting mould,

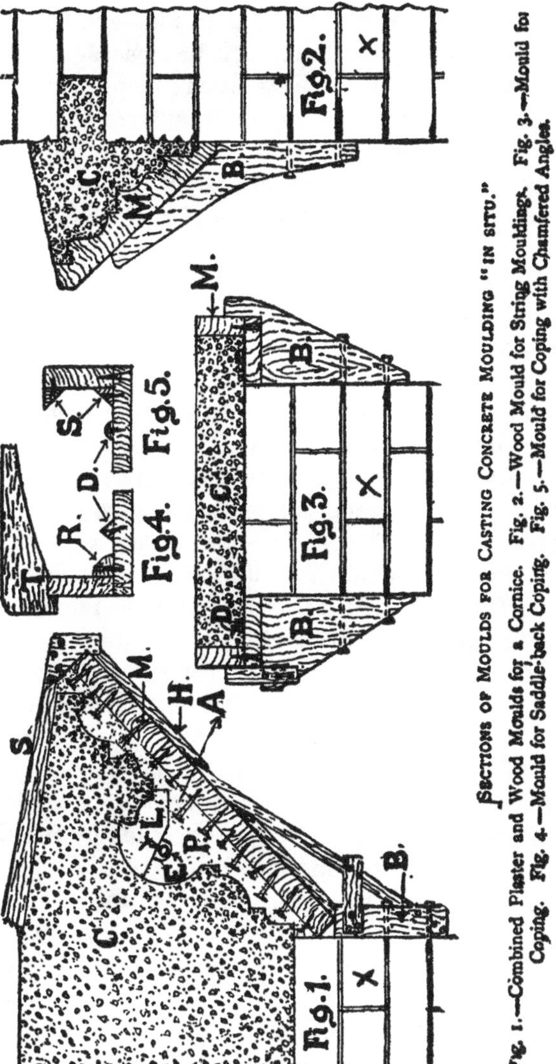

SECTIONS OF MOULDS FOR CASTING CONCRETE MOULDING "IN SITU."

Fig. 1.—Combined Plaster and Wood Moulds for a Cornice. Fig. 2.—Wood Mould for String Mouldings. Fig. 3.—Mould for Coping. Fig. 4.—Mould for Saddle-back Coping. Fig. 5.—Mould for Coping with Chamfered Angles.

NO. 30.

and supporting bracket. Wood moulds are generally used for small or plain mouldings, but where the profile is undercut or of an intricate nature, a plaster mould is preferable, as it is easier and cheaper to construct a plaster mould than cut the irons which are necessary for a wood mould for a special design. Fibrous plaster moulds may be used for this class of work, but to illustrate another method a combined wood and plaster mould is given. M is a moulding board to strengthen the plaster profile, and on which it is run. The board may be made in two or more pieces, each about 1 inch thick, and in width according to the depth of the moulding, and in length as required, the whole being held together by cleats H, which are nailed about 3 or 4 feet apart. Broad-headed nails are then driven in at random, leaving the heads projecting, to give a key for the plaster profile P. The profile is then run with a reverse running mould. It will be seen that this profile is undercut, therefore a loose piece L is required to enable the mould to draw off the moulding. The reverse mould and loose piece are constructed in the same way as described under the heading of "Reverse Mouldings." It may be here remarked that it is sometimes useful to have an "eye" inserted in the loose piece to give a better hold for the fingers when taking the loose piece off the moulding. The eyes are made by twisting a piece of strong wire round the handle of a tool bruch, leaving one end in the form of a ring, and the other bent outwards so as to form a key. The eyes are fixed about 3 or 4 feet apart, the fixing being done by cutting a hole in the loose piece and bedding the shank of the eye with plaster, and then cutting a slot in the main part of the mould to receive the ring of the eye as shown at E. The mould is held in position by the bracket B, fixed 4 or 5 feet apart. The mould is further secured by the stay S, the other or inner end of the stay is fixed on to the main wall. It will be understood that a plaster mould for this purpose should be dry and hard, and then well seasoned with linseed oil, or with a hot solution of paraffin wax. After the mould is fixed in position it is oiled, and then the concrete C is filled in, taking care that the surface of the mould is first covered with a thin coat of neat cement. The mould may be oiled with paraffin oil; but if the mould is inclined to "stick," oil it with "chalk oil," i. e., paraffin oil and French chalk, about the consistency of cream.

When the concrete is set, the brackets are removed, and the mould taken off. The mould in this case would draw in the line of the arrow A. The loose piece is then taken off. It is here that the use of the eyes will be found. Before removing the brackets it is advisable to prop the mould, in case it may drop off and break the fragile portions of the mould or parts of the cornice. A heavy mould hanging in this position, especially if the profile is flat, or in good working order, is apt to drop, hence the necessity of props. If the mould clings, or, as more generally called, "sticks fast," gentle tapping with a heavy hammer will ease or spring it, and allow it to be taken off. A heavy hammer is more effective in making the mould spring than a light hammer, as the force required for a light hammer is apt to injure the mould. This is why a heavy hammer with a flat head is best for plaster piece moulding.

Fig. 2 is the section of a string moulding with the casting mould and bracket. A chase is formed in the brickwork to allow it to bond, and the joints and the surface of the brickwork are cut out and hacked to give a further key to the moulding. M is the mould (in this case made of wood). The profile is drawn without any undercut parts, so as to allow the mould to draw off in one piece. B is the bracket, and C is the concrete. The same directions for casting Fig. 1 apply to this and the other moulding here shown. A drip member, as shown at the top member of both cornices, is generally used for exterior mouldings, to prevent the water running over the wall surface.

Fig. 3 is the section of a wall coping and the casting mould. M is the mould, a similar one being used for the other side. A mould for this purpose is best formed with flooring boards about 1 inch thick, and fixing them together as shown. The drip D is readily formed by sawing an inch bead through the centre, and nailing it on the bottom. Two forms of brackets, B and B, are here given. One is cut out of the solid, and the other made of two pieces of wood nailed together.

Fig. 4 is the section of a casting mould for a saddle-back coping. R is a quarter-round piece of wood fixed in the angle of the mould to form a cavetto, which is sometimes used in copings. D is an angular-shaped drip, sometimes used in place of a circular one. T is part of a template used for forming the saddle-back of the coping.

Fig. 5 is the section of a mould for a coping with splayed or chamfered angles. S is a triangular strip of wood fixed in the angle and the top of the mould to form the splays, and D is a circular drip.

Concrete mouldings that are deeply undercut or intricate in profile may be cast in situ by the use of the "Waste Mould Process."

Modelling in Fine Concrete.—Figures of the human and animal form, also emblems, trade signs, and buildings, are now being made in fine concrete. The work may be executed in situ, or in the moulding shop, and then fixed in position. For important works a plaster model is first made, and placed in position, so as to judge of the effect before committing it to the permanent material. For this purpose the model is first modelled in clay, and then it is waste-moulded, and a plaster cast obtained. After the model is approved it is moulded, and then cast in the fine concrete. The material is composed of Portland cement, and a light, but strong, aggregate; and the cast is made in a similar way to that described for casting vases. The material may be colored as required to suit the subject. The general method of executing figures "on the round" in fine concrete or Portland cement is to model the figure direct in the cement on an iron frame, and then to fix it in its permanent position. This is effected by first making a full-sized sketch of the proposed figure, then setting out on this the form of the necessary ironwork to serve as frame or skeleton to form an internal support. This iron frame also forms a core to enable the figure to be made hollow, and serves as a permanent support for thin parts and extremities of the figure. The quantity, size, and form of the iron frame is regulated by the size, form, and position of the figure. For instance, if the model of a full-size lion is required, first make a rectangular frame to suit the feet of the lion and the base on which the figure stands. The base frame is made of iron bars, 1½ inches wide by ¼ inch thick, fixed on edge. Then set out four leg-irons, and connect them on the base frame, and then set out one or two body-irons, and connect them with the leg-irons. After this set out a looped piece to fit the contour of the neck and head, and fix it to the body-iron. Now set out the tail-iron. This is best formed with an iron pipe, and it should be made to screw on to the body-iron. This allows the tail to be unscrewed when the model is finished, and screwed on after the model is fixed in position, thus enabling the model to be more freely handled, and with less risk of breakage when moving and fixing in its permanent position.

Having made the frame, place it on a stout modelling board, keeping the base frame from 1 to 3 inches above the board, according to the depth of the base; the frame being temporarily supported with four pieces of brick or stone. This is done to allow the base frame to be enveloped with concrete. This done, fix wood rules, cut to the depth of the base, on the board, so as to form a fence on all sides of the base. Then fill in the base with concrete; and when this is set, proceed with the coring out, so as to obtain a hollow model.

In order to decrease the weight of concrete figures "on the round," and to enable them to be more easily handled and hoisted when fixing them in their permanent positions, they should be made hollow. This is effected by making a round skeleton frame with hoop-iron, or with wire-netting, for the body, neck, and head, and other thick parts. This metal skeleton must be built on and securely fixed to the main iron frame. The whole, or parts of the figure, may also be cored out with shavings or tow, and held in position with tar bands or canvas strips, dipped in plaster. Tow is an excellent material for forming cores. By making up the inner parts with dry tow, and then dipping tow in plaster for the outside coat, the core can be made to any desired shape, and also leave the necessary thickness for the concrete. To prevent the material slipping down by its own weight, pieces of iron or wood, in the form of crosses, are fastened with copper wire or tar rope to the iron rods, which are used as single supports. These iron or wood pieces must be fixed in all directions, and in such a way that the material is held up by them. For small extremities, such as fingers of human figures, beaks of birds, fins of fishes, horns and tails of animals, iron rods should be fixed on the main frame, and the parts to be covered with cement must be notched or bound at intervals with copper wire or tar rope. The distance between the core and the finished face of the figure is of course the actual thickness of the model. This thickness may vary from 1 inch to 3 inches, or even 4 inches at some parts. An actual thickness of 2 inches will be sufficient to give the requisite strength.

When the core is made, cover it with a coat of Portland cement and old lime putty, in the proportion of 3 of the former to 1 of the latter, and add sufficient tow or hair to give tenacity. If there are open spaces in the skeleton iron work, bridge them over with bits of tiles and cement. The whole surface, after being coated, must be well scratched with a nail, to give a key for the roughing out coat. This scratched coat must be allowed to set before proceeding with the actual modelling. The stuff for roughing out is composed of 2 parts of Portland cement and 1 part of fine aggregate. Crushed bricks, stone, or pottery ware passed through a sieve having a 1/8 inch mesh may be used as aggregates. The finishing stuff is composed of fine sifted Portland cement. The addition of a fifth part of old lime putty to the cement makes the stuff more mellow, and works freer and sweeter. The modelling is done as described for in situ work. The finishing coat can be colored to any desired tint, as already described.

Concrete Fountains.—Fine concrete is an excellent material for the construction of fountains. It is obvious that a vast amount of cutting and consequent waste of material is involved in the executing of fountains, "on the round," when natural stone is employed. Saving of material, and a corresponding reduction in the cost, is effected by use of a material that can be easily cast, and is at the same time durable and impervious. These qualities combined are found in artificial stone composed of fine concrete. Being readily made in large blocks (any sized basin can be made in one piece), there is no jointing required, as is the case with terra cotta, which is another form of artificial stone. Fountains composed of fine concrete are made in a similar way to that described for making and casting vases.

Concrete Tanks.—Concrete tanks to contain water, and for a variety of manufacturing purposes, are now largely in use. They are strong and durable, and having hard smooth surfaces, they are easily washed and kept clean. Being impervious to vermin, damp, and atmospheric influences, they are the coolest and most sanitary water cisterns that can be used. Cattle troughs are best made in concrete. Concrete tanks have been used as water and silicate baths for indurating concrete casts, and during their constant use for over a decade no signs of cracks or damp are visible. They were made in one piece, varying in size from 6 feet up to 18 feet long, 3 feet to 7 feet wide, 2 feet 6 inches to

4 feet high, and from 3 to 4½ inches thick. Some were cast, but the large ones were made in situ. The method of construction (for in situ work) being simple and expeditious, the total cost is small. For a tank 9 feet long, 4 feet 6 inches wide, 2 feet 6 inches high, and 3½ inches thick, first frame up wood sides and ends to the above length, width, and height, then make inside boards, the lengths and widths being the same as above, less the tank thickness, and the heights less the bottom thickness. The sides and ends are hung by means of cross battens laid on the upper edges of the outside framing, and kept in position with inside stays. This leaves an open and continuous space at the sides, ends, and bottom. The constructive materials are 1 part of Portland cement and 2 of fine slag or granite, gauged stiff, and laid over the bottom. Next, the open sides and ends are filled up, taking great care that the whole mass is thoroughly consolidated by ramming. The stuff for the sides and ends should be laid in layers from 6 to 8 inches deep, each layer being well rammed before the next is laid.

The angles are strengthened by inserting angle irons during the process of filling in. As soon as the concrete is set the inner boards are removed, and if the surface is smooth or dry, it must be keyed with a coarse drag or a sharp hand pick. It is then swept and wetted to cleanse it and stop the suction, so as to ensure perfect cohesion, and allow the final coat to retain its moisture during the process of trowelling and the stuff setting.

The finishing coat is composed of neat cement, the finer ground the better, as percolation through concrete made with a finely ground cement is less liable than when made with a coarsely ground cement.

The final coat is laid about 3/16 inch thick, and preceded by brushing the surface with liquid cement to fill up all crevices, and afford better adhesion between the surface and the final coat. When the stuff is firm, it is well trowelled to a fine and close surface. The outer boards are then removed, and the surface finished in a similar way.

Concrete Sinks.—Concrete sinks can be made to any desired size or form. They are cast in wood or plaster moulds, and are composed of 1 part of Portland cement to 2 parts of fine crushed granite or other hard aggregate. They are made with rebated holes for traps. The ordinary size are as follows: 2 feet 6 inches by 1 foot 8 inches; 2 feet 9 inches by 1 foot 8 inches; and 3 feet by 2 feet, all 6 inches deep, and from 2 to 3 inches thick.

Garden Edging.—Plain and ornamented edgings are now made in concrete. They are made in various lengths. The most useful size is 3 feet long, 6 inches deep, and 2 inches thick. They can be made to any curve, and tinted to any shade.

Concrete Vases.—During the last half-century thousands of vases, composed of fine concrete—commonly called "artificial stone"—have been used for the decoration of buildings and practical use in gardens, conservatories, &c. For vases that are cast in sections the thickness of large and open parts, such as the "body," are regulated by means of a plaster core, which is placed in the open mould. The contour of the core must be so arranged that the cast will draw from the core, or vice versa. For some forms of vases, the core must be made in pieces similar to a piece mould. The method of making, moulding, and casting—the latter by the aid of a template instead of a core

Concrete Mantel Pieces.—Chimney-pieces of all sizes and shapes are now extensively made in fine concrete. They are generally made in wood moulds, plaster moulds being let in the main mould for ornamental parts. They are often made in colored concrete.

Colored Concrete.—Concrete casts, also work laid in situ, can be colored to imitate any natural stone. This is effected by mixing mineral oxides of the required color with the cement used for the surface coat. The color coat should not exceed 1/8 inch in thickness, as oxides are too expensive to use for the entire thickness of the cast. The quantity of oxide to be added to the cement depends upon the strength of the oxide. Some are much stronger than others. Five per cent. of a strong oxide will impart a close resemblance of the desired color to the concrete, but a weak oxide will require from 10 to 15 per cent., and even 20 per cent., to obtain the same color. Some of the red oxides range in color from scarlet or Turkey red, gradually deepening to chocolate. Some oxides contain 95 per cent. of pure ferric oxide, which is made from copperas, or, scientifically speaking, sulphate of iron. This is a by-product, and is frequently evolved from waste acid liquors at tinplate works, and is obtained in large quantities from South Wales. This kind of oxide is far more suitable for coloring concrete than ochres and most of the earthy oxides. Earthy colors, like Venetian red and umber, soon fade and have a sickly appearance. The oxides should be intimately mixed with the cement in a dry state before it is gauged. The mixing is generally done by hand, but better results are obtained by the use of grinding machine. It is a safe plan to try various proportions of color and cement and gauge small parts, and when set and dry select those most suitable for the desired purpose. All cast work, as soon as extracted from the moulds, should be examined, and any blubs stopped and chipped parts or other minor defects made good while the work is moist or green, using neat cement and colors in the same proportion as used for the surface stuff. Colored surfaces may be greatly improved by brushing the cast as soon as set with a solution of the same color as used for the surface coat. A color solution, made by mixing the color with water and a solution of alum, is very useful for coloring Portland cement, with or without sand. If this coloring solution is brushed over the surface while it is moist or semi-dry, a good standing color can be obtained without mixing color with dry cement. This method will be found useful for sgraffitto, &c.

A novel and color-saving method, for coloring the upper surfaces of slabs or other flat casts, is effected by first filling in the mould in the usual way, then placing the colored cement in a dry state in a hand sieve, and then violently shaking or tapping the sides of the sieve, so as to sprinkle the colored cement uniformly over the surface until it is nearly 1/16 inch thick. The surface is then trowelled in the usual way. The sprinkling must be done as soon as the main body of the stuff is ruled off, so as to obtain a homogeneous body. Another and a novel method which may be advantageously employed for finishing slab or other large surfaces in a mould is as follows: A fine finished face is more readily obtained by using a smoothing knife (for brevity termed a "shaver") than by a trowel. A shaver is a piece of polished steel about 3 inches wide and 3/8 inch thick, the length being regulated according to the width of the mould, and allowing about 8 inches at each end for handles. For instance, for a slab 2 feet wide, the shaver should be 3 feet long. This allows 2 feet for the surface of the cast, 3 inches to bear on the rims of the mould, each 1½ inches wide; 8 inches for the handles, each 4 inches long; and 1 inch for play. One edge or side is cut to an angle of 45°, so as to form a cutting edge. The method of filling in, coloring, and finishing the surface of the slab is as follows: First fill in the mould with the concrete, ramming and beating it as already described until the stuff is about 1/16 inch above the mould rims, then clean off the stuff on the rims with a wood template (rebated to fit the width of the rims), and lay the shaver flat on the rims, keeping the cutting edge outwards, and then push it forward, keeping it flat on the rims, so as to shave off the superfluous stuff. This done, sprinkle the colored cement, with the aid of a sieve, until about 1/16 inch thick; then clean the rims again, and pass the shaver forwards and backwards twice or thrice, which will leave a straight, smooth, and uniform-colored surface. This method effects a considerable saving in the amount of oxide and of time. The thickness of the coloring stratum is reduced mechanically to the minimum (about 1/32 inch), which is all sufficient for coloring purposes where the surface is not subjected to frictional wear.

As already mentioned, bullocks' blood mixed with cement gives a near resemblance to red brick, but it is not a desirable material to work with, and the same effect can be obtained by the use of red oxides. Red sand, brick, and stone, all finely ground, have been employed for coloring cement surfaces, but if too fine or in large quantities they weaken the surface; and if coarse-grained they possess little coloring effect, because the particles are liable to show singly, causing a spotty appearance, or the cement entirely covers the surface of each particle of sand. Powdered glass, marble, flint, alabaster, metal filings, and mineral coloring can be effectively employed for coloring concrete surfaces by mixing with the cement used for the surface coat. The surface is improved by rubbing and stoning, also polishing, after the work is dry. Other methods and quantities of colors for coloring Portland cement surfaces are given.

Fixing Blocks.—Concrete fixing blocks do not shrink, warp, or rot. Consequently they are superior to wood fillets, &c. They are principally used in concrete floors, stair landings, and walls, as bearings and fixing points for wire-lathing and fibrous plaster work. Floor boards may also be fixed to them. They are also built into brick walls for similar purposes, as well as for external wall tilings. For ceilings, stair soffits, and landings, the blocks are laid on the centrings where required, and permanently secured by laying concrete between and over them. For bearings and fixing flooring boards, they are secured flush.

TYPICAL SYSTEMS OF REINFORCED CONCRETE CONSTRUCTIONS FROM VARIOUS SOURCES.

Of the interesting features of modern civil engineering, interesting because of their extreme novelty and successful application, reinforced concrete is probably most noteworthy because of its unique adaptability. How striking is the influence of steel reinforcement is best exemplified by a reference to Fig. 1. There two beams are shown designed to carry ordinary floor loads, the one made entirely of concrete and the other of concrete with a sheet of expanded metal imbedded in the tensile portion of the beam. The saving in mere weight of concrete alone is apparent; and when we remember that the adoption of floor beams entirely of concrete means an increase of thickness of nine inches or assuming five to eight floors, an increase in the total height of the building (with extra cost and heavier walls, together with heavier foundations to carry them) of from four to six feet, we see that even as regards initial outlay for materials, the introduction of settle reinforcement into concrete construction is of importance.

So far as economy in initial cost of materials is concerned, reinforced concrete is undoubtedly cheaper than either concrete or steel alone. It is not very easy to demonstrate this economy except by comparative cost in individual cases, but an approach to a systematic comparison has been made by Mr. Walter Loring Webb, as follows: A cubic foot of steel weighs 490 pounds. Assume as an average price that it can be bought and placed for 4.5 cents per pound. The steel will therefore cost $22.05 per cubic foot. On the basis that concrete may be placed for $6 per cubic yard, the concrete will cost 22 cents per cubic foot which is 1 per cent of the cost of the steel. Therefore, on this basis if it is necessary to use as reinforcement an amount of steel whose volume is in excess of 1 per cent of the additional concrete which would do the same work, there is no economy in the reinforcement, even though the reinforcement is justified on account of the other considerations. Assuming 500 pounds per square inch as the working compressive strength of concrete, and 16,000 as the permissible stress in steel, it requires 3.125 per cent of steel to furnish the same compressive stress as concrete. On the above basis of cost, the compression is evidently obtained much more cheaply in concrete than in steel —in fact, at less than one-third of the cost. On the other hand, even if we allow 50 pounds per square inch tension in the concrete and 16,000 pounds in the steel, it requires only 0.21 per cent of steel to furnish the

Fig. 1.—These Beams Are Designed to Carry the Same Load. The Upper is of Reinforced Concrete, the Lower of Plain Concrete.

same strength as the concrete, which shows that, no matter what may be the variation in the comparative price, of concrete and steel, steel always furnishes tension at a far cheaper price than concrete, on the above basis at less than one-third of the cost. The practical meaning of this is, on the one hand, that a beam composed wholly of concrete is usually inadvisable, since its low tensile strength makes it uneconomical, if not actually impracticable, for it may be readily shown that, beyond a comparatively short span, a concrete beam will not support its own weight. On the other hand, on account of the cheaper compressive stress furnished by concrete, an all-steel beam is not so economical as

Fig. 2.—Types of Steel Reinforcing Rods.

a beam in which the concrete furnishes the compressive stress and the steel furnishes the tensile stress.

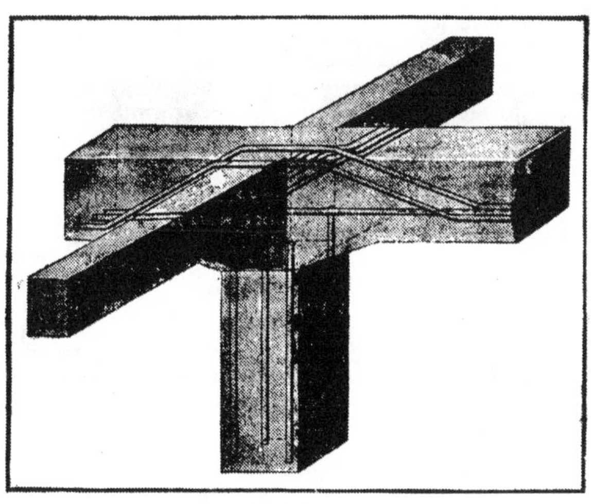

Fig. 3.—A Reinforced Concrete Pier for Railway Traffic.

This statement has been very frequently verified when comparing the cost of the construction of floors designed by using steel I-beams supporting a fire-proof concrete floor, and that of a concrete floor having a similar floor slab but making the beams as T-beams of reinforced concrete.

A good idea of reinforced concrete construction can be obtained from Fig. 3, which is an isometrical projection of a portion of a pier strong enough to carry the heaviest railway traffic. The disposition of the steel work is shown in the piles, the main girders, and beams; and the manner in which the steel rods running along the tensile or bottom side of the girders and beams are bent up over the top of the pile, which is here the tensile member (the beams being continuous), and then down again to the bottom of the girders and beams, is most instructive.

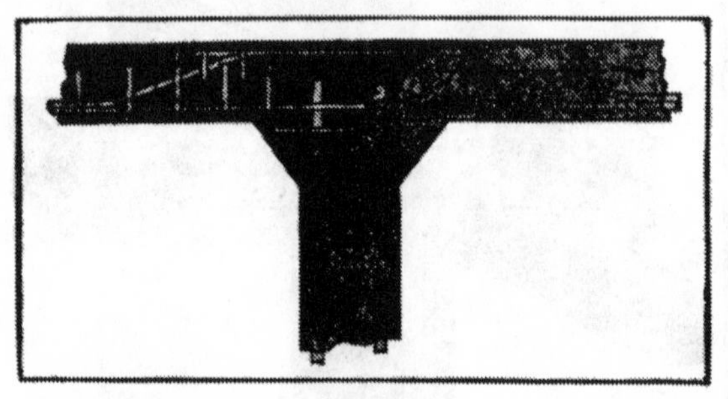

Fig. 4.—Method of Joining Columns and Floors.

The sections of the steel employed vary in different systems, being round, flat, square, angle, and tee—Fig. 2. In all cases the simplest section is the best, as it costs less, and readily allows the concrete to be rammed into the closest contact with the entire surface of the armoring. In America the Ransome system is most extensively used—a system in which a bar of twisted steel is employed. Small sections are better than large ones, for by their use we obtain a more uniform distribution of stress in the steel; we can also readily bend and work them into any required shape; and finally the most economical disposition of material is obtained, the metal being placed at the maximum distance from the neutral axis.

Fig. 5.—The Monier System.

Expanded metal meshing (Fig. 6) is increasingly employed, more particularly in the lighter forms of construction. It consists of sheets of metal which have been mechanically slit and expanded, so as to produce a network. This type of reinforcement has many and obvious advantages. Its mere existence is proof of good steel, and it forms an excellent key for concrete too thin to permit reinforcement in the form of rods; thus it is very useful for concrete plaster, ceiling, and partition wall work. A good example of reinforced concrete in which expanded metal is used may be found in the Monier system (Fig. 5). An improvement on this system is the Clinton method (Fig. 11) of using an electrically welded wire netting in combination with concrete. Clinton fabric consists of drawn wire of 6 to 10 gauge, which may be made in lengths up to 300 feet. The system is therefore a continuous bond system, which prevents the entire collapse of a span unless the weight imposed is sufficient to break all the wires.

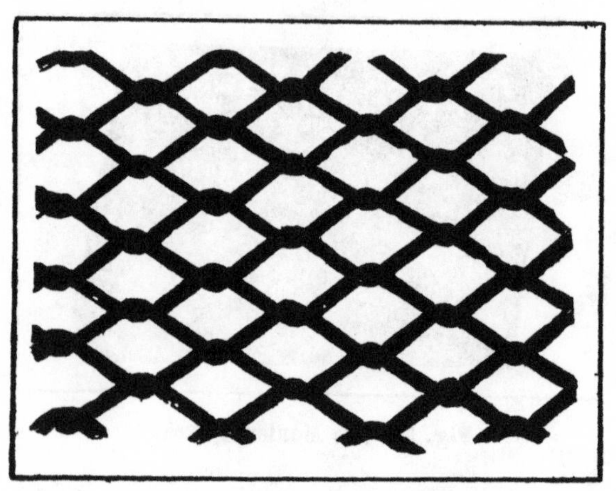

Fig. 6.—Expanded Metal.

Columns and Piles.—Reinforced columns are made with either square, rectangular, or circular sections. They are reinforced with from four to twenty rods, the diameters of which vary from 3/8 to 2 1/2 inches. The rods are placed as nearly as practicable to the circumference of the column, so as to give the greatest radius of gyration for the section; but they are never placed so near the surface that they have not at least one or two inches protective covering. The steel so disposed is able to take up the tensile stresses which may be induced in the column by eccentric loading, lateral shock, wind pressure, and the pull of belting.

Columns and piles are made in wooden boxes, each consisting of three permanent sides and a fourth side which is temporary and removable. Under the patent rights of Francois Hennebique the reinforcing is placed

Fig. 7.—Ransome System of Erecting Columns.

in these boxes, and adjusted by gauges to within one or two inches of the sides. The concrete is laid and rammed, about six inches at a time, with small hand rammers. The open side of the box is built up by battens fitting into grooves in the permanent sides, as the work proceeds; this enables inspection of the work to be made, and facilitates the placing of the ties at the proper positions. The ties are made of round wire 3/16

Fig. 8.—Wood Centering and Ransome Steel Bars for 50-foot Floor Span.

inch diameter and are dropped down over the top of the steel rods. They are spaced down two-inch centres at the bottom and top, to twelve-inch centres in the centre of length of the column, and are intended to prevent the steel rods from spreading out under the action of longitudinal loads. Fig. 4 shows the method of joining columns to the floor.

Fig. 9.—Concrete Power Plant in Course of Construction.

In the Ransome columns as exemplified in a recently constructed factory building (Fig. 7), the vertical reinforcement consists of round rods with the connections made about 12 inches above the floor line; in order that these rods might be continuous the ends were threaded and connected with sleeve nuts, thereby developing the full strength of the rods. Horizontal reinforcement was also used, consisting of hoops formed by a spiral

Fig. 10.—Slabs of Concrete Ready for Roof.

made from 1/4 inch diameter soft wire, having a pitch or spacing of 4 inches in the basement columns, and gradually increasing to a pitch of 6 inches in the top story (Fig. 12).

According to Mr. Henry Longcope the first innovation in concrete piles was the sand pile, produced by driving a wooden form in the ground and withdrawing it, the hole being filled with moist sand well rammed. The next method adopted was to drive a metal form into the ground and after withdrawal to fill the hole with concrete. This was not successful, as it was open to the serious objection that on withdrawing the form, the ground would collapse before the concrete could be inserted. Still another method was introduced, which consisted in dropping a cone-shaped five ton weight a number of times from a considerable height, in order to form a hole, which was afterward filled with concrete. This method never passed the experimental stage. Coming to more successful systems we may mention a method of moulding a pile of concrete, allowing it to stand, and then driving it into the ground, a cap being used to protect the head.

Fig. 11.—Clinton System Using Electrically Welded Fabric.

Of modern systems which have proven successful, Gilbreth's pile must first be re-

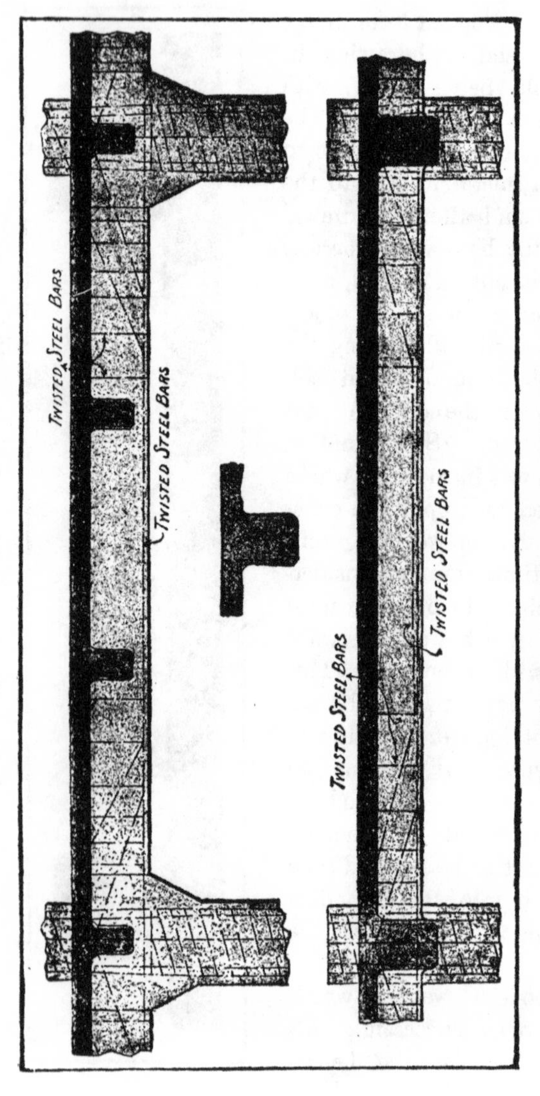

Fig. 12.—Ransome Floor System With Beams.

corded. Gilbreth used a molded corrugated taper pile, cast with core hole the entire length of the pile, which is jetted down by a water jet and finally settled by hammer blows.

Features which recommended the Gilbreth piles are the opportunities for complete inspection before driving and the fact that they save time because they can be cased while excavation is going on. After being driven they can be loaded immediately. Naturally they present considerable skin friction. The making of these piles above the ground surface also does away with the possibility of their being damaged or squeezed out of shape by the jar occasioned by driving forms for adjoining piles.

Still another method is used by Raymond. Under this system piles are usually put in by either of two methods, the jetting method or the pile core method. The water jet system is used only where the material penetrated is sand, quicksand, or soft material that will dissolve and flow up inside the pile when the water is forced through the pipe, thus causing the shell to settle until it comes in contact with the next shell, and so on until the desired depth has been reached. The shells are filled with concrete simultaneously with the sinking process, and when necessary spreads are attached to keep the hole in perfect line with the pipe. The ½ inch pipe is left in the centre of the pile and gives it greatly increased lateral strength. If desired, the lateral strength may be further increased by inserting rods near the outer surface of the concrete. By this method, piles of any size up to two feet in diameter at the bottom and four feet at the top can be put through any depth of water and to a suitable penetration in sand or silt (water sediment).

The pile-core method is the one most generally used for foundation work and consists of a collapsible steel pile core, conical in shape, which is incased in a thin, tight-fitting metal shell. The core and shell are driven into the ground by means of a pile driver. The core is so constructed that when the desired depth has been reached it is collapsed and loses contact with the shell, so that it is easily withdrawn, leaving the shell or casing in the ground, to act as a mold or form for the concrete. When the form is withdrawn, the shell or casing is filled with carefully mixed Portland cement concrete, which is thoroughly tamped during the filling process.

The simplex system uses another method in which the driving form consists of a strong steel tube, the lower end of which is fitted with powerful tooth jaws, which close together tightly, with a point capable of opening automatically to the full diameter of the tube while being withdrawn. The point of the form closely resembles the jaws of an alligator. At the same time the form is being withdrawn, the concrete is deposited.

It is so evident that concrete is vastly superior to wood in the construction of piles that it is almost superfluous to mention the points of superiority. Concrete is not subject to rot or the ravages of the teredo worm, neither can the piles constructed of concrete be destroyed by fire, and no cost is attached for repairs. While it is not possible to give accurate statistics as to the life of a wooden pile, as it varies so much under different conditions, yet we know that in some cases a wooden pile is rendered worthless in a very few years, especially when the surrounding material is composed of rotted vegetation, or where the pile is exposed by the rise and fall of tides. It is also impossible to state the exact cost of a concrete pile, as it varies also according to conditions. Ordinarily speaking, a concrete pile will cost from one and one-half times or two times as much as a wooden pile; but in order to illustrate where a saving can be made, the following extract is given from a report on the piles driven at the United States Naval Academy at Annapolis, Md.:

"The original plans called for 3,200 wooden piles cut off below low water with a capping of concrete. To get down to the low water level required sheet piling, shorting and pumping, and the excavating of nearly 5,000 cubic yards of earth. By substituting concrete piles, the work was reduced to driving 850 concrete piles, excavating 1,000 cubic yards of earth and placing of 1,000 cubic yards of concrete."

In the work mentioned, the first estimate for wooden piles placed the cost at $9.50 each, while the estimate for concrete piles was placed at $20 each, yet the estimate based on the use of wood piles aggregated $52,840, while the estimate based on the use of concrete piles was $25,403, or a total saving in favor of concrete of over $27,000.

In several instances piles have been uncovered to their full depth, and they were found to be perfectly sound in every particular. By surrounding the operation with the safeguards provided, it is almost impossible to make a faulty pile. The concrete is made as wet as good practice will allow. Constant ramming and dropping the concrete from a considerable height tend to the assurance of a solid mass, then the target on the ramming line or the introduction of an electric light into the form shows what is being done at the bottom of the form.

Floors, Slabs and Roofs.—The system of construction for floors, slabs, and roofs is determined by the extent of the work and the nature of the loads to be carried. If intended for small buildings and offices, the items can be made before erection (Figs. 9 and 10); but in the case of warehouses, factories, piers, and jetties, where live loads and vibrator stresses have to be borne, a monolithic structure is secured by building in molds directly on the site. For the lighter classes of monolithic structure, expanded metal is admirably suitable; it is also much used for the roofs of reservoirs, and for thin partitioned walls. The meshing is simply laid over the ribs or floor beams, which have been already erected, and the green concrete is applied to the acquired thickness, being supported from below by suitable supporting work, which is removed as soon as the concrete has set. In cold storage factories, the floor beams and ceilings are invariably erected first, the floor being laid afterward. The ceiling is then solid with the floor beams on their under side, and the floor is solid with them on their upper side, the air space between being a great aid to the maintenance of a low temperature for refrigeration.

In the Monier floors the reinforcement consists of round rods varying from ¼ inch to ⅝ inch diameter. The rods are spaced at about six times their diameter, and are crossed at right angles, being connected by iron wire bound round them. This artificial method of securing the rods takes considerable time, and is thus a somewhat costly process. To produce continuity of metal, the different lengths of rods are overlapped for about 8 to 16 inches, and bound with wire.

The Schluter are similar to the Monier floors, but the rods are crossed diagonally, and the longitudinal rods are of the same size as the transverse ones. The Cottancin floors have their rods interlaced like the canes of a chair seat or a basket, and the Hyatt floors have square rods with holes through which small transverse rods pass. Over fifty systems of reinforcing are in use, and in most cases the only points of difference are the shape of the section and the method of attachment and adjustment.

Beams.—It is obvious that, as the span increases, a limit will soon be reached beyond which it is not economical to use plain floor slabs, for their dead weight becomes of such magnitude as to prohibit their use. We have thus to resort to a division of the main span by cross beams resting on columns, and the floor is laid on these beams, which are arranged to take as much of the load as to render it possible to reduce the thickness of the floor within reasonable limits. Reinforced concrete beams are typical of the construction in which the merits of two component materials are made to serve a common end; but in the particular case of steel and concrete, the actual part played by the steel is not at all well understood.

Speaking generally, beams do not differ in constructional details from floors. The same reinforcement is used in both, the only difference being, that as beams are usually deeper than floors, the shearing stresses become more pronounced, the greater provision has to be made for them by a liberal use of stirrups or vertical binding rods. In some systems the reinforcement consists entirely of straight rods, disposed in any part of the beam where tensile stresses are likely to be called into play. In others, specially bent rods are joined or welded to straight rods, disposed and when welding has to be done it would appear that wrought iron is more suitable than steel.

It is usual to arrange the dimensions of the beams so that the whole of the compressive stresses are taken by that portion of the concrete on one side of the neutral axis; but in some cases, as with continuous beams or heavy beams of small depth, a portion of the reinforcement is disturbed along compressed portion of the beam, the steel rods either taking up the excess of compressive stress over that at which the concrete can be safely worked, or else taking up the tensile stresses at the places where they occur over the supports. As a general rule we may take it that the economical depth for a reinforced concrete beam, freely supported at both ends, is one-twentieth the span, and is thus approximately the same as that of a steel girder of equal strength. Reinforced concrete beams are now made for spans up to 100 feet for buildings, and 150 feet for bridges. But for each class of work beyond this limit, the weight becomes excessive. Several arched ribs, for much greater spans have, however, been successfully built.

The beams are made in much the same way as piles and columns; they can be made in sheds on the site, or in the actual position they are to occupy when finished. The ceiling and beams are erected first, the floor being afterward worked on the top of the beams. We thus obtain a very perfect monolithic structure in which any vibration set up by machinery, falling loads, etc., will be of much less extent than with any ordinary type of building, in which there is often a great want of rigidity, the beams and arches being loose and able to vibrate independently of other parts of the structure.

Concrete being as weak in shear as in tension, provision is also required to take the shearing stresses. Some American designers have to this end patented special forms of reinforcement bar, in which each main tension bar has projecting upward from it ties inclined at the angle of 45 deg. (Kahn system.) These extend to the top of the bar and take the tensile stresses arising from the shear. The corresponding compressive stress at right angles to this is carried by the concrete. The system is efficient and on large spans, where weight must be reduced to a minimum, it has its advantages.

Thus, in the Ransome system (Fig. 12), the shearing stresses at the end of a beam are taken up by inclined reinforcing rods imbedded in the concrete at the junction of beam with column.

Arches.—Concrete has long had an extensive application in the building of arches, but until the introduction of reinforced concrete the arches that could be economically and safely constructed were limited to spans of a few feet. The general rule that the line of resistance fell within the middle third had to be observed for simple concrete arches, as for those in brickwork and masonry; and the thickness of the arches at the crown was thus approximately the same whether built in either of these materials. The introduction of steel reinforcement, however, made it possible not only to reduce the thickness of the ring of a given load-

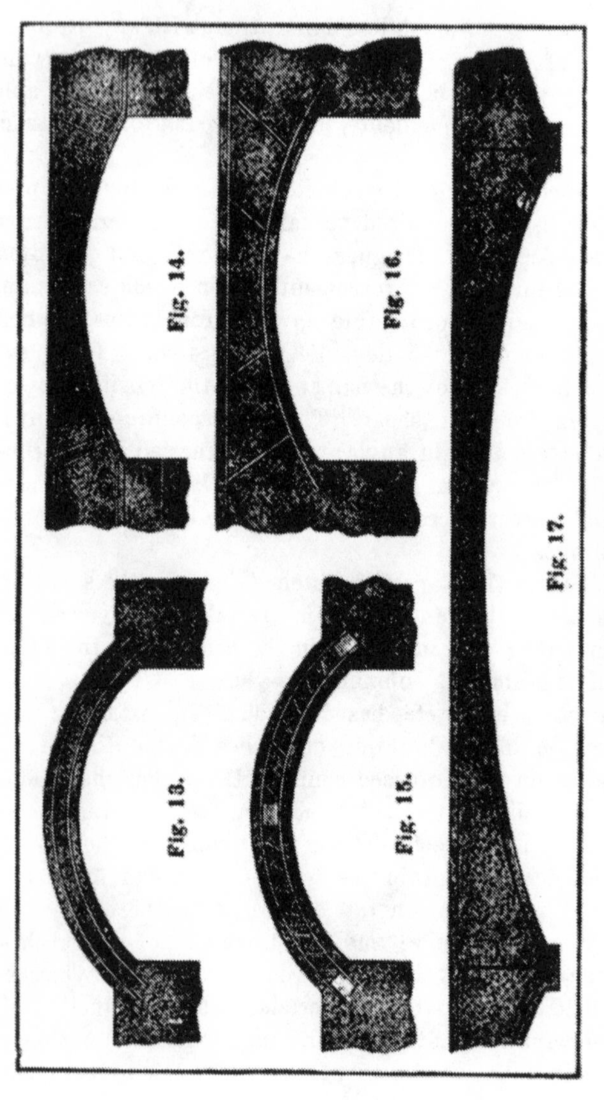

Types of Reinforced Concrete Arches.

carrying capacity, but by suitably providing for the tensile stresses to enable arches of much greater span and smaller rise to be built. Some general types of arches in reinforced concrete are shown in Figs. 13, 14, 15 and 16. Fig. 13 shows an ordinary arch with top and bottom armature. In many cases where the tensile stresses can safely be carried by the concrete the top armature can be omitted. In the Melane arches, shown in Fig. 14, the top and bottom armatures are connected by ligatures, and in the Hennebique arches (Fig. 15) stirrups are used. As a general rule, hinges should be built at the stringings and the crown, for the calculations are much simplified, and the line of resistance goes through the hinges; the arches also adjust themselves better to the load and to any slow temperature changes, and when the centering is struck the arch can better take its bearings without cracking. The methods of calculations for arches are as numerous as those for beams, and generally speaking are as irrational. The Monier system is the one most generally adopted, and over 400 bridges built on this system now exist in Europe. In America expanded metal and Clinton electrically-welded fabric are often used. An example of the latter construction will be found in Fig. 17.

SOME MISCELLANEOUS ITEMS.

Lintels.—Concrete lintels and beams are fast superseding those made of stone and wood. Lintels are generally cast and then fixed.

A Spiral Staircase built on the Hennebique principle.

Concrete Walls.—Many ingenious plans have been introduced as substitutes for wood framing for retaining concrete while constructing walls and partitions. The most simple method is as follows: Cast a number of concrete angle slabs with an L section, and then place them level in contrary directions, thus [[, spaced to the width of the proposed partition or wall until the desired length of wall is completed, and fill the openings with rough concrete. When set, place another row on this (taking care to break the joints by overlapping), and so on, until the desired height is obtained. Concrete for walls formed in situ should be deposited in layers, taking care that each layer is thoroughly rammed and keyed, as described under the heading of "Ramming." A suitable finish for ordinary purposes, for rough walls built in situ, may be obtained by "rough trowelling." This is done by first gauging 1 part of Portland cement, 1 part of old lime putty, and 2 parts of sand. The adding of lime renders the stuff more plastic and easy to work, without decreasing the impermeability of the work. This "limed cement" is applied with a hand-float, and is thoroughly worked into the crevices of the concrete, but leaving no body on the surface. The surface is then finished by brushing with a wet stock-brush. The walls should be well wetted before the stuff is applied.

Strong Rooms.—Concrete is frequently employed in the construction of strong-rooms that are situated underground, and are rendered damp-proof as well as burglar-proof, which is useful for the storage of documents.

Concrete Coffins and Cementation.—The great improvements in the manufacture of Portland cement during the last decade has so cheapened and improved the quality as to bring it more and more to the front as one of the most useful and important materials for a variety of purposes. One of the latest uses found for it is in the construction of coffins, by the author, whose invented and registered idea was that such a coffin, made of specially prepared metallic concrete, would be impermeable, and practically indestructible, and that it would obviate the danger of spreading the poisons of disease by preventing the escape of noxious gases. The lid having a strong piece of plate glass embedded in the concrete, and directly over the face, enabled the mourners to see the features of the departed. The edge of the open coffin had a sunk groove, and the lid a corresponding projection, only smaller, to allow for a coat of fine cement. When the joints were bedded and pressed together until the excess cement oozed out, the coffin was hermetically sealed. The coffin should be left uncovered by cement for identification, and so that friends could view it until the time of removal to the cemetery. The face could then be covered with quick-setting cement, which, joining with the other portion of cement, would permanently embalm the body, which would further be protected by fixing the lid in a similar way. If the properties of this class of coffin are taken into consideration, the expense will be comparatively less than that of wood. If expense is not a special consideration, the coffin can be enriched with armorial bearings or other devices. The concrete may also be polished like real granite. One objection was raised as to the weight, but the old stone coffins and those of oak lined with lead were also heavy. Besides, the weight would be a protection against body-snatchers, and bearing in mind that a coffin is only moved about once in a lifetime, or rather at death, the question of weight is unimportant. Cementation, from a sanitary point of view, would be equal if not superior to cremation. In case of an epidemic, the coffins could be cemented at once, and stacked in the cemetery until graves or vaults were prepared for them. It may be safely said that it is a clean, safe, effectual, rapid and sanitary method of disposing of the dead. If their manufacture should not cause any great amount of extra employment for plasterers, the latter can at least make their own coffins, in frosty weather, when most works are stopped, and they could use them as baths during their lifetime.

Stonette.—Stonette is a composition of Portland cement and fine aggregate, to imitate any kind of stone, and so made that it can be carved the same as natural stone. The Portland cement must be thoroughly air-slaked, finely sifted, and gauged with the natural aggregate in the proportion of 2 of cement to 7 of aggregate. The aggregate is composed of finely crushed natural stone, the same as that to be imitated. This should be passed through a fine sieve. It is necessary, when imitating some stones, to add a small portion of oxide to counteract the color of the cement. If a very white stone is being imitated, the addition of a small proportion of whiting or French chalk or well-slaked white limestone, is necessary to obtain the desired color. The material should be gauged stiff, and then well rammed into the mould. The carving is best done while the cast blocks are green.

Tile Fixing.—Tile fixing is in some places a separate branch of the building trade, but it is generally recruited from the ranks of plasterers, and in some districts it is done by plasterers. As regards the process of placing the tiles, it is best to work from the centre of the space, and if the design be intricate, to lay out a portion of the pavement according to the plan, upon a smooth floor, fitting the tiles together as they are to be laid. Lines being stretched over the foundation at right angles, the fixing may proceed, both the tiles and the foundation being previously soaked in cold water, to prevent the too rapid drying of the cement, and to secure better adhesion. The border should be left until the last. Its position and that of the tiles are to be obtained from the drawing, or by measuring the tiles when laid loosely upon the floor. The cement for fixing should be mixed thin, in small quantities, and without sand. It is best to float the tiles to their places, so as to exclude air, and fill the spaces between them and the foundation. For fixing tiles in grate cheeks, sides and backs of fire-places, etc., equal parts of sand, plaster and hair mortar may be used. These materials are sometimes mixed with hot glue to the consistency of mortar. The tiles should be well soaked in warm water. Keen's or other white cements are used as fixing materials for wall tiles, neat Portland cement (very often killed) being generally used for floor work. Tiles may be cut in the following manner: Draw a line with a pencil or sharp point where the break is desired, then placing the tile on a form board, or embedding it in sand on a flagstone, tap it moderately with a sharp chisel and a hammer along the line, up and down, or scratch it with a file. The tile may then be broken in the hand by a gentle blow at the back. The edges, if required, may be smoothed by grinding or by rubbing with sand and water on a flat stone. Tiles may also be sawn to any desired size. Cement should not be allowed to harden upon the surface of the tile if it can be prevented, as it is difficult to remove it after it has set. Stains or dirt adhering to tiles may be removed by wetting with diluted muriatic acid ("spirits of salts"), care being taken that the acid is all wiped off, and, after washing, the superfluous moisture must be wiped off with a clean, dry cloth. In order to obtain a sound and straight foundation, which is imperative for good permanent tile fixing, the substratum, whether on walls or floors, should be composed of Portland cement gauged with strong sand or similar aggregate in proportion of 1 of the former to 3 of the latter. The surface must be ruled fair and left rough, so as to form a fair bed and key for the fixing materials and tiles.

Setting Floor and Wall Tile.—As this work properly belongs to the plasterer, where no regular tile setter is available, I have thought it proper to publish the following instructions for doing this work, which are taken from a treatise prepared for the Tile Manufacturers of the United States. This treatise, in pamphlet form, was intended for distribution among buyers and workers in tiles, and the directions and suggestions laid down in it are of the best, and quite suited to the wants of the workingmen:

Foundations.—A good foundation is always necessary, and should be both solid and perfectly level. Tile should always be laid upon concrete foundation, prepared from the best quality of Portland cement and clean, sharp sand and gravel, or other hard material.

(Cinders should never be used, as they have a tendency to destroy the life of the cement and cause it to disintegrate.) A foundation, however, may also be formed of brick or hollow tile embedded solidly in and covered with cement mortar. Concrete should be allowed to thoroughly harden before laying the floor, and should be well soaked with water before laying the tile.

Lime mortar should never be mixed with concreting.

Concrete should consist of one part Portland cement, two parts clean sharp sand, two parts clean gravel, and thoroughly mixed with sufficient water to form a hard, solid mass when well beaten down into a bed, which should be from 2½ inches to 3 inches thick. If the concrete bed can be made over three inches in thickness, the concrete can then be made of one part Louisville cement, one part clean sharp sand, one part clean gravel and thoroughly mixed with sufficient water, as above described.

For Floors.—The surface of the concrete must be level and finished to within one (1) inch of the finished floor line, when tile ½ inch thick is used, which will leave a space of ½ inch for cement mortar, composed of equal parts of the very best quality Portland cement and clean sharp sand. The distance below the surface of the finished floor line, however, should be governed by the thickness of the tile.

For Wood Floors.—When tiles are to be laid on wood flooring in new buildings the joists should be set five inches below the intended finished floor line and spaced about 12 inches apart and thoroughly bridged, so as to make a stiff floor, and covered with one-inch boards not over six inches wide (boards three inches wide preferred), and thoroughly nailed, and the joints ⅛ inch apart to allow for swelling. (See No. 31.) (A layer of heavy tar paper on top of wood flooring will protect the boards from the moisture of the concrete, and will also prevent any moisture from dripping through to a ceiling below.)

Fig. 31.

In Old Buildings.—Cleats are nailed to joists five inches below the intended finished floor line, and short pieces of boards ⅛ inch apart fitted in between the

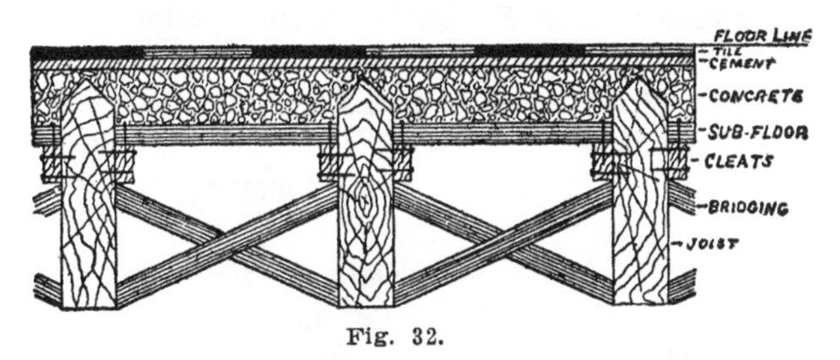

Fig. 32.

joists upon the cleats and well nailed, and the joists thoroughly bridged. The corners on the upper edge of the joists should be chamfered off to a sharp point (see Fig. 32), as the flat surface of the joists will give an uneven foundation. When the strength of the joists will permit, it is best to cut an inch or more off the top. (Where joists are too weak, strengthen by thoroughly nailing cleats six inches wide full length of joists.) When the solid wood foundation is thus prepared, concrete is placed upon it as above directed.

Where Steel Beams and hollow tile arches are used, frequently very little space is left for preparing a proper foundation for setting tile, as the rough coating is usually put in by the hollow tile contractor to protect his work, but this covering should always conform

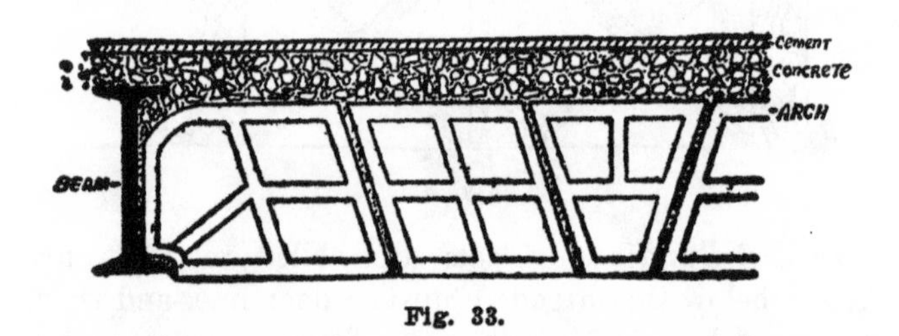

Fig. 33.

to the requirements for a solid tile foundation. Should this not be the case, the tile contractor should remove sufficient of the covering to allow him to put down a foundation that will insure a satisfactory tile floor. (Cinders, lime, mortar or inferior material must never be used.)

The tops of iron beams should be from three to four inches below the finished floor line, to prevent floors, when finished, showing lines of the beams.

For Hearths.—The foundation for hearths should be placed upon a brick arch, if possible, to ensure perfect fire protection, and then covered with concrete in the same manner as directed for tile floors. If placed upon a sub-foundation of wood, the concreting should be at least six inches thick. (See Figs. 34 and 35.)

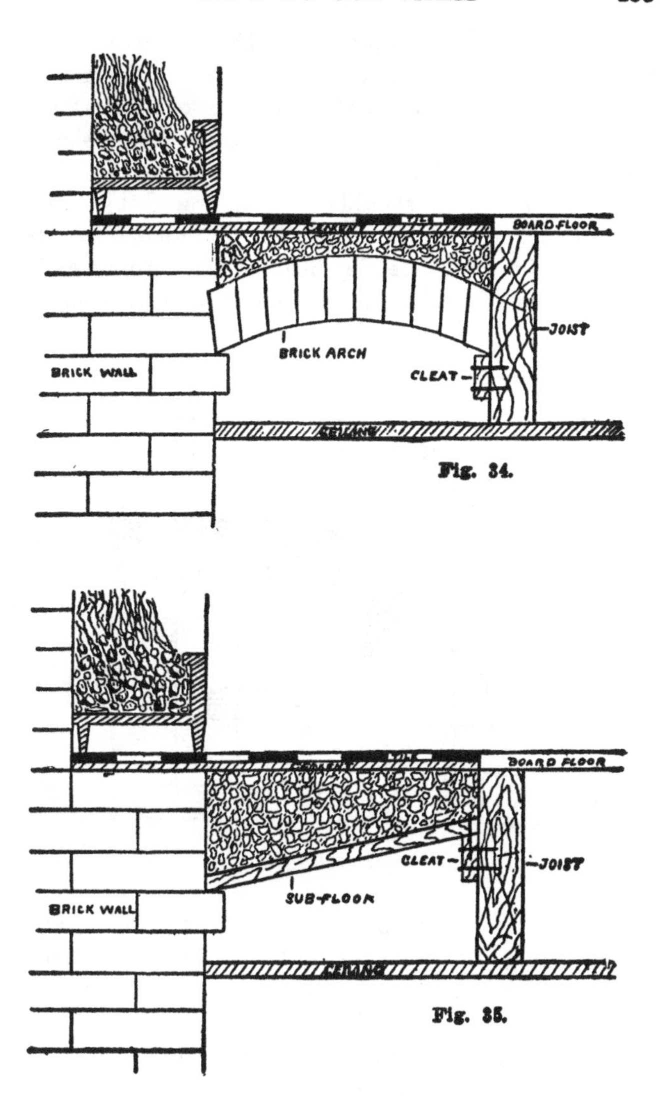
BOARD FLOOR
JOIST
BRICK ARCH
CLEAT
BRICK WALL
BOARD FLOOR
CLEAT
JOIST
SUB-FLOOR
BRICK WALL

Fig. 34.

Fig. 35.

For Walls.—When tiles are to be laid on old brick walls the plaster must be all removed and the mortar raked out of the joints of the brick work to form a key for the cement. On new brick walls the points should not be pointed. When tiles are to be placed on studding, the studding should be well braced by filling in between the studding with brick set in mortar to the height of tile work (see Fig. 36); or brick work may be omitted and extra studding put in and thoroughly

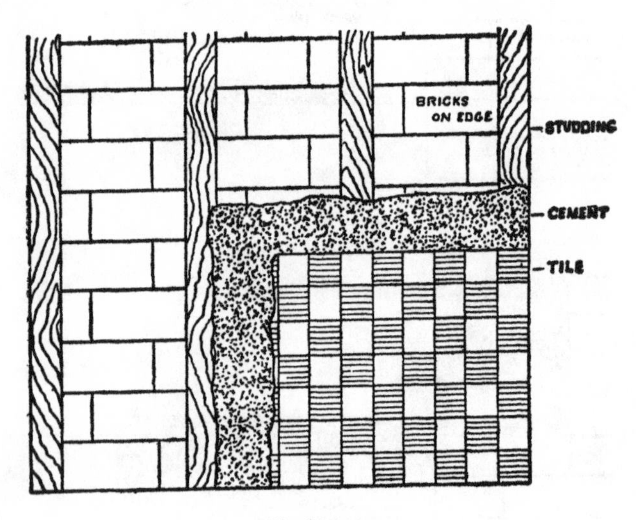

Fig. 36.

bridged, so as to have as little spring as possible, and this studding then covered with sheet metal lathing. (See Fig. 37.) (*Tile must never be placed on wood lath or on old plaster.*) The brick walls must be well wet with water and then covered with a rough coating of cement mortar, composed of one part Portland cement and two parts clean sharp sand. When tiles are placed on metal lathing, hair should be mixed with the cement mortar to make it adhere more closely to the lath. The cement mortar should be ½ inch thick, or sufficient to make an even and true surface to within one (1) inch of the intended finished surface of the tile, when tile ½ inch thick is used, which will allow

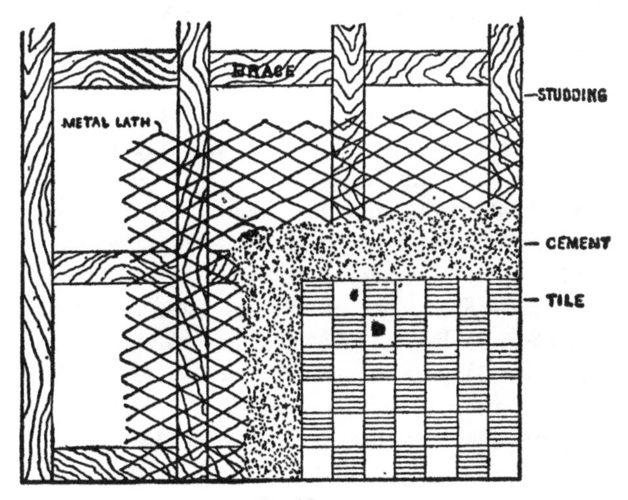

Fig. 37.

a space of ½ inch for the cement mortar, composed as above for rough coating the walls. The face of the cement foundation should be roughly scratched and allowed to harden for at least one day before commencing to lay the tile. If any lime is mixed with the cement mortar for setting the tiles, it should never exceed 10 per cent., and great care must be used to have the lime well slaked, and made free from all lumps by running through a coarse sieve, in order to guard against "heaving" or "swelling," and thus loosening or "lifting" the tiles.

Important.—The foundation for both floor and wall tiling should be thoroughly brushed, to remove all dust and small particles adhering to it, and then well wet before putting on the cement mortar. To ensure a perfect bond it is best to coat the foundation by brushing over it pure cement mixed in water.

Cement.—The very best quality of Portland cement should always be used for setting either floor or wall tile and for grouting the floors, and the very best quality of Keene's Imported Cement for filling the joints in the wall tiling.

Sand.—Clean, sharp grit sand, free from all salt, loam or other matter, and perfectly screened before mixing with the cement, should always be used.

Mortar.—For floors or vitreous tiles, should be composed of equal parts of cement and sand, and for wall tiles one (1) part of cement and two (2) parts sand. The mortar should not be too wet, but should be rather stiff, and should always be used fresh, as mortar, when allowed to set before using, loses a portion of its strength.

Soaking.—Tiles must always be thoroughly soaked in water before setting, which makes the cement unite to the tiles.

The Tiles for the Floors are first laid out to ascertain if they are all right and compared with the plan provided for laying the floors. Strips are then set, beginning at one end of and in the centre of the room, and level with the intended finished floor line. Two sets of guide strips running parallel about 18, to 30 inches apart should be set first. (See Fig. 38.) The mortar is then spread between them for about six to ten feet at a time, and level with a screed notched at each end, to allow for the thickness of the tiles. The tiles are placed upon the mortar, which must be stiff enough to prevent the mortar from working up be-

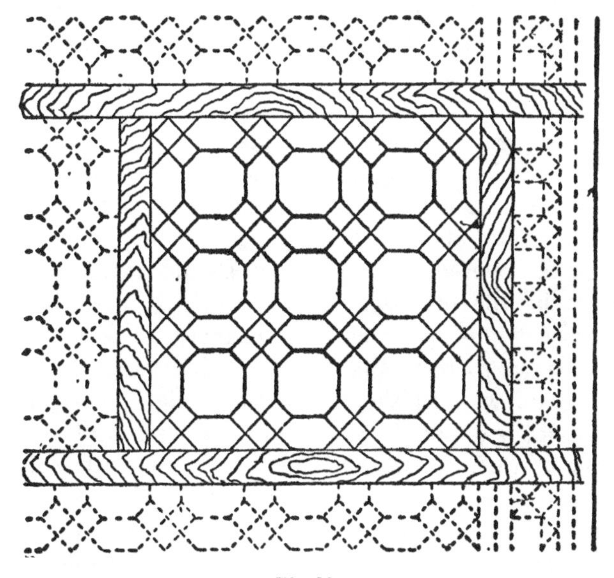

Fig. 38.

tween the joints. The tiles are to be firmly pressed into the mortar and tamped down with a block and hammer until they are exactly level with the strips. When the space between the strips is completed, the strips on one side of the tile is moved out 18 to 30 inches and placed in proper position for laying another section of tile, using the tiles which have been laid for one end of the screed, and the laying of the tile continued in the same manner until the floor is finished. When the cement is sufficiently set, which should be in about two days, the floor should be well scrubbed with clean water and a broom, and the joints thoroughly grouted with pure cement (mixed with water to the consistency of cream). As soon as this begins to stiffen, it must be carefully rubbed off with sawdust or fine shavings and the floor left perfectly clean.

Ceramics.—The foundation and cement mortar for ceramics are the same as for plain or vitreous floors, and the guide strips used in the same manner. The cement mortar is then spread evenly and the tile sheets laid carefully on it with the paper side up. After the batch is covered, the tile setter should commence to press the tile into the mortar, gently at first, firmly afterwards, using block and hammer, thus leveling the tile as correctly as possible. The tile should be beaten down until the mortar is visible in the joints through the paper; however, without breaking it. The paper is then moistened, and after it is well soaked and can be easily removed, it is pulled off backwards, starting from a corner. After removing the paper, the tile should be sprinkled with white sand before finishing the beating, so that the tiles will not adhere to the beater, owing to the paste which is used in mounting them. Corrections of the surface are then made by leveling it with block and hammer. The filling of the joints and cleaning of the surface is a delicate operation, as the looks of this work depends largely upon it. The joints are to be filled with clean Portland cement mixed with water. This mixture is forced into the joints with a flat trowel (not with a broom, which often scrapes out the joints). After the joints are

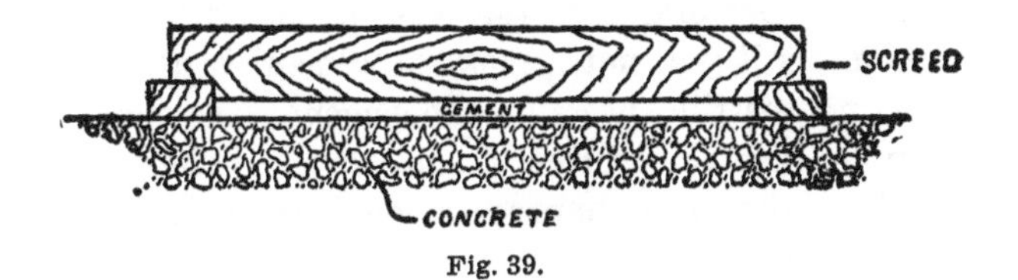

Fig. 39.

filled, the surplus cement is removed from the surface by drawing a wet piece of canton flannel over it.

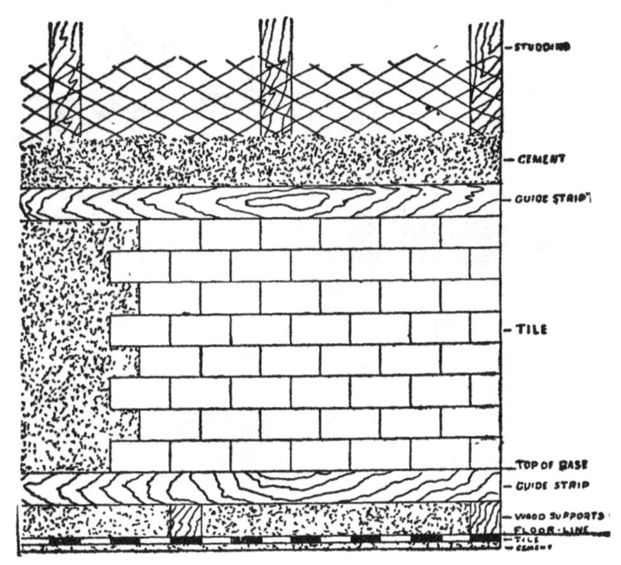

Fig. 40.

This piece of cloth must be washed out frequently with clean water. After the floor is cleaned, it should be allowed to stand for a day or two, when the whole floor is to be rubbed with sharp sand and a board of soft lumber. This treatment, which the last traces of cement, is preferable to the washing off with an acid solution, as it will not attack the cement in the joints. In laying the tile sheets on the cement, care should be taken to have the widths of joints spaced the same as the tile on the sheets to prevent the floor having a block appearance.

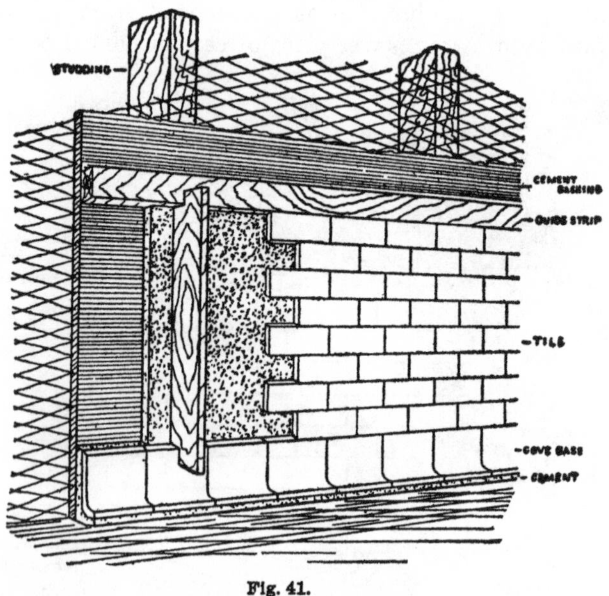

Fig. 41.

The Tiles for the Walls or Wainscoting are first laid out and compared with the plan provided for setting them. Guide strips are then placed on the wall parallel and about two feet apart, the bottom one being so arranged as to allow the base to be set after the body is in place. (See Fig. 40.) When a cove base is used it may be necessary to set it first, but in all cases must be well supported on the concrete. (See Fig. 41.) The strips must be placed plumb and even with the intended finished wall line. The method of setting wall tile is governed to some extent by the conditions of the wall on which they are to be set, and must be decided by the mechanic at the time, which process he will use, whether buttering or floating, as equally good work can be done by either, by following the instructions, as stated below.

Floating Wall Tile.—The mortar is spread between the guide strips for about five feet at a time and levelled with a screed notched at each end to allow for the thickness of the tile. (See Fig. 39.) The tiles are placed in position and tamped until they are firmly united to the cement and level with the strips. When the space between the strips is completed, which should be one side of the room, the strips are removed and the work continued in the same manner until completed. When the tiles are all set, the joints must be carefully washed out and neatly filled with thinly mixed pure Keene's Cement, and all cement remaining on the tile carefully wiped off.

Buttering Wall Tiles.—The cement mortar is spread on the back of each tile, and the tile placed on the wall, and tapped gently until firmly united to the wall and plumb with the guide strips. When the tiles are all set, the joints must be carefully washed out and filled with Keene's Cement, and the tiles cleaned as directed above.

When fixtures of any kind are to be placed on the

tile work, such as plumbing in bathroom, provision should be made for them by fastening wood strips on the wall before the rough or first coating of cement mortar is put on, the strips to be the same thickness as the rough coating. The tiles can be placed over the strips by covering them with cement mortar, and when thoroughly set, holes can be bored in the tiles for fastening the fixtures without injuring the tiling.

Hearth and Facing Tile are set in the same manner as for floors and walls.

Cleaning.—It is absolutely necessary to remove with sawdust, and afterwards with a flannel cloth and water, all traces of cement which may have been left on the surface of the tile, as it is hard to remove after it is set.

After thoroughly cleaning the floor, it should be covered with sawdust and boards placed on the floor for several days where there is walking upon it.

A white scum sometimes appears on the surface of the tile, caused by the cement. This can generally be removed by washing frequently with plenty of soap and water. If this does not remove it, then use a weak solution of 15 parts muriatic acid and 85 parts water, which should only be allowed to remain on the tile for a few minutes, and then thoroughly washed off.

Cutting of Tile.—When it is found necessary to cut tile the following directions are given:

Tools.—The chisels used should be made of the best tool steel, and should always be sharp. They should be of small size, the edge not being wider than one-fourth inch. The hammer should be light, weighing about six ounces, having a slender handle. After the exact shape of the tile has been determined, lines should be drawn on the surface of the tile with a lead pencil, giving the exact direction of the cut desired. This line should be followed with the chisel, which is held at right angles with the surface, the hammer giving the chisel sharp, decisive raps. After the line has been repeatedly traversed with the chisel, a few sharp blows against the back of the tile opposite the mark on the face will break it at the place thus marked.

To cut glazed or enamel tiles, they should be scratched on the surface with a tool at the place where it is desired to break them, and then gently tapped on the back opposite the scratch.

Caution should be used not to allow any one to walk upon or carry anything heavy over the floor, or have any pounding about wall work for several days, or until the tiles are firmly set. Unless these precautions are taken it will be impossible to guarantee a first-class job. Tile work is frequently condemned when the fault lies with the rush of other contractors to finish their work.

Laying Tile on Wood.—A new material called "Monolith," manufactured by The Wisconsin Mantel & Tile Co., that enables the workman to lay tiles on a wooden floor. There are many places where tile could be used, but on account of the added weight to the floor by the use of cement, concrete foundation, it is impracticable to lay in many places, but by the use of Monolith, the only weight that is added is the tile itself and the Monolith bed it is laid in. Both materials are only five-eighths of an inch in thickness when laid.

Fig. 42.

The illustration, Fig. 42, shows the method of laying the tile. The paper to which the small pieces of tiles are glued is seen on top of tiles. The dark part shows the patent cement, or Monolith.

I show herewith, at Nos. 43 and 44, twelve designs for decorative borders of various kinds, and in 45 and 46 I show two designs well suited for vestibules, store entrances or for hearths in fire-places.

Good Concrete.—In determining the proportions of the aggregates and cement for a certain piece of work, it is necessary usually to take samples of the broken stone (or gravel) and sand which are most available to the site and make measurements of the percentage of voids in the stone which must be filled by the sand and the percentage of voids in the sand which must be filled by the cement. This is done by taking a cubic foot box and filling it with broken stone in a thoroughly wet state. The box is then filled with as much water as is required to completely fill it, in addition to the stone, which upon being poured off gives the relation between the volume of the voids and the volume of the stone. The required amount of local sand thus determined is then measured out and placed in the box with the stone in a damp state. Water is then used to determine the percentage of voids left in the sand, which gives the approximate amount of cement required, although an excess of cement is almost invariably used. Engineers everywhere differ regarding the best proportion to be used, but in general the above test, roughly made, will determine it well enough. The proportions which are most universally used are as follows: 1 cement, 2 sand, 4 broken stone; where extremely strong work is desired. Tests

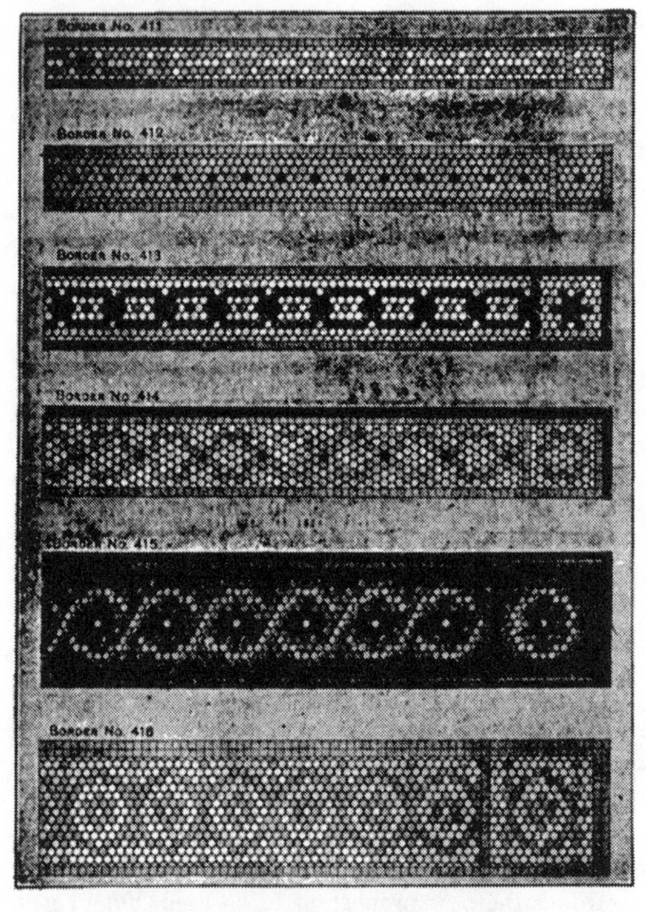

Decorative Borders in Round, Square and One Inch Hexagons of Various Colors.

Fig. 43.

A Series of Borders in Square Tiles, Each in a Variety of Colors.

Fig. 44.

show that a 6-inch thickness of 1-2-4 concrete properly made is waterproof up to about 50 pounds to the square inch. This concrete is frequently used for facing dams. 1-3-6 is the proportion generally used for the interior of dams and large structures. It is entirely suitable for large foundations. 1-4-8 is frequently used for foundation work, and when properly mixed

Fig. 45.

makes good concrete, although it is about the limit of what is considered good work, and would not be suitable for very important structures. 1-5-10 is equal to any concrete made with natural cement. It is a well-known fact that the volume of concrete when mixed with water is somewhat less than the volume of the aggregate and cement before mixing. The contractors' rule is that the volume of mixed concrete is equal to the volume of the stone plus one-half to one-third the volume of sand.

There has been much discussion among engineers and others as to the amount of water that should be added to the aggregates and cement for making the best concrete, and while it is not the purpose of this paper to enter into this controversy, it might be said that the modern tendency is toward wet concrete. The old way was to add just enough water so that when all

Fig. 46.

the concrete was in the form and tamped, it would show moisture on the surface. The tamping is a very important part of the operation, and the quality of the work is dependent upon how well this is superintended, as unless it is well and thoroughly done the concrete is liable to be honeycombed and imperfect, especially near the forms. With the growth of the use of concrete the old method of putting it in the forms nearly dry and depending on tamping to consolidate it has been more or less abandoned, and the more modern way is to put the concrete in quite wet, as less tamping is required and much labor and expense saved. One of the great objections to this scheme is that if care is not taken the water will tend to wash the cement from the stone and sand; in other words, unmix it. However, it may be said that it is now generally understood that rather wet concrete properly handled makes better work. The amount of water to be added to the aggregates and cement varies from 1 water to 3 cement by measurement to 12 per cent of water by weight. Mr. Carey, of Newhaven, England, says that 23 gallons water per cubic yard of cement was the best mixture. Quite frequently salt water is used in mixing concrete in cold weather to prevent freezing, and it seems to have no ill effects on the resulting mixture.

Reinforced Concrete.—Up to the last few years the use of concrete as a building material was chiefly confined to the construction of foundations, piers, reservoir dams and similar purposes, in which the stresses to be met were almost entirely simple pressures. Indeed, even fifteen years ago, many engineers looked askance on the use of concrete for arches, considering it for this purpose much inferior to brick. Much of the caution shown in extending the use of this valuable material doubtless arose from the frequency with which concrete masonry exhibited unsightly cracks, due largely to the material being allowed to get too dry while hardening. At the same time, careful examination has shown that cracks of the same character are common in masonry of all kinds, but are unnoticed, because they follow the regular joints of the structure; whereas, on the smooth uniform surface of the concrete, cracks of much less significance are immediately visible.

The plan of reinforcing the material with metal, of which several systems have been introduced during the last four years, has greatly extended the possible use of concrete; and it appears that in many cases a reinforced concrete bridge may compete, even in first cost, with a steel girder; while as regards upkeep, it has, of course, many advantages. Small bridge culverts of this material were extensively used by Russian engineers in building the Manchurian Railway. For openings of some 7-foot span, flat slabs of concrete reinforced with rails were used, the thickness being 8¼ inches. A similar system was used for spans up to 21 feet, the concrete, however, being thickened at the center as the span increased, the depth at this point being 2 feet 6¼ inches for the 21-foot span, and proportionately less for smaller openings. The thickness at the bearings was, however, the same in all cases, viz., 8¼ inches. The line was thrown over the spans as little as seven days after completion. The concrete consisted of one part cement, two sand and five broken stone. The system in this case had great advantages, as stone for masonry was unobtainable, and could, moreover, only be used for arches, which would have necessitated the use of higher embankments than were required with the ferro-concrete, used as described. Much larger spans have, of course, been built than those mentioned. One, of 153-foot span, carrying four main line tracks, has recently been built for the Lake Shore and Michigan Southern Railroad, while Mr. Edwin Thacker, M. Am. Soc. C. E., states he considers the system feasible for spans up to 500 feet, and has actually got out designs for a span 300 feet, the cost comparing favorably with that of a steel bridge.

One great drawback to the extension of the system lies in the difficulty in proportioning structures thus built in a thoroughly rational manner. In the case of steel bridges certain simple assumptions as to the elasticity and strength of the material suffice. These assumptions are doubtless not absolutely exact, but are sufficiently near the truth for practical purposes. The elastic properties of concrete are, however, very different from those of steel; Hooke's law is not even approximately correct, and, moreover, the material always takes a permanent set when first loaded. The true distribution of the stress and strain on a concrete beam is thus a much more complicated matter than it is in the case of a steel joist, in which it is permissible, within working limits of stress, to assume the accuracy of Hooke's law. The assumption generally made in the case of ferro-concrete is that plane sections of a concrete beam remain plane after bending. This postulate is, of course, that commonly made in proportioning steel work; and in the latter case, stress being proportional to strain, the usual formula for the working strength of beams is readily reduced. In the case of concrete, however, the stress-strain curve is much more complex. Nevertheless, M. Considere has shown that by making experiments on concrete in simple tension and compression, and plotting the corresponding stress-strain curves, it is possible to deduce from these with fair accuracy the load-deflection curve of a ferro-concrete beam.

This method, though logical, leads, however, to no simple formula for the strength; and in applying this method the working load of any particular concrete beam would have to be deduced by the tedious process of scaling off the stress-strain curves at a number of points, and combining the results. A further question arises as to whether this stress-strain curve should be the initial stress-strain of the concrete, or that obtained after repeated loadings. Probably the latter is the best to choose, but in that case it by no means follows that the metal reinforcement is free from initial stresses when the load is applied to the beam; and if the metal is subject to initial stress, it is obvious that similar ones must exist in the concrete. In fact, M. Considere has shown that this is necessarily the case in any circumstances, since, if the concrete is allowed to harden under water, it tends to expand, and this expansion is resisted by the metal reinforcement. If, on the other hand, the hardening takes place in air the concrete tends to contract; and this contraction being again resisted by the metal, a series of fine hair cracks are produced which, visible at low loads, are readily detected on the tension side of a heavily loaded ferro-concrete beam.

In view of the uncertainties introduced by the different factors above mentioned, it is really questionable whether, after all, the theoretically objectionable formula of M. Hennebique is not as good as any other. The latter all involve a preliminary calculation of the position of the neutral axis, which varies with the percentage of metal used, and with the type of stress-strain curve assumed for the concrete; and also with the maximum stress at any particular section. Thus, in a centrally-loaded beam, its position at the ends is entirely different from what it is at the centre. M. Hennebique, on the other hand, makes no attempt to locate this neutral axis, and simply assumes that one-half of his beam resists compression, and that the stress is uniformly distributed over this half. The moment of this compression about the centre of the section equates to half the moment due to the load, and the other half of the moment due to the load he equates to the moment about the centre of the section of the tensile stress on the metal reinforcement. The working strength of concrete in compression, he takes as 350 pounds per square inch, and neglects entirely its strength in tension. The working tensile stress on the steel reinforcement he takes as 14,000 pounds per square inch. This method is, of course, totally illogical, yet many thousand cubic yards of ferro-concrete have been successfully designed on these lines; and a comparison of the strength of ferro-concrete beams as calculated by this formula, and by those of a more rational type, shows very little difference between the two for a considerable range of metal to concrete. On the other hand, it must not be forgotten that formulae which are non-rational in form are always risky when applied to extreme conditions.

Concrete being as weak in shear as in tension, provision is also required to take the shearing stresses. Some American designers have to this end patented special forms of reinforcement bar, in which each main tension bar has projecting upward from the ties inclined at an angle of 45 degrees. These extend to the top of the bar and take the tensile stresses arising from the shear. The corresponding compressive stress at right angles to this is carried by the concrete. The system is doubtless efficient, and on large spans, where weight must be reduced to a minimum it may have some advantage; but in work of ordinary proportions it seems to be little superior to the Hennebique system, in which the necessary strengthening is provided by stirrups of flat iron bent into a U shape. The main reinforcing bars rest in these stirrups at the lower ends. The spacing of the stirrups depends upon the "web stresses" to be taken, which can easily be calculated by assuming the reinforced beam to be a latticed girder, the lower chord of which is represented by the metal reinforcement, the upper one by the centre of the compression half of the beam, while the stirrups represent vertical ties, which may be taken as connected together at top and bottom by inclined imaginary struts. The advantage of this simple method of reinforcing for shear lies in the possibility of using common rolled sections for the whole of the reinforcement.

M. Hennebique constructs most of his ferro-concrete work on the monolithic system, girders, piers, columns and floors being solidly connected together. It is, therefore, necessary to provide for the reversed bending moments over the point of support, which is done by bending up half of the total reinforcement bars, so that the ends of the span are close to the upper surface of the beam, and thus in a position to take the heavy tensile stresses which ensue at these points when the monolithic system of construction is followed. The exact calculation of the reactions and bending moments here is impracticable, if not actually impossible; and those engineers who attach much importance to having all structures statically determinate will doubtless object to the plan, but experience shows that the advantages gained are very considerable. The structure then resists as a unit, and in particular its rigidity is marvelous.

Some comparative tests on this point, made by the Railway Company, showed that with a ferro-concrete floor subjected to blows four times as heavy as were applied to an equivalent floor constructed of brick arches on steel joists, the deflection was only one-seventh as great.

The extreme rigidity attainable with the monolithic system of construction was also very evident in the case of the large Hennebique bridge at Purfleet. Since a structure fails by strain rather than by stress, the small deformation noted with ferro-concrete are evident that as an average the material is relatively little tried by the loads carried. It must, however, be admitted that this low average strain is quite compatible with extremely severe strain at particular points; but it is, of course, the business of the designer, by suitably disposing his material to avoid these possible local abnormalities.

Occasionally, doubts have been expressed as to whether the metallic reinforcement may not suffer from corrosion as time goes on. This would be extremely dangerous if it occurred, since the metal being out of sight, its loss of strength might remain undetected until, some day, the structure might fall under its ordinary working load. Fortunately, much evidence is available to the effect that steel or iron thoroughly imbedded in concrete is permanently protected from rust. Americans, indeed, are so positive on this point that they have recently constructed a number of reservoir dams in ferro-concrete. In some cases these have been arched, but in others they have been straight. The cross-section in the latter case is generally a hollow triangle, the sides of which are connected together by diaphragm walls from point to point. The dam is also anchored to its site, though generally the weight provided is sufficient to make the structure safe against overturning, quite apart from the help received from the anchor-bars.

Progress in the use of reinforced concrete has been somewhat slow in England. The railway engineers, in view of their enormous responsibilities, have not unnaturally hesitated to adopt a material in which it was impossible to calculate the strength with accuracy, and of which experience as to its reliability was very recent. In the larger cities, moreover, its use has, quite apart from this, been restricted by the inelastic nature of the building regulations, which have been reached upon the assumption that finality had been reached in the matter of building construction. Hence, permission to erect warehouses and factories in ferro-concrete has always been difficult—and often impossible—to obtain, though experience has shown that the new material is most excellent as a fire-resister. At the great Baltimore fire it was found that the concrete exposed to the flames was seldom damaged to a greater depth than one-half inch, though projecting corners suffered somewhat more, being rounded off by the flames to a radius of about two inches, pointing to the advisability of constructing the concrete with well-rounded corners in the first instance. The only reasonable grounds of objection to any proposed system of building construction are its dangers from a structural sanitary or fire-risk point of view. As a result of much investigation and experiment, the following conclusions were arrived at for the guidance of the designer and constructor of reinforced concrete:

1. What drawings and details should be prepared before work is commenced.

2. The nature of the materials which may be employed and the standards to which these should comply, i. e.,

   (a) the metal in reinforcement,

   (b) the matrix,

   (c) the sand,

   (d) the gravel, stone, clinker or other aggregate,

   (e) water.

3. What are the proportions for concrete to be used in different cases.

4. How the ingredients for concrete are to be mixed and deposited on the work.

5. The distances to be allowed between the reinforcing bars and what covering of concrete is necessary.

6. What precautions are necessary in the design and erection of centring and false work, and how long the whole or portion of centring and false work should remain in position.

7. The rules which should be used in determining the dimensions of the several parts necessary for security, and what safe stresses should be allowed.

8. The supervision necessary and the special matters to which it should be directed.

9. The fire-resisting properties of reinforced concrete.

10. Its adaptability for structures where resistance to liquid pressure is essential, and what special precautions may be advisable under these conditions.

11. What are the necessary conditions for its permanence; resistance to rusting of metal, disintegration of concrete or effects of vibration.

12. The testing of the materials employed and of the finished structures.

13. What provisions are desirable in Building Laws or Government regulations relating to buildings and other structures so far as these affect the use of reinforced concrete.

REINFORCED CONCRETE.

The engineer who is designing a steel structure specifies that tests shall be made at the shops which will give a clear indication of the character of the materials used. These tests refer to the ultimate strength, elastic limit, ultimate elongation and reduction of area. He also inspects the construction of his structure, and bad workmanship is getting more and more rare. If poor work is sometimes done it can be discovered by careful inspection, and when the structure is tested on completion nothing unexpected will take place, if its type and design are based on practical experience. Thus the deflections which steel structures show under their test loads are found to be almost identical with those computed for them and their determination is, therefore, not of great value.

The measuring and observation of the local deformations, on the contrary, furnish valuable information on the distribution of stresses, and enable the engineer to appreciate the advantages and disadvantages of the various types of construction; but it is very seldom that they disclose faulty construction or bad material. It can thus be said that for steel or iron structures the preliminary tests of the materials used and the inspection of construction and erection furnish all the necessary assurances. Quite different is the case with concrete-steel structures, because laboratory tests tell us only of the quality of the materials employed, and the most active inspection will not be able to prevent positively poor workmanship and faulty construction which can destroy the strength of structures made of the best materials.

In fact, the proportions of the concrete may, in spite of careful watching, not be in all parts in accordance with the specifications; the quantity of water used in mixing must, in order to produce identical results, vary within a wide range, according to the condition of moisture in the materials and the atmosphere, and it is quite sure that it will be sometimes badly proportioned. If too much water be added the strength of the concrete, and especially its coefficient of elasticity, will be decreased to a degree which may be considerable; if too little water be added the adhesion of the concrete to the reinforcing metal will not be sufficient. The thoroughness of the tamping has a still greater influence on the strength of the work. To the faults of execution, faults of design may be added. The latter must especially be guarded against in a new type of construction, the theory of which is not yet fully established.

Whatever the results of the tests of the materials may be, very little information on the strength of a concrete-steel structure can be obtained without direct tests of the structure itself. But observed deformations will furnish really useful indications only when compared to the normal deformations which, according to the computations, should have been caused in accordance with the quality and disposition of the materials. Hitherto no method has been established to enable the engineer to compute these normal deformations. However, at one time it was assumed that reinforced concrete, whatever its deformation, preserves the coefficient of elasticity as determined in ordinary tension tests, and at another that the resistance of the concrete in tension can be neglected in reinforced members. Sometimes it has also been assumed that the resistance of concrete in tension can be neglected only when its deformations exceed the elongation which causes rupture in common tension tests. None of these assumptions has given results agreeing with the actual behavior of reinforced concrete. We may conclude that in reinforced concrete construction certainly some particular phenomena occur, a knowledge of which is necessary to predict their resistance and deformations.

Concrete in compression is generally not reinforced and it cannot be expected that the phenomena mentioned in the preceding section will be found to be caused by it. It suffices to recall the well-known law of deformation of concrete in compression and to make it more precise by naming the ratio of an infinitely small variation of compression to the variation of length caused by it, the "instantaneous coefficient of elasticity."

When the compression increases, but remains within an amount which, in general, is nearly a third of the ultimate strength, the instantaneous coefficient of elasticity decreases, but in a very small degree. When the stress increases still more the change in the elasticity gradually increases; it is appreciable for a compressive stress near one-half the value of the ultimate, and it then increases so rapidly before failure that the instantaneous coefficient may fall below one-twentieth of its value under a light stress. This aspect of the deformation is similar to the one generally observed on all materials. The simple law which determines the deformation of concrete in compression thus cannot furnish the explanation of observed irregularities, and it must be looked for in the phenomena which are produced in tension.

It appears to be evident that the test loads should not be heavier than the amount required to insure the safety of the structure. Even smaller loads could, no doubt, be employed if a comparison of the computed deformations and those actually observed is made, as has been proposed in this chapter, so as to obtain by means of moderate test loads the coefficient of elasticity, the elastic limit and the tensile resistance of the concrete of the tested beams. It is, besides, known that the compressive resistance is almost proportional to the tensile resistance and it is consequently evident that a test with a moderate load will suffice to furnish information on all the properties of the concrete employed.

To the preliminary tests of the materials to be employed the direct tests of reinforced concrete structures must be added to obtain sufficient assurance of safety.

The tests will not show their full usefulness unless the deformations which should normally be expected be first computed and then compared to the observed deformations.

The computation of the deformations to be expected must be based on the knowledge of the laws of deformation of concrete reinforced by metal, and it appears that above the elastic limit, these laws are different from the laws which determine the deformations of unreinforced concrete.

The deformations of members in flexure appear to be influenced by the shearing stresses, by the character of the surroundings in which the concrete has set and was kept and by the action of any transverse reinforcing members.

The investigation and study of these phenomena is still more important because the strength of a member is intimately connected with its deformations.

It is easier to compute the elongations and shortenings which should be expected to take place, under normal conditions, in a given section than the deflection of a beam, which is the resultant of the deformations of all of its sections. The measuring of the local deformations deserves, therefore, to be recommended and at least to take its place side by side with the measuring of deflections.

Concretes placed under water and gradually hardened there show a tendency to swell in all directions, and the more so the richer their proportions of cement. This swelling varies from 0.1 to 0.2 per cent, for pure cement mortar and from 0.02 to 0.05 per cent, for concrete poor in cement.

When the swelling cannot take place freely, compressive stresses are developed in the masonry, which may reach much higher values than the stresses caused by the shrinking in the air. Experiments were made which were intended to establish the law of relation between the deformations, prevented from exceeding certain limits by external means or metal reinforcing, and the stresses developed at the same time. An idea of the importance of these stresses will be formed by the fact that, in a rectangular prism 2.36 by 0.98 inch, made of neat cement and reinforced in its axis by an iron rod 0.4 inch diameter, there have been developed, after ten months in water, internal and opposing stresses of about 2,200 pounds, equivalent to a compressive stress of about 90 pounds per square inch in the concrete and a tensile stress of about 17,500 pounds per square inch in the iron. The tension in the iron was measured directly, and computed as accurately as possible by multiplying the coefficient of elasticity by the shortening of the rod caused at the instant when the surrounding cement which prevented it from taking its natural length was carefully removed.

The internal stresses caused by the prevention of the

swelling of mortar or concrete members by the reinforcing rods are, in general, favorable to their resistance, because these stresses increase the compressive stresses and decrease the tensile stresses of the materials which can resist the former ten times better than the latter. They have especially the effect of consolidating building joints and all sections of small resistance to tension by preventing cracks in them. Obvious advantages result therefrom for the resistance of masonry kept under water and the durability of the concrete and its reinforcing metal.

Differences in the swelling of layers of different age must, however, be guarded against as they cause parallel stresses in the joints, which seem to be injurious to the adhesion. But, contrary to what takes place in the case of shrinking, it is here the oldest masonry in which tensile stresses are caused, and its resistance being superior to that of the superimposed masonry the possibly dangerous effect is decreased. However, the author has no experimental proof as to the dangers due to the different swelling of parts of masonry. In general an exaggerated account of the internal stresses should be avoided because their effects combine according to little-known laws with the stresses caused by the external forces, and it may be possible that in some places their actions should be added together.

It seems, therefore, to be proper not to raise the proportions of cement in concrete above the limits which insure sufficient impermeability and long life to the submerged concrete. It appears to be of advantage not to exceed 1,300 to 1,500 pounds of cement to the cubic yard of concrete, which proportion gives the greatest resistance, except for work exposed to the waves, where rapidity of setting is a necessary condition for successful work. From all the above considerations it follows that reinforced concrete masonry will give still better results for hydraulic work than for structures exposed to the air, and the success of these has been proved by experience.

It should be stated that, in the computations of the resistances of concrete masonry structures in which the free change of volume is in any way prevented, these changes should be considered. On this basis the author recently showed that in the floor of a dock only harmless stresses could be produced in spite of the fact that this floor was of a thickness which would have caused excessive stresses if the increase in volume had not strongly compressed the floor against the foundations of the side walls.

It is well known that all the materials employed in masonry show an increase in volume when they absorb water and a decrease when their moisture is reduced. The author has found these changes in volume to be much greater than is given by Busing and Schumann in their work on cement. A prism of neat cement, not reinforced, which was kept in dry air during two years elongated 0.024 per cent. of its length after three weeks of immersion in water. A prism of mortar, not reinforced, containing 730 pounds of cement to the cubic yard of sand, which was kept fifteen months in water, shortened 0.05 per cent. after being two months in dry air. From the observations made it appears that contrary to what has taken place in the changes of volume due to the gradual hardening of the cement, the variations in volume produced by changes in the state of moisture on hardened mortar do not increase with the higher proportions of cement. The contrary rather takes place.

There is still another radical difference between the effects which the two causes of change in volume have on reinforced concrete members. During the hardening the mortar possesses at the beginning a very high degree of plasticity, which gradually decreases. This results in causing the mortar, which has gradually hardened, to yield to a large extent to the stresses which the reinforcing rods produce in it. Thus reinforced members which have set in the open air remain of a greater length than that which they would have taken freely without restraint from the reinforcing. The crystallizations which take place during the setting are between the artificially separated molecules, and a decrease in density, elasticity, and resistance is the result.

The opposite should be caused in reinforced members which have hardened in water, but the author has not had the occasion to verify whether an improvement in the quality of the concrete actually takes place. The effects of the variations in the hygrometric condition on completely hardened mortars are very different from those resulting from gradual hardening. There is a struggle between the two associated materials, the coefficients of elasticity of which have arrived at their final values, and the difference between the length which each material tries to assume and the one it is compelled to take by the combination is inversely proportional to its coefficient of elasticity.

From these considerations it follows that account should be taken of the fact that the difference in the variations of length which take place in a mortar according to whether it is reinforced or not will be considerably greater during the beginning of the hardening than during the following hygrometric changes. Experience has confirmed this fact. It also follows that the variations in volume which the hygrometric changes tend to produce in hardened mortars are smaller than those produced during gradual hardening, since internal stresses, and especially tensile stresses in the reinforcing rods, may be caused, which attain 5,500 to 8,500 pounds per square inch. Contrary to what takes place during the slow hardening of mortar, the hygrometric variations appear to be the more dangerous the less rich in cement the mortar is, because its resistance is smaller while the internal stresses are, at least, as great.

It should be added that these disadvantages are practically of no account for masonry always exposed to the air because the changes in the proportions of moisture in the air have a very small effect. The question is only of importance for members made in the open air which begin to harden before being put in water where they finally remain submerged, as in the case of piles, caissons, etc. By keeping them moistened until put in place, not only will the cracks which are often caused, as has been shown by experience, be prevented, but also the changes in the internal stresses, which cannot be of any advantage. It would be both interesting and useful to determine experimentally the results to be obtained by keeping reinforced concrete members, to be permanently exposed to the air, as moist as possible by abundant and repeated sprinkling for several weeks. It is obvious that the final shrinking, as well as the disadvantages resulting therefrom, would be decreased.

In concluding attention should be called to a fact worthy of research. Reinforced concrete members previously subjected to test loads have shown very little effect due to changes of the moisture in them. This will seem probable when it is remembered that the test load reduces the coefficient of elasticity of the concrete very considerably.

The first idea which presented itself to engineers to increase the resistance of concrete in compression was to reinforce it, similarly to tension pieces, by rods laid longitudinally in the direction of the stress. For purposes of construction, to keep the rods better in place, the reinforcing rods were tied together by a network or a belt of smaller rods. Some engineers understood that these belts perform another important role, that they protect the longitudinal rods from premature flexure and retard the swelling of the concrete and, hence, its ultimate failure.

It will be seen below that by hooping or completely surrounding the concrete by steel rods a considerably higher resistance can be obtained, and it is evident that between this method, supplemented by the addition of longitudinal rods, on one side, and the method of reinforcing by longitudinal main rods tied together by belts of lighter material on the other side, there is an intermediate continuous series of methods of reinforcing. The conclusions reached by this study will enable us to foresee the effects of these complex combinations, but before making the synthesis the influence of each element should be investigated separately. Concrete reinforced by longitudinal rods tied together by netting or belts of dimensions too small or spaced too far apart to exert noticeable influence on the resistance of concrete will, therefore, be treated first.

It was admitted, up to the present time, that the different varieties of stone, mortars, and concrete, when under compression, always fail by shearing along planes which are inclined to the direction of the stress. The recent experiments made in Germany by Foeppel and repeated by Mesnager at the laboratory of l'Ecole des Ponts et Chaussees have proved that this mode of failure is due to the friction exerted on the lower planes of the test specimens by the plates transmitting the pressure.

And it has further been proved that by sufficiently reducing this friction by the introduction of a greased surface, the failure will take place along surfaces which will be parallel to the direction of the pressure.

It is not clear how longitudinal reinforcing bars, which are parallel to the lines of rupture, could prevent the separation of the molecules and increase the resistance of the concrete, and it seems that the only effect of longitudinal reinforcing in compression members consists in adding the resistance of the steel to that of the concrete without strengthening the latter. Experience has shown that such is the case. The effects of the reinforcing bars are, however, complicated, for the reasons which follow.

As has been shown, the tendency to shrink which concrete shows when hardening in air causes in reinforced concrete internal stresses of great intensity; tension in the concrete and compression in the metal. Experiments made in 1902 at the laboratory of l'Ecole des Ponts et Chaussees, according to the program laid out by the French Commission on Concrete-Steel, have determined the effect due to the shrinking of large concrete-steel specimens of the most commonly employed mixture, 420 pounds of Portland cement to the cubic yard of sand and 1-inch gravel in the proportion of 1:2. Measurement of the variations in length of the reinforcing bars has shown that after three months the shrinking of the concrete had compressed the metal, 6,540 pounds per square inch, in prisms 6.5 feet long of a section about 4x4 inches and reinforced near the edges by 4 iron wires 1/4 inch in diameter. The compressive stress in the metal has reached 10,800 to 14,200 pounds per square inch in beams 13.1 feet long having a cross-section about 8x16 inches and reinforced near one of the smaller sides by 4 metal rods of 7/8-inch diameter placed 1.3 inches from the face. The latter specimens were prepared to be tested for bending.

It is superfluous to point out the importance of the above statement as to the magnitude of the interior stresses in members of the usual mixtures and of dimensions similar to those met in practice. Neglecting this kind of stresses, some engineers have made grave mistakes in the interpretation of bending experiments and have established incorrect formulas and rules, especially on the subject of stresses in compression members. They have assumed that if a certain specimen has undergone a shortening, i, its reinforcing bars, which had a coefficient of elasticity E, were compressed to a stress $E\ i$, neglecting the addition which has to be made to the latter stress for the shrinking of the concrete, if it has hardened in air, and which usually exceeds it in amount. The above considerations are sufficient to compute the stresses in compression members as long as the elastic limits have not been surpassed, neither in the concrete nor in the metal; but this is only one side of the question.

Without entering into a discussion of the unit stresses which may be allowed for the various elements of reinforced concrete structures, it is evident that the basis of any computation must be the knowledge of the stresses which are induced in these elements at the instant at which, for the first time, there appears any danger for the one or the other of them. It is, therefore, important to know the stress caused by the reinforcing steel in a member in compression at the instant where it begins to fail by the crushing of the concrete, which takes place a long time before that of the steel.

A concrete of common quality can stand without crushing a reduction in length of 0.07 to 0.10 per cent. and sometimes more. Such a compression will cause a stress in the metal of 20,000 to 29,000 pounds per square inch, if the coefficient of elasticity be 29,000,000 pounds. This stress added to the previous stress of 7,000 to 14,000 pounds, gives a total of 27,000 to 43,000 pounds per square inch of the metal, which is equal and even superior to the elastic limit of the iron and mild steel which is usually employed. Therefore, before the crushing of the concrete, the reinforcing bars are almost always stressed up to their elastic limit, unless the elastic limit of the bars be exceptionally high or the concrete exceptionally poor.

This stress cannot be appreciably surpassed because a very great decrease takes place in the value of the coefficient of elasticity of the metal as soon as the elastic limit has been exceeded, and the stresses increase, therefore, with an extreme slowness which is limited by the small deformations which the concrete can still undergo without crushing.

Whatever the mode of rupture of concrete in compression, the crushing of the same must be retarded by the use of reinforcing rods put in planes perpendicular to the direction of the external pressure and sufficiently near to each other. The tendency to slide along oblique planes is, indeed, resisted by reinforcing bars which cut these planes, whether parallel or perpendicular to the direction of the pressure. Rupturing along surfaces parallel to the pressure is directly opposed by transverse reinforcing.

The idea of using transverse reinforcing is not new, and, while it may be still older, it is sufficient to mention that it was experimented upon in 1892 by Koenen and Wayss. Since then Harel de la Noe has theoretically explained the advantages of transverse reinforcing and has made and inspired some very interesting applications. The transverse reinforcing may consist of a series of rods placed on diameters, all passing through the center of the section, or of a net with rectangular openings, or of circumferential rods which constitute hoops embedded in the concrete to a depth required to protect the metal from the action of atmospheric influences.

The author has not made any experiments on the first system which concentrates the metal around the center where it is the least useful. He has limited his preliminary experiments to reinforcing consisting either of circumferential hoops or of netting wires at right angles and parallel to the sides of the section. For equal weights of metal the resistance to crushing was appreciably more than twice as great for the circumferential reinforcing as for the wire netting.

Without entering into a theoretical discussion, the above result can be explained by a simple observation. If the external layers of a prism reinforced by rectangular wire nets are considered the lateral thrust outwards to which they are subjected by the pressure at their base will in nowise be resisted by the rods parallel to these layers or faces, and nothing prevents them from separating from the central mass simultaneously with the concrete in which they are embedded. Of course, the bars at right angles to the faces considered offer a resistance to the outward thrust, but only to such extent as they adhere to the concrete. This adhesion is proportional to the area of contact, and is zero at the ends and only increases in intensity as the distance along the bars increases from the faces, but these faces are just the layers most exposed to crushing. To remedy this fault the author has first employed iron rods so connected as to support each other, and then nets of wires interwoven in a manner which promised the best results. After all these arrangements the crushing beginning at the face has gradually spread toward the center and it became apparent why, for equal weights of steel, not more than one-half of the resistance shown by the hooped concrete was obtained. It was as a result of the above experiments that all further investigations were directed to concrete reinforced by hoop-like rods.

The inner forces acting in solid bodies are often placed in two different classes. The name, cohesion, is generally given to the inter-molecular action, and it is known that it varies in proportion to the distances of the molecules from each other up to a certain point which is called the "elastic limit." As a premise nothing is supposed to be known of the effects produced by cohesion above the elastic limit; but at the same time it is generally admitted that friction exerts an action in the interior of bodies similar to that exerted on their surface.

However, this division, which may appear arbitrary, is not generally accepted and the deductions made from it may be disputed. We will leave the purely theoretical considerations and will attempt to attain the practical aim of the engineer, which is to formulate rules which will enable him to predict the mechanical properties of the materials. The following method was adopted for investigation:

A certain number of prisms of concrete of different qualities and surrounded by hoops of various arrangements and sizes was prepared. Some had, also, longitudinal reinforcing rods. These prisms were submitted to increasing pressures and the shortenings produced were measured together with the loads. By a well-known formula for the thrust of a granular mass, the resistance was computed which would be offered by a prism of the same dimensions, reinforced in the same way if sand without cohesion were put in place of the concrete. The same co-efficient of friction was assumed and the same percentage of swelling of cross-section to decrease of length. This was computed for each observed deformation. It is evident that the excess of the observed resistance of a concrete prism over the similar resistance of sand corresponding to the same deformation can only be attributed to the direct or indirect effects of the cohesion of the concrete. Without entering into a discussion on the character of this difference in resistance and without attributing to the name a precise scientific meaning, we shall call this excess the "specific resistance of the concrete."

From this definition it follows that to determine the total compressive resistance of a hooped concrete prism it will suffice to add the specific resistance of the concrete to the resistance of a prism of sand having the same hooping and the same coefficients of friction and transverse swelling. The latter resistance can be computed. To make use of this arbitrary distinction it must be possible to predict the specific resistance of the concrete in hooped members from the resistance of concrete of the same quality not hooped. It will be seen that this can be done as far as is required.

CONCRETES, CEMENTS, MORTARS, PLASTERS AND STUCCO

QUESTIONS

1. Give a description of the lime principally used for internal plastering.
2. Give a description of those which are known as "Hydraulic Limes" and the properties they possess.
3. Give a description of "artificial hydraulic limes" and how they may be mixed.
4. Give a description of the process termed "slaking" and how to effect it thoroughly, and what lime will slake quicker than others.

QUESTIONS

5. Give a description of how the lime should be "run."
6. Give a description of the two important purposes for which sand is used in the composition of plaster.
7. Give a description of the composition and properties of sand for the several purposes for which it is best adapted.
8. Give the general rule for the proportion of sand to lime in the composition of plaster.
9. Give a description of where sand is obtained, and what kind should be avoided, and the reason for doing so.
10. Give a description of river sand, its properties, and for what class of work it is used.
11. Give a description of the purpose of hair in the composition of plaster, the kind generally used, its characteristic qualities, and proper method in its manipulation.
12. Give a description for what purposes Portland Cement with a large proportion of sand, may be utilized.
13. Give the designations of the "setting cements" that are generally the stronger.
14. Give a description of "Roman Cement," its disadvantages, and its utility for certain purposes.
15. Give the names of other "natural cements" very similar to Roman, and that are also useful where quick setting is required.
16. Give a description of "Parian Cement," for what kind of work it is best adapted, and the qualities it possesses.

17. Give a description of "Keene's Cement," its dominant property over other kinds, and the utility to which it may be adapted.
18. Give a description of "Martin's Cement," the properties it possesses, and for what purpose is it principally utilized.
19. Give a description of some of the advantages derived from the use of "Robinson's Cement."
20. Give a description of "Adamant," and the properties it possesses.
21. Give a description of "Selenitic Cement," the properties it possesses, and its utility.
22. Give a description of "Plaster of Paris," its proportion to ordinary lime putty, and its utility for various purposes.
23. For what purpose are pine, cedar and metal laths used?
24. Describe the defects that are to be avoided in laths, and the reason for their rejection.
25. Give the description of "Riven Laths."
26. Give the three sizes in which laths may be obtained, and the terms applicable to each respectively.
27. Give a description where the "thicker" and "thinner" laths should be used respectively, and the reasons why so described.
28. Give a description of how laths are usually spaced.
29. Give a description of what is meant by "A Bunch of Laths," what it contains, the number of superficial yards it will cover, and the number of nails required when nailed to joists 1 ft. from center to center.
30. Give a description of the lengths of laths.

QUESTIONS

31. Give a description of how laths are best nailed so as to break joint entirely.
32. Give a description of how "Lap Joints" at the end of laths should be treated.
33. Give a description of how joists that are thicker than 2 inches should be treated.
34. Give a description of the qualities possessed by "Metal Lathing" and why it is now extensively used.
35. Give a description of the various kinds of "lathing nails" and the different purposes for which they are used.
36. Give a description of the purposes for which Portland cement is best adapted, and the qualities it possesses.
37. Give a description of the composition of the cement for "rendering."
38. Give a description of the plastering operations of "External Facades in Portland Cement."
39. Give a description of how the key for external plastering on brick work may be obtained.
40. Should fat lime be mixed with Portland cement?
41. Give a description of the term "Stucco" and to what it is applied.
42. Give a description of "common stucco," its composition and how employed.
43. Give a description of "rough stucco," how it is utilized and manipulated.
44. Give a description of "Bastard Stucco and Trowelled Stucco," their composition and purposes for which they are adapted and how manipulated.
45. Give a description of the term "Sgraffito," and how patterns may be obtained.

46. Give a description of "the design for the "Sgraffito."
47. Give a description of "rough cast," its composition, qualities, and method of manipulation.
48. Give a description of "Depeter," the qualities it possesses, and the several methods of manipulating it.
49. Give a description of "Lime plastering," its composition, and manner of its application.
50. Give a description of what is meant by "one-coat work" in plaster work operations.
51. Give a description of "two-coat work" in plaster work operations.
52. Give a description of "three-coat work" in plaster work operations.
53. Give a description of the several processes in plastering ordinary three-coat work.
54. Give a description of "Gauged stuff," its composition, the purposes for which it is used, and manner of its manipulation.
55. Give a description of "the white cements," their composition, and manner of adaptation.
56. Give a description of some of the causes that produce the cracks often observable in plaster work.
57. Give a description of how the joist lines on ceilings are caused, and how they may be prevented.
58. Give a description of the process termed "Pugging," and the purposes for which it is intended.
59. Give a description of "Mineral Wool," its comparison with ordinary pugging, its qualities, and purposes for which it is adapted.

QUESTIONS

60. Give a description of "Lime Whiting or Whitewash," its composition, and purposes for which it is adapted.
61. Give a description of "fibrous plaster," its composition, and the adaptability of the qualities it possesses.
62. Give a description of the methods in which ornamental plaster ceilings may be treated.
63. Give details separately of the 17 rules that are embraced under "Specification Clauses" and relative to materials and workmanship.
64. Give a description of the preparation of Bill of Quantities.
65. Give a description of "Laths Generally," the method of manipulating them, and the different kinds of nails used.
66. Give a description of the "Hoes and Drags" used by the plasterer, and the purposes for which they are utilized.
67. Give a description of the article known as "The Hawk," and for what purpose it is used.
68. Give a description of the "Mortar Board," and for what purpose it is used.
69. Give a description of the different kinds of "Trowels," and the respective purposes for which they are utilized.
70. Give a description of the different kinds of "Floats," and the respective purposes for which they are adapted.
71. Give a description of "Moulds," how they are made and for what purposes they are utilized.
72. Give a description of "Center-Moulds," and the principle upon which they are made.

73. Give a description of the tool termed "The Pointer," and for what it is chiefly used.
74. Give a description of the process termed lime burning or calcination.
75. Give a description of what is meant by the term "Mortar," its composition and the processes which are adopted in its manipulation.
76. Give a description of what is meant by "the adhesive strength" of mortar.
77. Give a description of the causes that operate in the "hardening of mortar."
78. Give a description of some of the qualities pertaining to "Mastic," and for what purpose is it sometimes used?
79. Give a description of the various processes in the manipulation of "Mastic."
80. Give a description of the composition of "Scotch Mastic."
81. Give a description of the composition of "Common Mastic."
82. Give a description of the process termed "Scratching," the tool employed and method of manipulation.
83. Give a description of the process termed "Rendering," and how it should be properly done.
84. Give a description of how to manipulate the wall and ceiling "screeds."
85. Give a description of the term "Flanking" and the method of performing the operation.
86. Give a description of the process in "Scouring coarse stuff."
87. Give a description of the process termed "keying" in plaster work, and method of manipulation.

QUESTIONS

88. Give a description of what is termed "Setting Stuff," and method of manipulating it.
89. Give a description of the term "Scouring setting stuff," and method of manipulation.
90. Give a description of the processes known as "Trowelling and brushing setting stuff."
91. Give some general remarks on "Setting," and the best method of making joints and setting stuff, where it is inconvenient to lay and finish the whole surface in one operation.
92. Give a description of "Common Setting" for walls and ceilings, and methods of manipulation.
93. Give a description of the process termed "Skimming," and method of manipulation.
94. Give a description of the process termed "Colored Setting," its composition, and method of manipulation.
95. Give a detailed description of how to set out and construct Corinthian Entablature, including the cornice, enrichments, coffers, modillion blocks, and paterae.
96. Give a description of the method of setting out and constructing a mould intended for forming the moulding and miters in one operation.
97. Give a description of how the fixing of enrichments should be executed, and what has to be avoided during the operation.
98. Give a description of how the mitering of enrichments is to be performed, and what should be done in fixing medallion blocks, dentils or paterae.
99. Give the description of a column trammel, and the method of its manipulation.

CEMENTS AND CONCRETES

100. Give a description of the method of constructing plain diminished columns.
101. Give a description of how to set out the flutes of a diminished column.
102. Give a description of how to construct diminished fluted columns.
103. Give a description of diminished fluted pilasters, and the method that should be adopted in their construction.
104. Give a description of diminished mouldings, and the methods that are adopted in their construction.
105. Give a description of the "diminished rule method" for running double diminished mouldings.
106. Give a description of the "top rule method" of running double diminished mouldings.
107. Give a description of the method of constructing the plaster work of cupolas.
108. Give a description of templates for running elliptical mouldings, and methods of their manipulation.
109. Give a description of the methods adopted in the formation of coved ceilings.
110. Give a description of the methods adopted in the formation of circle mouldings on circular surfaces.
111. Give a description of the formation of niches or recesses in walls, and for what purposes they are adapted.
112. Give a description of the process termed "Fresco," and how the plaster is to be prepared for the reception of the decorative operations.

QUESTIONS

113. Give a description of "Indian Fresco and Marble Plaster," the process of its composition and the purposes for which it is adapted.

114. Give a description of "Scagliola," its excellent qualities, durability, and the purposes for which it is adapted.

115. Give a description of the colors and quantities that are used for the following marbles, respectively, namely, Penzance marble, Egyptian Green, Dark Porphyry and Green Genoa.

116. Give a description of the process of the polishing of "Scagliola."

117. Give a description of the process in the manufacture of "Marezzo," and the purposes for which it is adapted.

118. Give a description of the method of executing granite plaster work, and how it is manipulated in its composition.

119. Give a description of concrete in general and some of the uses to which it is applied.

120. Give a description of what the term "matrix" is applied to when considering the qualities of any material.

121. Give a description of what is meant by the term "Compound Aggregates," and explain the difference between an inferior and superior aggregate by an example.

122. Give a description of the "Voids in Aggregates," and what method is used to ascertain the voids.

123. Give a description of the "crushing strength of concrete" and upon what it depends.

124. Give a description of the "ramming of concrete" and the effect that is produced.

125. Give a description of the thickness of concrete paving and its relation to the foundations, and to the amount of traffic on street sidewalks, stable floors and yards.

126. Give a description of "Eureka Paving," its manipulation, and the purposes for which it is best adapted.

127. Give a description of the method of preparing the aggregate for Eureka, and the quantities for the rough coat and topping.

128. Give a description of the "levelling and adjustment of the requisite falls" in the laying of concrete pavements and flooring.

129. Give a description of the two parts in the composition of foundations, and the method of manipulation.

130. Give a description of the "laying concrete pavements" and the processes to be employed in order to leave the surface uniform, straight and solid.

131. Give a description of "trowelling concrete" and how the best effects may be attained.

132. Give a description of the process termed "grouting," and when it is adopted.

133. Give a description of the methods of composition of materials that are sometimes adopted for "non-slippery pavements."

134. Give a description of the preparation of "grooved and roughened surfaces," that are required for stables, yards, etc.

135. Give a description of the process employed in coloring cement work, and how the best results may be obtained, also some of the materials to be used in producing the color desired.

QUESTIONS

136. Give a description of the method of depositing concrete, and what should be avoided in the process.
137. Give a description of the process termed "Retempering," and the conditions upon which the proper setting of concrete depends.
138. Give a description of how to treat operations in concrete during freezing weather.
139. Give a description of "Rubble Concrete," its composition and method of manipulation.
140. Give a description of how to face concrete, the composition employed, and how it is prepared.
141. Give a description of the "top dressing or wearing surface" for finished walks, and the method of mixing the mortar.
142. Give a description of the composition of "Basement Floors" and the method of their treatment.
143. Give a description of the construction of concrete stable floors and driveways.
144. Give a description of concrete steps, their manner of construction, and in what places they may be advantageously adopted.
145. Give a detailed description of wood framing in the construction of concrete stairs.
146. Give a description of the materials required for a concrete staircase, and how to manipulate them for the several purposes required.
147. Give a description of "Modelling in Fine Concrete" and the several stages in the development of the process to obtain the proper execution of the figure or design required.
148. Give a description of how concrete fountains are constructed, and how a saving of material may be effected.

149. Give a description of the construction of concrete tanks, and the manipulation of the materials for the purposes desired.

150. Give a description of the composition of "concrete vases," and the method of manipulating the materials.

INDEX

INDEX

INDEX

INDEX

INDEX

INDEX

INDEX

INDEX